Source Book in Chemistry, 1900-1950

Edited by Henry M. Leicester

University of the Pacific

SOURCE BOOK
IN CHEMISTRY
1900-1950

Harvard University Press

Cambridge, Massachusetts

1968

General Editor's Preface

The Source Books in this series are collections of classical papers that have shaped the structures of the various sciences. Some of these classics are not readily available and many of them have never been translated into English, thus being lost to the general reader and frequently to the scientist himself. The point of this series is to make these texts readily accessible and to provide good translations of the ones that either have not been translated at all or have been translated only poorly.

The series was planned originally to include volumes in all the major sciences from the Renaissance through the nineteenth century. It has been extended to include ancient and medieval Western science and the development of the sciences in the first half of the present century. Many of these books have been published already and several more are in various stages of preparation.

The Carnegie Corporation originally financed the series by a grant to the American Philosophical Association. The History of Science Society and the American Association for the Advancement of Science have approved the project and are represented on the Editorial Advisory Board. This Board at present consists of the following members.

Marshall Clagett, History of Science, University of Wisconsin
I. Bernard Cohen, History of Science, Harvard University
C. J. Ducasse, Philosophy, Brown University
Ernst Mayr, Zoology, Harvard University
Ernest A. Moody, Philosophy, University of California at Los Angeles
Ernest Nagel, Philosophy, Columbia University
Harlow Shapley, Astronomy, Harvard University
Harry Woolf, History of Science, Johns Hopkins University

The series was begun and sustained by the devoted labors of Gregory D. Walcott and Everett W. Hall, the first two General Editors. I am indebted to them, to the members of the Advisory Board, and to Joseph D. Elder, Science Editor of Harvard University Press, for their indispensable aid in guiding the course of the Source Books.

Edward H. Madden
General Editor

Department of Philosophy
State University of New York at Buffalo
Buffalo, New York

Preface

The problem of selecting papers for a source book in chemistry covering the years 1900 to 1950 is almost exactly the opposite of that involved in preparing one for the years 1400 to 1900. In the latter case, the classic papers are fairly well known, and the compiler is faced chiefly with the task of securing the often rare publications in which the selections appeared. In the modern case, the journals desired are usually available in any large scientific library, but who can be so presumptuous as to say exactly what papers are vital to a science that is still using a large part of the material published during these years? Certainly no two individuals would make the same selections, and it is unlikely that any reader will not disagree, perhaps forcefully, with the choice of citations.

Since this is the case, I can only indicate the ideas in my mind when I made the choices that follow. I have tried to select not only the papers that seem to me to lie at the foundations of the most significant movements of the present day, but also to include, wherever possible, statements by the authors of why they chose to do what they did. Admittedly in modern times, with the pressure for space in the journals, authors of scientific papers seldom reveal all their mistakes and emotions as frankly as did Priestley, for instance, in his outspoken accounts of his work. However, there is often some indication in the first papers in a given field of what went on in the mind of the investigator, and these have been sought.

Since it is hoped that these selections will be of value in years to come to the general historian of chemistry or, more widely, of science, the attempt has been made to avoid selections that are almost entirely mathematical, such as the original papers of Debye and Hückel or of Heitler and London. Rather I have chosen selections that explain the ideas behind the mathematical symbolism. Of course, where mathematics is essential as part of a general paper, it has been included.

It will be noted that more papers from the early part of this half century have been included than from the later part. There is little doubt that the first thirty years of the twentieth century were years of great development in chemical theory and techniques, and much of the more recent work is firmly founded on the earlier material. However, the historian who compiles the selections for the years

1950 to 2000 will undoubtedly find more articles of basic value in the latter half of the period here discussed than can be recognized now.

Many individuals have given valuable suggestions in the course of this work, but I particularly wish to acknowledge the advice and aid of my colleagues G. V. Bykov, A. T. Cape, Eduard Farber, Erwin N. Hiebert, Frederick O. Koenig, and Adolf Pabst. Dr. Herbert S. Klickstein, with whom I prepared the *Source Book* for 1400 to 1900, was unable to devote the time required for the preparation of the present volume, but offered many important and helpful suggestions. However, the responsibility for choosing the final selections, for making the translations from German and French, and for all errors and omissions lies with me.

I wish to thank the following for permission to reprint copyrighted material from the sources indicated. The exact volume and page references precede each selection. Akademie der Wissenschaften in Göttingen; Akademische Verlagsgellschaft for material from *Ergebnisse der Enzymforschung* and *Zeitschrift für Physikalische Chemie;* American Chemical Society for material from *Chemical Reviews* and *The Journal of the American Chemical Society;* American Institute of Physics for material from *The Journal of Chemical Physics;* American Society of Biological Chemists for material from *The Journal of Biological Chemistry;* Johann Ambrosius Barth Verlag for material from *Annalen der Physik;* J. F. Bergman-Verlagsbuchhandlung for material from *Verhandlungen der Deutschen Gesellschaft für Innere Medizin;* The Chemical Society for material from *Journal of the Chemical Society;* J. and A. Churchill for material from *Quantitative Organic Microanalysis* by F. Pregl; Walter de Gruyter & Co. for material from *Hoppe-Seylers Zeitschrift für Physiologische Chemie;* The Faraday Society for material from its *Transactions;* Gauthier-Villars for material from *Comptes Rendus Hebdomadaires des Seances de l'Academie des Sciences;* Gebrüder Borntraeger for material from *Berichte der Deutschen Botanischen Gesellschaft; The Biochemical Journal;* British Association for the Advancement of Science for material from its *Annual Reports; The Journal of Physiology (London); Le Journal de Physique et Le Radium; The Lancet;* J. B. Lippincott Co. for material from *Endocrinology;* National Academy of Sciences for material from its *Proceedings; Nature; Die Naturwissenschaften;* Nederlandse Chemische Vereniging for material from *Recueil des Travaux Chimiques des Pays-Bas; The Physical Review;* Rockefeller Institute Press for material from *The Journal of General Physiology;* Royal Society (London) for material from its *Proceedings; Science;* Springer-Verlag for material from *Beiträge zur Chemischen Physiologie und Pathologie Biochemische Zeitschrift, Klinische Wochenschrift,* and *Zeitschrift für Physik;* Dr. Dietrich Steinkopff Verlag for material from *Kolloid-Zeitschrift;* Taylor and Francis for material from *The London, Edinburgh and Dublin Philosophical Magazine;* Uitgeverij Dr. W. Junk for material from *Enzymologia;* Verlag Chemie for material from *Berichte der Deutschen Chemischen Gesellschaft, Zeitschrift für Angewandte Chemie,* and *Zeitschrift für Elektrochemie;* John Wiley & Sons for material in *Advances in Enzymology and Related Subjects of Biochemistry.*

Henry M. Leicester

San Francisco, California
May 1965

Contents

Source Book in Chemistry, 1900-1950

Introduction

The diversification of science into various separate fields that became apparent in the seventeenth century had become so pronounced in the nineteenth century that the followers of any specialty had very little contact with those of another. By the end of the century it could be said that chemists and physicists scarcely spoke to one another as scientists, and both regarded the biologist as hardly a scientist at all. Even within a particular science this tendency to extreme specialization showed itself. Organic chemists and physical chemists were inclined to regard each other with a kind of veiled contempt.

Along with this narrow outlook the physical sciences seemed at this time to have reached a plateau in their development. Physics had seen great advances in the study of electricity and in the understanding of the various forms of energy, but along with them had come an increasing satisfaction with the mathematical description of phenomena at the expense of a deeper inquiry into the mechanisms involved. Whether electricity should be accounted for by a one-fluid or a two-fluid theory did not matter, since the mathematics could account for either. Atoms were not needed to account for thermal behavior. The search for the next decimal place seemed to be the chief goal of the investigator in the physical sciences. Biology was almost entirely descriptive, and only a small beginning had been made in laboratory studies in physiology.

Chemistry shared in this rather narrow and self-satisfied outlook. At the beginning of the nineteenth century the problem of affinity—that is, the mechanism by which compounds were held together—and the nature of chemical reactions had been among the chief interests of chemists. The great advances in organic chemistry during the century led to the concept of valence, but it was a static and formalized valence that could be represented by lines in a structural formula without much concern as to what the lines actually meant. The periodic law gave order to a mass of facts that had been accumulating in more or less random fashion, but again it tended to formalize the chemistry of the elements in a rigid framework that discouraged inquiry into the reasons for the periodic phenomena it described. It was essential for the progress of chemistry that this stage of rigidity should be brought about, but once established, it

1

laid a stultifying hand on further advances. Thus chemistry had reached its own plateau. Chemists were busy preparing new compounds but the interpretation of the reactions by which they were prepared seemed of little interest. Even the physical chemists, exponents of the newest branch of chemistry, tried to explain affinity solely from the statistical viewpoint of thermodynamics and so did not consider the basic nature of the valence forces they were using.

A change was now at hand. The physicists began this change when the discovery of X-rays and radioactivity at the end of the century brought them face to face with phenomena outside the forces they had been studying. In the first two decades of the twentieth century the whole outlook changed. Concepts of quanta and relativity further forced them into a search for the deeper meanings behind natural phenomena, and their discoveries were soon extended to other sciences.

In spite of the general acceptance of the status quo, some chemists at the beginning of the century were questioning the rigidity of the structural viewpoint; see H. M. Leicester and H. S. Klickstein, *A Source Book in Chemistry 1400–1900* (Harvard University Press, Cambridge, Massachusetts, 1952). Werner (p. 516) in inorganic chemistry and Nef and Gomberg (p. 512) in organic were challenging the older ideas. The Curies (p. 521) were extending the work of the physicist on radioactivity by their chemical separation of polonium and radium. It took a decade for the new concepts of physics to reach deeper into chemistry, but once started, progress was rapid. Interest in mechanisms revived, and with it came new understandings of the nature of the chemical bond, chemical kinetics, and reaction mechanisms. New techniques opened whole new fields for chemical study.

Inevitably this expanded vision led to closer contacts among chemists of every specialty, and also with scientists in other fields. Physics and physical chemistry were applied to organic compounds and new substances that could not have been foreseen by the older theories were prepared. Reaction mechanisms were generalized. New borderline sciences sprang up. Chemical physics and biochemistry became sciences in their own right. Chemistry thus became a link between physics and biology. This growing interdependence of the sciences was one of the most characteristic features of the first half of the twentieth century. The selections given in this book are classified into the usual branches of the science, but the reader cannot fail to note how the discoveries in any one branch were taken up and used in most of the others.

Part I   Techniques

Libavius in 1597 defined chemistry as "the art of producing magisteria [compounds] and of extracting pure essences by separating bodies from mixtures." (Leicester and Klickstein, *Source Book*, p. 21.) These remained and remain among the chief aims of chemistry, and as methods for carrying them out have improved, so have all other phases of the science.

In the twentieth century, progress in the second of these aims has been especially rapid, and completely new methods have been devised. At the beginning of the century chemists were analyzing compounds by methods that had been worked out in principle over a hundred years before, and for separation they were using the methods of distillation, crystallization, and sublimation which had been standard among the alchemists of the sixteenth century. Such methods worked well for separating compounds with widely differing properties, but they became exceedingly laborious and sometimes impossible when complex, highly reactive, or very similar compounds were involved.

The problem became especially acute when attempts were made to study natural mixtures, whether of inorganic or organic origin. Colloidal mixtures were especially difficult to separate and purify. Among these, the proteins offered a particular challenge, as did mixtures of alkaloids or pigments found in plant materials. Even if fractional crystallization or distillation could be employed, often only minute amounts of material could be obtained. Chemists of the first half of the twentieth century therefore developed many new ways for handling their compounds. They drew heavily on the work of the physicists for some of the new methods, especially on the various types of spectra: ultraviolet, infrared, Raman, and nuclear resonance. These gave particular help in rapid determinations of organic structures, where the classical methods often took months or even years. Though the application of these methods by the chemist has

3

been exceedingly useful to him, they remain essentially physical phenomena, and hence are not included in the selections of this section. Instead,
attention is centered on newer analytical methods and the completely
new methods for separating mixtures and following compounds through
the changes that may occur in chemical reactions.

ANALYTICAL METHODS

MICROANALYSIS. A very severe limitation on analytical work in
chemistry had always been the amount of material required for study.
This was especially true for natural compounds, where often only very
small quantities were available. This difficulty was particularly and first
apparent in biological materials, but as the chemistry of rarer elements
came to be studied, the limitation was felt there also.

At the beginning of the nineteenth century, Proust had found it necessary
to use as much as 100 pounds of copper in his analytical samples (Leicester
and Klickstein, *Source Book*, p. 202). By the beginning of the twentieth
century only a fraction of a gram was needed for good analytical work, but
the limitations of analytical balances prevented further decrease in sample
size. However, balances for assaying had been steadily improved and by
1910 W. Kuhlmann in Hamburg was constructing a balance that could
weigh accurately to a few hundredths of a milligram. Friedrich Emich in
Graz had begun to use such a balance early in the century and by 1910 had
already developed micromethods for both inorganic and organic substances.
At this time his associate, Fritz Pregl, was studying the bile acids and
obtained one compound in extremely small amounts; he began to work
on micromethods for organic analysis. Emich turned this branch over to
Pregl, retaining for himself the subject of inorganic micromethods. During
the next fifteen years Pregl—and soon many others—had adapted the
methods of chemical analysis to work on a microscale, and new possibilities in the study of natural products, rare minerals, and reaction mechanisms became available. The selections by Emich and Pregl indicate how
this came about.

The following selection is from pages 28–30 of *Berichte der Deutschen
Chemischen Gesellschaft*, **43,** 10–45 (1910).

On Microchemistry, with Special Attention to the Work of H. Behrens

F. EMICH

The paper opens with a review of the microchemical methods used up
to its date.

Quantitative microchemical analysis is still just beginning. Among the older methods, which were more estimations than quantitative determinations, but which certainly used only very small quantities, we should mention the "forked procedure" of Oswald Richter. It assumes that when a certain substance is put through a series of reactions whose different sensitivities are known to be characteristic, then it can be established which reactions occur and which do not and from this draw a conclusion as to the unknown quantity. B. H. Behrens has also made an approximate determination of the carbon content of iron in which he burns the powdered sample with saltpeter, precipitates the carbonate with strontium or calcium, and compares the amount of precipitate with that from iron samples of known carbon content. Further examples of quantitative microanalysis have already appeared.

At last we have been able, by means of microfilters, to carry out many determinations which end with the weighing of a precipitate, since the microbalance satisfies the requirements of quantitative analysis. Thus it can be considered a favorable combination of circumstances that by reducing in size the entire quantitative apparatus there is no essential decrease in accuracy with the precipitate. The microfilter is a small circular disc, 6–8 mm. in diameter, greased at the edges, which is laid on the capillary filter. This is connected to a receiver in the middle of an aspirator. A reduced pressure of a few decimeters of water is produced. When the precipitate has been deposited on the filter, it is washed with 5–10 drops of water. The weighing (perhaps also the ashing or drying) takes place after wrapping the filter in platinum foil ("in its case") or placing it in the receptacle of the microbalance which has a small cover for this purpose. The results obtained up to now show errors up to $\frac{1}{2}\%$. The weighing of the substance and the filtering, washing, and weighing of the precipitate under favorable conditions require an expenditure of time of about half an hour; the expenditure of material amounts to several milligrams. The process can thus be called the "milligram process" in distinction from the usual "decigram process." There is still possible an intermediate "centigram process." Balances that can safely be considered accurate to one to two hundredths of a milligram are repeatedly being built today (for example, by Kuhlmann in Hamburg) and for a load of 20 g. are not expensive. Thus with about the same accuracy as for the usual analytical process it is possible to save a great deal in material and time, and to have the satisfaction that a single crucible, disk, etc. can be weighed directly, which, as is well known, is not always possible with a microbalance. Such determinations have been carried out repeatedly, but perhaps have not yet been tested systematically.

A detailed account of analyses that have been made concludes the paper.

The following selection is from pages 1–4 of the first English edition of Pregl's book, *Quantitative Organic Microanalysis* (J. and A. Churchill, London, 1924); it is a direct translation of the passage as given in both the first and second German editions. The first German edition of the book was published in Berlin in 1917; the first English edition was a translation of the second German edition.

Quantitative Organic Microanalysis

F. PREGL

In the course of a lengthy investigation in the summer of the year 1910, I obtained a fission product which was only obtainable at the time in extremely small quantity. Thus a decision had to be arrived at, either to continue the investigation with exceptionally large quantities of the original material or so to modify the quantitative analysis of organic substances that it should be possible to obtain correct analytical figures with quantities of material hitherto unheard of, so that formulae could be determined with certainty. I had more particularly in view the necessity for working out a quantitative microanalytical method for the determination of carbon and hydrogen and also of nitrogen by measurement of the gas volume.

As no experimental material of this kind existed, it appeared to me all the more interesting to work at this entirely neglected problem. I was encouraged by the fact that Emich had already shown the essential reliability and advantages of working with small amounts of material in various inorganic determinations; this was a factor which enabled me to attack the problem which I had set myself with great confidence, in spite of the difference of the objective.

By the end of 1911 this problem had been essentially solved; the methods elaborated by that date and described in detail in E. Abderhalden's "Handbuch der biochemischen Arbeitsmethoden," vol. 5, pp. 1307–1356, enabled carbon and hydrogen to be determined in 7 to 13 mgm. of organic material even in the presence of nitrogen and of small amounts of halogen and sulfur; also of nitrogen in 4 to 8 mgm. of material, either by measurement of the gas volume or alkalimetrically, and the determination of sulphur and halogen, also in 4 to 8 mgm. of material by Carius' method. Thus the fundamental applicability of elementary organic microanalysis had been proved for a series of elements, although various observed effects awaited explanation and required further modification of the methods.

In this direction the years 1912 and 1913 were very fruitful. In the determination of carbon the necessity for passing the gases through the combustion tube twice was rendered unnecessary by increasing the tube filling and replacing the mercury gas holder by a Mariotte flask. The quantity of material required was successfully reduced to 2 mgm. by the discovery of a series of hitherto unnoticed effects, for instance, recognition of the fact that new india-rubber tubing led to serious contamination of the gases passing through it; and by the determination of the necessary conditions for the complete decomposition of the organic material, and their quantitative expression with regard to the velocity of the gases and time of contact with the heated filling of the combustion tube, instead of the ambiguous terms "rapid" and "slow." The influence and efficiency of various fillings for the combustion tube were also investigated, more particularly in the case of substances containing much halogen and sulphur.

The origin of the admixture of other gases in the determination of nitrogen by the gas volume, which had hitherto necessitated a deduction of 10 per cent of the actual reading, was discovered, and methods of preventing their formation were found. An essentially new method of determining halogen and sulphur was also developed, based on the complete destruction of the organic material by combustion in a stream of oxygen. Practical requirements led to the discovery of a microanalytical method of determining copper electrolytically and also of determining molecular weight by rise of boiling point. A method of microanalytical determination of methoxyl was also elaborated during this period together with initial attempts at the determination of methyl attached to nitrogen.

During these investigations I was very greatly assisted by my co-workers, namely by my former assistants, Dr. Max de Crinis and Dr. S. Edlbacher, also by Dr. Heinrich Poda, Dr. Emil Schwinger, of Graz, Dr. Johann Dubsky, of Zürich, and more particularly by my present assistant, Dr. Hans Lieb. At a low and superficial estimate the experimental material for working out methods of organic microanalysis necessitated about 10,000 exact weighings.

Acknowledgment of the work of a number of colleagues is given.

These circumstances provided me, assisted by Dr. Lieb, with ample opportunity to discover which precautions and manipulations could be generally recommended and which not, and in this way the experimental material was effectively increased. By these means, knowledge of organic microanalysis was spread and found adherents without publication by me of the experience which had been gained, as I avoided publicity until full assurance had been obtained that each of the methods recommended was accurate, apart from unknown imperfections which might have been hidden by compensating errors, and that everything which had appeared to require it had found a satisfactory explanation; for a large series of analytical data in agreement with the theory is no proof of the reliability of an analytical method until all the necessary fundamental conditions have been realised, tested and established. Our experience was considerably increased by the fact that Dr. Hans Lieb willingly undertook to carry out the most varied microanalyses for large numbers of colleagues; this gave me the opportunity, not only to investigate substances of very varied constitution, but also to investigate numerous cases in which all manner of disturbing phenomena were met with and thus to learn how to overcome them.

Thus the microanalytical processes which will be described do not rest merely on theoretical considerations and occasional experiments, but have been elaborated by actual practical experience, and may, therefore, claim to be adapted to practical purposes.

PHYSIOCHEMICAL ANALYSIS. The work of J. Willard Gibbs in the years 1875 to 1878 (Leicester and Klickstein, *Source Book*, p. 475) had shown the importance of the phase rule for determining the compounds that co-existed in mixtures under varying conditions of temperature, pressure, and composition. Metallurgists and mineralogists in particular studied the phase diagrams of alloys and minerals as the conditions were varied. Early in the century Kurnakov noted that the formation of compounds in such mixtures could be detected by study of the physical properties, such as thermal responses, hardness, or conductivity. Eventually he generalized this into his method of physicochemical analysis which has been widely used, especially in the U.S.S.R. The generalized statement of his method was given in 1912–1913.

The following selection is from pages 481–483 of *Zeitschrift für Physikalische Chemie 83*, 481–506 (1913); an earlier paper appeared in the *Journal of the Russian Physical Chemical Society* (translated title) *44*, 1964–1991 (1912).

The Inner Friction of Binary Mixtures. Characteristics of Definite Compounds

N. S. KURNAKOV AND S. F. ZHEMCHUZHNYI

In recent times the use of various physicochemical methods for the study of equilibrium systems has made great progress. The fusion method, which for a number of years was used chiefly for the study of metallic alloys, has now, under the new name of "thermal analysis," been greatly extended for a most varied group of substances. Moreover, the newly discovered connections between chemical composition and a whole series of physical properties, such as conductivity, thermoelectric force, and hardness, permits fine determination of differences in the state of test substances which would have been completely undiscovered by the more usual methods of chemical investigation.

There is particular value in the study of the properties of hardness and the resistance of a material to alteration of its form.

For plastic substances it has already been shown that there is a complete parallelism between the hardness and the flow pressure.

There is complete correspondence between the Brinell hardness number, which is obtained by pressing a steel ball into the test substance, and the pressure required to force the substance from an opening or canal of known diameter in the form of a thread. Under certain conditions there is a simple proportionality between the two values.

We can draw a general conclusion from this.

The flow pressure doubtless depends on the internal friction of the plastic substance. For this substance the hardness is closely connected with the internal friction and appears as one of the manifestations of this most interesting, but up to now little studied property.

In our laboratory the inner connections between chemical composition and hardness of binary systems have often been studied, and now we can consider the general character of the diagrams which correspond to the chief types of reciprocal action of the components to be firmly established.

In the great majority of cases the process of formation of a definite chemical compound that occurs with evolution of heat will be accompanied by an increase in hardness. If this property is directly connected with internal friction, then obviously the latter is also increased by the same process.

As a clear indication of this conclusion, we have numerous examples of the formation of solid compounds by the reciprocal action of gaseous and liquid components.

However, the change from the gaseous into the liquid or solid states will in itself be accompanied by an enormous increase in the internal friction, and therefore this type of case cannot be considered sufficient for a strong indication.

Thus, for example, we have a comparison of the coefficient of internal friction for water and its gaseous components, hydrogen and oxygen, as follows:

$$\text{Coefficient of internal friction } (\eta)$$

Hydrogen	at 0°	$8.22 \cdot 10^{-5}$
Oxygen	at 20°	$21.20 \cdot 10^{-5}$
Water as vapor	at 0°	$9.2 \ \cdot 10^{-5}$
Water as liquid	at 0.37°	$1757 \ \cdot 10^{-5}$
Ice	at 0°	$\begin{cases} 0.38 \cdot 10^{13} \\ 0.95 \cdot 10^{13} \end{cases}$

The values for ice are the observations of B. P. Weinberg on the ice of the Neva River and the glacier "Hintereisferner" in the Tyrol.

As can be seen, the act of binding the oxygen with hydrogen in the gaseous state has very little influence on the internal friction; the value for gaseous water lies between the corresponding values of the constituents.

The transition of water vapor to liquid water and especially to ice is characterized by an enormous increase in internal friction, of about 10^3 and 10^{18} times.

It is clear that for determination of a change of this magnitude in the formation of liquid and solid compounds, comparative observations on systems that occur in the same physical state are essential.

POLAROGRAPHY. A new and very sensitive method for determination of small amounts of ions and electrically reducible organic compounds, even in mixtures, came from the studies of Heyrovský on reactions at a dropping mercury cathode. Early in the course of his work he recognized the value of his method for chemical analysis and in his report to the Faraday Society in 1924 he pointed this out.

The following selection is from pages 692–695 and 698–702 of *Transactions of the Faraday Society 19*, 692–702 (1924).

The Processes at the Mercury Dropping Cathode.
Part I. The Deposition of Metals

JAROSSLAV HEYROVSKY

Introduction

The methods hitherto employed of following electrode potentials during polarisations contrast markedly—as regard exactness—with the E. M. F. determinations of primary galvanic cells; this is due to the circumstance that for polarisations more or less considerable current densities are used, whereas galvanic cells are studied in a "currentless' condition. Thus the polarisation "current-voltage" diagrams bear the character of a technical research rather than of exactly reproducible measurements, which would show strict thermodynamic relationships.

To approach nearer to the stage of reversibility in investigating the polarisation phenomena the author has applied to the study of electrolytic processes a dropping mercury cathode as used by B. Kučera in the determination of the interfacial tension of polarised mercury.

Figure 1 shows a suitable form of the electrolytic vessel.

Through a rubber or cork stopper A, placed at the top of a long-necked conical flask so as not to contaminate the solutions, the

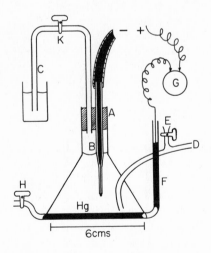

Fig. 1

mercury cathode B is inserted, consisting of a thick-walled capillary, the lower end of which is drawn into a tip allowing mercury to drop out slowly. The upper end of the capillary is connected by a rubber tubing, ca. 50 cms. long, to a mercury reservoir, by the level of which the rate of dropping can be regulated; the usual drop time was ca. 3 seconds.

In order to expel air and remove oxidising impurities from the solution in the vessel pure hydrogen is let in before electrolysis through the glass tube D, it passes the solution and escapes through the syphon C. The large bottom mercury layer Hg serves as the anode, from which a platinum contact leads to the connection in F.

Through the tap H the solution or mercury may be let out, and through E fresh mercury can be poured in, if required.

When the solution is properly reduced by hydrogen, which is effected after two or three hours of slow passage, the siphon C is lowered and filled with the solution, thus establishing a connection with a normal calomel electrode, to which the potential of the bottom mercury layer is referred. The negative pole of the polarising source is then connected to the mercury reservoir, making the drops cathode, whilst the mercury layer is joined with the positive pole; the polarising E. M. F. is then slowly increased and the current which passes through the solution is determined by a sensitive galvanometer (a d'Arsonval with 4 mm. deflection corresponding to 10^{-8} amp.).

The constant renewal of mercury surface at the dropping cathode, which prevents "concentration-polarisation" and hydrogen evolution, effects slight fluctuations due to the charge acquired by the spreading of the mercury surface (the electrocapillary phenomenon), which causes the galvanometer mirror to oscillate 1–2 millimeters of the scale-division, corresponding to changes in intensity of 2–5 $\times$ 10^{-9} amp.; the current which passes the cell before electrolysis of the solution sets in is of the order of 10^{-8}–10^{-7} amp.

Electrodeposition in Mercury

If a properly reduced solution be polarised, the current must all be due to the ionic deposition in the mercury drop; it is therefore important to avoid in the solution traces of mercury salts, which would deposit already at very small polarisations. Even very sparingly soluble salts such as mercurous chloride or mercuric oxide cause by their presence a large increase of current; this is especially marked in more concentrated (ca. normal) solutions of alkali hydroxides or chlorides, showing that these solutions then contain mercury in complex ions. Solutions of bromides and iodides, when standing longer over mercury, show the presence of such complexes so strongly that only concentrations from decinormal downwards can be used for electrolysis in this method. A trace of cupric hydroxide when added to the alkaline solution brings the galvanometer mirror off the scale even at 0.2–0.3 volt polarisation.

If all such impurities of nobler metals are absent, the current passing the solution is very small and the oscillations of the mirror are slight, vanishing entirely at the potential at which the interfacial tension of mercury in the solution is maximal (*i.e.*, ca.—0.56 volt from the calomel electrode); this, then, tests the purity of the solution and furnishes a check for the right adjustment of the arrangement.

Figure 2 shows some of the characteristic "current–voltage" curves as obtained by the method. All measurements were carried out at room temperature varying between 18°–20°C.

During polarisation ions are discharged at the drops, causing thereby a back E.M.F. equal and opposite to the polarising force; the current due to this deposition is minute, 10^{-8}–10^{-7} amp. per sq. mm., as will be observed on the horizontal part of the curves.

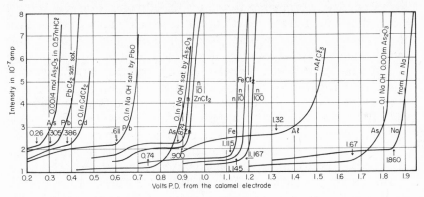

Fig. 2

However, at a certain potential of the polarised drop, termed the "deposition potential," and denoted on the diagram by arrows, a sudden increase of current begins.

Three processes might cause this increase, provided oxidising agents are absent and the ions in the solution are at their lowest stage of oxidation:

(1) Combination with mercury and diffusion into the drops.

(2) A new phase of formation at the mercury drop surface.

(3) Diffusion of a deposited volatile product into the surrounding solution.

These cases are discussed in detail. The paper then continues with a discussion of applications of the method, first to ionic equilibria, and then to analysis.

Qualitative Electro-Analysis. An important feature observable on the curves in Fig. 3 [not included here] is the turn to the horizontal in solutions with a very small amount of the metal, down from 10^{-4} gram-ions per litre. Evidently the current of about 10^{-7} amp., depositing every second at the cathode 10^{-12} gram-ions from the few cubic mm. in the immediate neighbourhood of the dropping cathode, which contain at this dilution some 10^{-10} gram-ions of the metal, must soon exhaust the space round the drop, and the current intensity then depends chiefly on the amount diffused to. The metal in solution reveals itself in the form of a "wave" on the current-voltage curve quite distinctly when present in 10^{-6} gram-mols per litre, and even smaller amounts are still detectable.

The "wave" due to an admixture of 3×10^{-5} mols PbO per litre of a normal sodium hydroxide solution begins at -0.758 *v.*, and is about ten times more prominent than the "wave" due to a 3×10^{-6} PbO impurity, which rises at about -0.782 volts from the calomel electrode. The latter "wave" again is much more distinct than that due to 4×10^{-7} gr.-mm. PbO. The same thing is observable in the case of dilute zincates in alkalis; here, of course, the potential of polarisation at which the wave due to zinc deposition begins is much more negative than in the case of lead.

It is obvious that by the determination of the position and size of such waves on the "current-voltage" curves traces of some metallic impurities in solutions can be identified; in other words, that this method can serve as a means of *qualitative electro-analysis.* Some instances of this are graphically represented in Fig. 4.

The curve (1) Zn was obtained from electrolysis of a normal zinc chloride solution, which was prepared by the solution of the equivalent amount of pure (Merck's "pro analysi") zinc in normal hydrochloric acid, so that no metallic residue was left. Two big waves appear (at -0.41 and -0.59 volt), which bring the galvanometer deflexion off the scale before the actual deposition of zinc ions in mercury can be reached. The proper value of the zinc deposition potential is observed only when an excess of the metal is treated with hydrochloric acid, and the presence of the metallic phase does not allow impurities of a more noble character than that of zinc to enter the solution. In this way the curve (2) Zn was obtained. That -0.874 is the true value of zinc deposition, and that it does not relate to another substance, is ascertained on subsequent dilutions, when only a regular shift (by about 28 millivolts per tenfold dilution) is observable, until the curves turn into the form of "waves" at about 10^{-5} gr.-mols of Zn per litre. Such extreme dilutions have to be made up with a conducting solution, *e.g.*, in a pure 0.1 n potassium

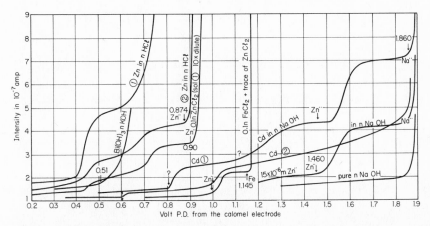

Fig. 4

chloride, which does not interfere with the deposition of zinc. If the resistance of the solutions is large, the slope of the ascending branch of the curve is lessened and the turning point becomes indistinct.

A tenfold dilution of the solution (1) Zn causes a great diminution of the two waves, so that the determination of the zinc deposition at 0.900 $v.$ appears within the galvanometer scale.

Evidently the very pure zinc contains at least two impurities of nobler metals in an amount of about 1 part in 100,000, *i.e.*, 0.001 per cent. Judging from their potential positions, they are probably indium and lead. The first wave (at -0.41) appears near the cadmium normal deposition potential; however, sulphuretted hydrogen produced only a faint yellow coloration in this solution, showing that there is so little of cadmium present that its deposition could not begin before -0.50 volt. It has been ascertained later on, that the first wave is due to lead and the second to indium impurities.

The next curve shows the electrolysis of a ferrous solution with an addition of 5×10^{-6} mols of zinc chloride per litre. Zinc, of course, deposits before iron, behaving at the mercury electrode as a more noble metal.

The curve denoted "Cd (1)" shows the polarisation current obtained in a normal sodium hydroxide solution, which was allowed to act for three months on a thin strip of pure (Kahlbaum's "pro analysi") cadmium. Although cadmium apparently does not dissolve in alkaline solutions, yet it gives rise after some weeks to a precipitate of cadmium hydroxide, and the metallic surface turns black and seems corroded. The alkaline extract contains zinc, as it is evident from the large wave coinciding in size and position with an artificial zinc addition to normal sodium hydroxide (see curve below "Cd (2)"). The alkaline extract when filtered and neutralised by pure hydrochloric acid gave the curve denoted "Cd (2)". In this the zinc impurity is found to deposit in the expected place at $-1.00\ v.$ (it has been also ascertained as zinc micro-analytically). The other impurity, producing a wave at $-0.81\ v.$ in the alkaline and at $-0.61\ v.$ in the neutralised solution, must be due to an amphoteric substance, perhaps cadmium hydroxide itself, if it possesses a faintly acidic character.

The more markedly pronounced acidity of bismuth hydroxide, which manifests itself in dissolving in very concentrated alkalis, is easily shown from the polarisation curve of normal sodium hydroxide to which some bismuth hydroxide has been added; the increase of current due to bismuth deposition starts near -0.5 volt.

These examples suggest the possibility of working out a systematic method of analysis by means of the dropping cathode.

HYDROGEN ION CONCENTRATION; PH. The concept of acids as substances that give up hydrogen ion was destined to be considerably expanded during the twentieth century, but the importance of the hydrogen ion concentration, especially in biological systems, was recognized early. In the course of a study of enzyme reactions, Sörensen was led to formulate a simple method of expressing hydrogen ion concentration. His utilization of this concept of the empirically derived term pH, although not strictly speaking a technique, is now so widely used in all branches of chemistry that it ranks as a major tool of the modern chemist. Sörensen's derivation of the term is shown here.

The following selection is from pages 131–134 and 159–160 of *Biochemische Zeitschrift 21*, 131–200 (1909); the paper also appeared in *Comptes rendus des Travaux du Laboratoire de Carlsberg 8*, 1 (1909).

Enzyme Studies II. The Measurement and Meaning of Hydrogen Ion Concentration in Enzymatic Processes

S. P. L. SÖRENSEN

1. Degree of Acidity—Hydrogen Ion Concentration

It is a well-known fact that the rate at which enzymatic splitting takes place depends among other things on the degree of acidity or alkalinity of the solution used. Usually—in fact, we may say always—the degree of acidity or alkalinity in enzymatic processes is calculated from the total amount of acid or base added and is expressed by this; it is not at all customary to call attention to the dissociation constant of the acid or base used; still more rarely is the ability of the solutions to bind acids or bases considered.

There can be no doubt that in such a case the ideas on the nature of solutions involved in the Arrhenius theory of electrolytic dissociation can be applied. If, for example, pepsin digestion takes place in a hydrochloric acid solution which is 0.1 normal with respect to the total content of hydrochloric acid, we cannot fail to consider that 0.1 normal hydrochloric acid is not fully dissociated and that the "actual degree of acidity" must rationally be considered *the hydrogen ion concentration*, because this is somewhat less than 0.1 normal. We must equally consider how much the solution of salts such as phosphates can exchange with the hydrochloric acid or what is the content of other substances which can influence the hydrogen ion concentration; specifically, we cannot foget that the substrate, in this special case an available protein, can bind acids. Since the hydrogen ion concentration of the solution is dependent only on the amount of free dissociated acid present, and, of course, since the amount of acid bound to the protein depends on the nature and amount of this substance, it is immediately clear that two solutions of which, for example, one contains 1 g. of protein, the other 5 g. in 100 cc of 0.1 N hydrochloric acid, and which, consequently, are of the same degree of acidity according to the usual method of expression, have very different "actual degrees of acidity," very different hydrogen ion concentrations.

These ideas of the effect of degree of acidity and hydrogen ion concentration on pepsin digestion are valid for all enzymatic processes. I have chosen pepsin-splitting as an example because this process takes place best at a greater hydrogen ion concentration and therefore the relationship is clearer and is also known to some extent. However, exactly the same considerations must also apply to enzymatic behavior which is found to be best in weakly acid, neutral, or alkaline solutions. In the last section of this paper we will give examples of the significance of hydrogen ion concentration in other enzymatic reactions, just as in pepsin digestion; the difference is found only in the order of magnitude of the hydrogen ion concentration with which we must reckon in different cases.

2. The Significance of Hydrogen Ion Concentration. The Hydrogen Ion Exponent

If we denote the concentration of hydrogen ions, of hydroxyl ions, and of water in a water solution by $C_{H^\cdot}$, $C_{OH'}$, and C_{H_2O}, then, as is well known, the following equation holds, by virtue of the law of chemical mass action.

$$\frac{C_{H^\cdot} \times C_{OH'}}{C_{H_2O}} = \text{constant}.$$

Since C_{H_2O} for a somewhat dilute solution can be considered to be constant, then too the product

$$C_{H^\cdot} \times C_{OH'} = \text{a constant}.$$

This product, which usually, and also in this paper, is called the *dissociation constant of water*, at 18° equals 0.64×10^{-14}; in a series of measurements which have been carried out here in our laboratory and which are described in a later section, we have found the average value of 0.72×10^{-14}, or, written in another way, $10^{-14.14}$. As is easily seen, this value permits calculation of the hydrogen ion concentration of aqueous solutions if the concentration of the hydroxyl ion is known, or vice versa. Naturally, since the value for the dissociation constant of water is affected by errors and also the concentration of hydrogen ions is usually easier to determine more exactly than that of the hydroxyl ions, it is more rational, as H. Friedenthal has reported, so far as possible always to determine the hydrogen ion concentration of a solution and to introduce it into the calculation even when the solution has an alkaline reaction. This procedure will therefore be used in what follows since, for example, a solution whose normality based on hydrogen ions equals 0.01 is denoted by 0.01 N; it can be denoted briefly by 10^{-2} without using normalities. In the same way the hydrogen ion concentration of a solution which is based on hydroxyl ions, for example 0.01 normal, is given by $10^{-12.14}$, since $10^{-12.14} \times 10^{-2} = 10^{-14.14}$. Completely pure water and a truly neutral solution, using the same expression, will have a hydrogen ion concentration of $10^{-7.07}$, since $10^{-7.07} \times 10^{-7.07} = 10^{-14.14}$.

The value of the hydrogen ion concentration will accordingly be expressed by the hydrogen ion based on the normality factor of the solution used, and this factor will have the form of a *negative power of 10*. Since in the following section I usually refer to this, I will explain here that *I use the name "hydrogen ion exponent" and the designation P_H for the numerical value of the exponents of this power*. In the three examples given above, the P_H will therefore be 2, 12.40, and 7.07, respectively. . . .

C_P, which is based on the normality factor of the solution on hydrogen ions, or, in other words, means the number of gram atoms of hydrogen ion per liter, is less than 1 in all the cases treated in this paper, and can thus be placed equal to 10^{-P}. *For the number P, I have chosen the name "hydrogen ion exponent" and the written expression P_H. By the hydrogen ion exponent (P_H) of a solution we understand the Briggs logarithm of the reciprocal value of the normality factor of the solution based on the hydrogen ions.*[1]

OPTICAL METHODS

THE ULTRAMICROSCOPE. Probably the first major advance in colloid chemistry came from the studies of Zsigmondy on ruby glasses in which the color was due to colloidal gold particles. His method of ultramicroscopy permitted visualization of these colloidal preparations, and was soon extended to other branches of colloidal chemistry, as he predicted it would be in the paper in which he first described his method.

The following selection is from pages 1–5 of *Annalen der Physik 10,* 1–39 (1903).

On Making Visible and Determining the Size of Ultramicroscopic[2] Particles with Special Attention to Gold Ruby Glasses

H. SIEDENTOPF AND R. ZSIGMONDY

The existence of a series of gold-containing glasses in which the gold was present in the most varied colored states (blue, violet, red, in different shades), as well as in larger particles no longer coloured but cloudy, gave us the opportunity for a detailed optical study which we report in the following communication.

Up to now no one has been able to state anything definite about the size or other properties of the individual small gold particles in ruby glass; it has been stated only that they were no longer visible microscopically and their size had to be under that of a half light

[1] I have chosen the above definition of the hydrogen ion exponent because only rarely will it be necessary to take account of a hydrogen ion solution stronger than 1 normal. It will therefore usually be a positive number, and only in rare, exceptional cases will it be negative in dealing with a stronger hydrogen ion concentration than 1 normal.

[2] Since in this paper we must very often mention particles whose dimensions are below the limits of resolution for microscopic observation in the Abbe-Helmboltz sense, we have decided to call them ultramicroscopic for brevity.

wave. The above-mentioned series of gold glasses therefore permitted a closer study of this question. We first set ourselves the problem of working out a method which as far as possible would make the gold particles themselves available for direct observation.

We should note to begin with that after a year and a half of improvement of this method, which is discussed in more detail in what follows, we have progressed so far that we believe we are very close to the limits which can be attained. We have been able to make visible by its help gold particles whose size is not far from molecular dimensions. We further emphasize that our method is capable of general use and that we ourselves have already extended the investigation with some success to the study of colloidal solutions and turbid media. However, since such studies have more chemical or medical interest, we must limit ourselves here to a discussion of the optical conditions of the method and a description of it. This forms the content of the first part of the following report. Then in the second part we will describe the attempt to determine the order of magnitude of the observed ultramicroscopic particles, and in the third we will conclude with the observations made here on the gold glasses.

1. On a Method for Making Ultramicroscopic
Particles Visible

The colored ruby glasses which are the starting point of this work show no turbidity by ordinary microscopic methods, even with dark field illumination, but appear homogeneous. We might expect in them some hint of heterogeneity, since in thin sections the gold glasses should behave like colored bacterial preparations. Of course, the whole problem might seem pointless, especially if it were considered that the size of the particles to be made visible could not be approached by the resolving power of the best microscopes. However, a simple reflection based on previous observations permits us to be sure that the problem can be solved. If we consider that at any division self-illuminating particles of very high specific radiating power at average distances are still resolvable microscopically, we will be able to observe the diffraction disks produced from them in a microscope even if the particles are smaller than about half a wave length of visible light. It is only necessary that the product of the specific intensity at the surface of the illuminated particle and the square of the sine of the effective light angle be greater than the lower boundary for the light sensitivity of the eye. The image itself is liable to the same limitations as those of the stars through a telescope. From these considerations we can make the objects visible by bright illumination through a narrow slit which can be produced on a silvered glass surface; the width of the slit can be about 0.1 μ or less.

Here we must so illuminate that we obtain a limit for disappearance of the image lower than that established by Abbe and Helmholtz for similar images. From these remarks follow the requirements for making the smallest particles visible. Since in general optically detected particles are not, or almost not, self-illuminated with sufficient intensity we must at once turn to artificial illumination, and specifically to brighter sources than arc lights or sunlight. Because of their smallness, the illuminated particles exert no noteworthy influence on the phases of the illuminating rays, so that they act like self-illuminated particles from the light rays scattered by them. In size and direction of amplitude the rays of the diffraction cone are different, according to the investigations of Rayleigh. The size of the diffracted rays that lie in the direction of the illuminating rays is double that scattered in a perpendicular plane, and the direction of the amplitude of the diffracted rays agrees with the diffraction plane in a simple way.

The intensity of the illuminating rays is in general markedly higher than that of the diffracted ones. Therefore, in order to make the smaller particles visible through their diffraction cone it is *a main requirement so to arrange the lighting that none of the illuminating rays are contained in the diffraction cone used to make them visible.* Such an arrangement would in principle come to a so-called dark field illumination. However, such an arrangement, using arc light or sunlight, gives such a large number of reflections on the numerous lens surfaces of the condenser and the microscope objective that the principle of dark field illumination in practice becomes illusory.

However, if the arrangement is such that the axis of the illumination cone is perpendicular to the axis of the diffraction cone for making the particles visible, and both cones are of such a size that they do not interpenetrate, the resulting reflections in the condenser do not affect the observation objective perpendicular to them in the microscope, and it becomes impossible for one of the illuminating rays in the latter to penetrate directly (Fig. 1). Accordingly, the method here discussed is supplementary to the so-called dark field illumination; it makes possible in particular the use of the brightest light sources for illumination.

There is still another way to characterize the method. It is known that the dust particles that float freely in the air of a closed space become visible as soon as a ray of sunlight comes through a slit into a dark room and the eye of the observer sees them in a plane nearly perpendicular to the sun's rays. If the illumination is strengthened and the observation made through the use of a condenser and

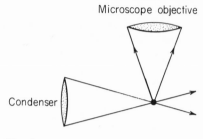

Fig. 1

a microscope system in the arrangement of Fig. 1, the principle of our method has likewise been sketched.

In the remainder of the paper a detailed description of the apparatus is given.

METHODS OF SEPARATION

It was in the field of separation of chemically similar substances that some of the greatest advances in methodology were made during the first half of the twentieth century. Such substances were particularly difficult to separate by the older methods of distillation or crystallization because their boiling points and solubilities were often very similar. However, closer studies of other physical properties showed that such features as ease of adsorption, size, or electrical charge could frequently show great differences. The newer methods were applications of such principles.

CHROMATOGRAPHY. The groups of plant pigments represented by the chlorophylls and carotenoids offered a challenge to the nineteenth-century chemist because of their vivid colors and obvious importance to plants, and because of the difficulty of separating them into individual components. The problem of their separation was solved early in the new century by the brilliant work of Tswett, who utilized the properties of differential adsorption rates and color in the process he called chromatography. In his first widely disseminated paper on this subject, the first selection given below, he not only showed how to obtain an easy and complete separation of the plant pigments, but intimated many of the later developments of the method. At first not much use was made of his discovery, but by about 1930 it came into general use for purification of plant pigments. The discovery of the structures of carotene and vitamin A (see p. 303) would have been difficult without it. It was soon extended to other colored compounds, then to colorless ones revealed by reactions that produced colored compounds or by ultraviolet fluorescence; and then, as new adsorption materials were developed, such as ion exchange resins or cellulose derivatives, including, very significantly, paper, the method acquired very wide distribution. Such diverse substances as amino acids and rare earth compounds could be separated by chromatographic methods. The selections by Martin and Spedding which follow the first citation below illustrate such widening of the applicability of chromatography.

The following selection is from pages 316–317 and 318–323 of *Berichte der Deutschen Botanischen Gesellschaft 24*, 316–323 (1906).

Physical Chemical Studies on Chlorophyll Adsorptions

M. TSWETT

It is a fact, already long known, that different organic liquids that serve as solvents for chlorophyll are very unequally suitable for the extraction of leaf green from leaves. While alcohol or ether gives intensive dark green extracts, other solvents, such as the aliphatic or cyclic hydrocarbons and carbon disulfide, give more yellowish extracts, much poorer in chlorophyll even when extraction of dry material is carried out. The most characteristic in this respect are petroleum ether and petroleum benzine, which when brought into contact with fresh leaves or those dried at low temperature give mostly more or less pure yellow extracts, colored by carotin, on which property Arnaud based his process for preparation of this pigment from leaves.

If the chlorophyll itself is completely soluble in petroleum ether, as is generally accepted, why is it not removed from fresh or dried leaves in this solvent? Why is only a yellow portion dissolved?

This problem, no less important for the question of the physical constitution and chemical composition of the chlorophyll apparatus, has remained unsolved up to now. Because of the brilliant development of the chemistry of chlorophyll derivatives, many questions of broad physiological interest have been neglected. The few investigators who have turned their attention to the phenomena with which we are concerned have offered different and contradictory explanations, among which not one can be said to stand on a broad experimental basis.

A review of previous work is given.

Thus far the literature dealing with our problem. When I turn to the experimental treatment of this question, it has first of all seemed worthwhile to me to test more closely *in situ* the effect of various indifferent organic solvents on the leaf pigments.

Among the numerous materials used I found especially suitable *Plantago* species and *Lamium album*. The softness of the *Lamium* leaves and the approximate neutrality of their tissue juice marked them as especially suitable objects.

Their behavior toward the leaf pigments permits us to divide the solvents tested into three groups:

1. Alcohols (methyl, ethyl, amyl), acetone, acetaldehyde, ether, chloroform. These solvents, acting on fresh (ground) or dry leaves, dissolve all the pigments equally and abundantly.

2. Petroleum ether and petroleum benzine. Fresh leaves finely ground with sand or emery and again ground under the solvent give more or less pure yellow extracts that are chiefly colored by carotin, but also contain traces of the other pigments. The carotin can be completely extracted in this way. Dried leaves (dried at low temperature!) likewise give their carotin to the solvent, and in somewhat purer condition. Tissues cooked or warmed at higher temperatures, however, when ground with this solvent give a green extract, a fact which will be explained later.

3. Benzene, xylene, toluene, carbon disulfide. They have an action on leaf pigments intermediate between the solvents of the first groups.

As mentioned, petroleum ether dissolves only traces of the other pigments besides carotin. However, it is enough to add some absolute alcohol (10 per cent for fresh leaves, 1 per cent for dry ones) in order to obtain a richly colored, beautiful green solution. Acetone or ether has an analogous action.

The total chlorophyll can be extracted with petroleum ether containing alcohol. What is the significance of this "solubilizing" action of the alcohol? Since, with pure petroleum ether, one component of the chlorophyll, carotin, is very well extracted, we cannot believe that the solvent does not reach the chlorophyll. A chemical action of the alcohol is excluded here, as the following investigation shows. Fresh leaves were ground with emery and the resulting homogenate was treated with about 40 per cent alcohol. If the material was then immediately treated with petroleum ether, a green solution resulted, but if it was dried at 45°, petroleum ether gave only the usual yellow carotin solution. The alcohol must therefore act simply by its presence physically, and not chemically. Actually, the pigments, recognizably soluble in pure petroleum ether, after alcohol extraction can again become insoluble in this solvent.

My first study (1901, III) in this direction was as follows. Alcohol-petroleum ether solutions of chorophyll were digested in a flask with several strips of filter paper and the solvent was distilled off in a vacuum; by this treatment the pigment was taken up by the paper. The dry green paper now behaved toward solvents exactly like the green leaves, and pure petroleum ether took up only the carotin, while the addition of alcohol produced decolorization of the paper at once.

The phenomena mentioned at the beginning of this paper, which still remained puzzling, therefore depended on adsorption of the pigments, on the mechanical, molecular affinity of the substances for the chloroplast stroma which could indeed be overcome by alcohol, ether, etc., but not by petroleum hydrocarbons. However, if the pigments were removed from the sphere of molecular forces, as, for example, by cooking or warming the tissues, which, as is well known, forces little green droplets from the chloroplasts, then these pigments dissolved easily in petroleum ether and the dark green extract was obtained.

It follows from the foregoing that it is impossible for chlorophyll to be enclosed in the chloroplasts in the form of microscopically definable grana and it must be that the grana themselves possess an insoluble adsorbing substrate. Moreover, the grana theory is not well grounded micrographically.

It was mentioned above that the chlorophyll pigments (except for carotin) bound to the filter paper from the petroleum ether were held firmly by an adsorption force. As expected, these pigments were taken from the petroleum ether solution by the filter paper. However, not only cellulose but *all solid bodies insoluble in petroleum hydrocarbons* adsorb chlorophyll and, if used in finely powdered condition, decolorize petroleum ether partly or completely. From this point of view I have studied more than a hundred substances belonging to different chemical systems and always with essentially the same result. I will give here a short summary of the substances tested.

Simple substances (S, Si, Zn, Fe, Al, Pb, Sb); oxides (SiO_2, MgO, MnO_2, PbO, Sb_2O_3, Fe_2O_3, Ag_2O, HgO, U_3O_8); hydroxides ($B(OH)_3$, NaOH, $Ba(OH)_2$, $Al(OH)_3$); inorganic chlorides (Na, K, NH_4, Ca, Mg, Al, Fe, Co, Cu, Hg); chlorates (K, Ba); potassium bromide, potassium iodate; nitrates (K, Ca, Ba, Pb, Ag, Cu, U); phosphates (K, Na, NH_4, Fe); sulfides (K, Hg); sulfite (Na); sulfates (K, Ca, Mg, Ba, Zn, Fe, Mn, Cu); carbonates (Na, K, Ca, Mg, Fe); silicates (K, asbestos); ammonium molybdate, potassium permanganate, potassium ferricyanide and potassium ferrocyanide, oxalic acid, tartaric acid, citric acid, quinic acid, tannic acid, uric acid, picric acid, phenolphthalein; oxalates (NH_4, Mn); acetates (Pb, Cu); amides (urea, asparagine); higher alcohols and carbohydrates (mannite, dulcite, sucrose, galactose, inulin, dextrin, amylose); proteins (egg albumin, peptone, hemoglobin); trioxymethylene, chloral hydrate, hydroquinone, resorcin, pyrogallol, aniline dyes (gentian violet, chrysoidin, etc.); finally a series of chemically undefined substances (bone meal and blood meal, soil, kieselguhr).

Some of these substances can also carry down carotin from its petroleum ether solution ($HgCl_2$, $CaCl_2$, PbS, etc.). Many bodies decompose the pigments adsorbed on them. Some, for example (MnO_2, $KMnO_4$, U_3O_8), destroy the chlorophyll completely, obviously by oxidation. Others act on the chlorophyllines in the well-known manner of acids; these include the acids mentioned, acid salts, and many neutral salts whose water solutions can acquire an acid reaction by hydrolysis. This is not the place to discuss more fully the type and manner of these chemical reactions. We shall speak more fully of the method of adsorption and its analytical use. In order to obtain a petroleum ether solution, the best procedure is the following. Fresh leaves (best from *Lamium*) were ground in a mortar with fine emery and again extracted with petroleum ether containing alcohol (10 per cent). The green solution was repeatedly washed with twice the volume of water in a separatory funnel.

The alcohol had a greater affinity for water than for petroleum ether and so it could be separated practically completely from the petroleum ether in this way. The washed green solution, usually somewhat cloudy, was now clarified by centrifuging or filtration and was suitable for adsorption studies.

The most suitable adsorptive materials were precipitated calcium carbonate, inulin, or sucrose (powdered).

If the petroleum ether chlorophyll solution was then shaken with the adsorptive material, the latter carried down the pigment, and with a certain excess of this, only the carotin remained in solution, escaping adsorption. In this way a green precipitate and a pure yellow, fluorescence-free carotin solution were obtained (test for fluorescence in my luminoscope). This carotin solution showed a spectrum with absorption bands at 492–475 and 460–445$\mu\mu$. If it was shaken with 80 per cent alcohol, the lower alcohol-water phase remained completely colorless.

The green precipitate was then brought onto a filter and carefully washed with petroleum ether to separate the last traces of carotin. The filtered yellow liquid could be immediately regenerated with bone meal. Then the precipitate was treated with petroleum ether containing alcohol, which completely decolored it and gave a beautiful green solution which could then be separated by 80 per cent alcohol by the method of Kraus. The petroleum ether phase, colored blue-green, contained chiefly the chlorophyllines, while the lower yellow phase contained chiefly the xanthophylls.

If the petroleum ether solution of the chlorophyll was treated with the adsorption material not in excess, but in portions until the fluorescence vanished, then along with the carotin the xanthophylls also remained in solution. These could be freed from carotin by again treating the decanted solution with the adsorption material and liberating the pigment from the resulting adsorption compound with petroleum ether containing alcohol. The solution of xanthophyll mixture thus obtained shows the following absorption spectrum: 480–470 and 452–440 $\mu\mu$. If it was shaken with 80 per cent alcohol, the pigment remained almost completely in the alcoholic phase.

The physical interpretation of the adsorption phenomena that we have considered will be discussed elsewhere. However, here we can mention some related regularities and the resulting applications. The adsorption material saturated with a pigment can still take up another member of a certain mixture and hold it firmly. Substitution can also occur. For example, the xanthophylls can be partly displaced from their adsorption compounds by the chorophyllines, but not the reverse. There is a definite adsorption series according to which the substances can substitute. The following important application comes from this rule. If a petroleum ether solution of chlorophyll filters through a column of an adsorption material (I use chiefly calcium carbonate which is firmly pressed into a narrow glass tube), the pigments will separate according to the adsorption series from above downward in differently colored zones, and the more strongly adsorbed pigments will displace the more weakly held ones which will move downward. This separation will be practically complete if, after one passage of the pigment solution it is followed, by a stream of pure solvent through the adsorbing column. Like the light rays of the spectrum, the different components of a pigment mixture in the calcium carbonate column will be separated regularly from each other, and can be determined qualitatively and also quantitatively. I call such a preparation a *chromatogram* and the corresponding method the *chromatographic method*. In the near future I will give a later report on this. It is perhaps not superfluous to mention here that this method in its principle and also in the exceptional ease of carrying it out has nothing to do with so-called capillary analysis.

Up to now we have considered only the adsorption of chlorophyll pigments from petroleum ether solution. However, adsorption also occurs from benzene, xylene, toluene, and carbon disulfide solutions. From benzene indeed almost the chlorophyllines alone are adsorbed, in much less degree than from petroleum ether. It seems, however, that adsorption from a CS_2 solution obtained simply by treatment of the ground leaves with the solvent is especially suitable for chromatographic analysis. In CS_2 the different pigment zones have a much brighter color than in petroleum ether, especially the xanthophylls which in it are very sharply differentiated from each other. Carotin passes through as a rose-colored solution.

It is obvious that the adsorption phenomena described are suitable not only for chlorophyll pigments, and it can be assumed that any sorts of colored or colorless chemical compounds will follow the same rules. Up to now I have studied lecithin, alkannin, prodigiosin, sudan, cyanin, and solanorubin as well as the acid derivatives of chlorophyllines with positive results.

The following selection is from pages 224–225 of *The Biochemical Journal 38*, 224–232 (1944).

Qualitative Analysis of Proteins:
A Partition Chromatographic Method Using Paper

R. CONSDEN, A. H. GORDON, AND A. J. P. MARTIN

Gordon, Martin and Synge attempted to separate amino-acids on a silica gel partition chromatogram, but found it impracticable owing to adsorption by the silica of various amino-acids. They obtained, however, good separations by using cellulose in the form of strips of filter paper. Following further work along these lines, the present paper describes a qualitative micro-analytical technique for proteins. Using only 200 μg of wool, it is possible by this method to demonstrate the presence of all the amino-acids which have been shown to be there by other methods.

The method is rather similar to the capillary analysis method of Schönbein and Goppelsroeder (reviewed by Rheinboldt) except that the separation depends on the differences in partition coefficient between the mobile phase and water-saturated cellulose, instead of differences in adsorption by the cellulose. That adsorption of the amino-acids by the cellulose plays no significant part is seen from Table 1 [not included here], where the partition coefficient calculated from the rates of movement of the bands are compared with those found directly by England and Cohn. Too much stress should not be laid upon the agreement of these figures, which are based upon an assumed water content of the saturated cellulose and the assumption that the ratio of the weight of n-butanol to paper is constant in all parts of the strip. This assumption does not hold accurately. Nevertheless, the conclusion seems justified that the cellulose is playing the role of an inert support.

The most satisfactory solvents are those which are partially miscible with water. Within a homologous series of solvents the corresponding rates of movement of the amino-acids change in the same direction as the water solubility of the solvent: solvents completely miscible with water can be employed provided that the water content is not too high. In this case, presumably, the cellulose, by a "salting out" effect, allows the system to function as a partition chromatogram. However, the amino-acid bands obtained are much broader than is the case with immiscible solvents. This is no doubt due to a variation in the composition of the phases caused by the presence of the amino-acids. This effect has been noticed in the n-butanol-water system by England and Cohn and is the limiting factor in the amount of amino-acid that can be employed in a given chromatogram. It is reasonable to suppose that the phases will be more easily disturbed by employing a miscible rather than an immiscible solvent. The main effect of temperature on the rates of movement of the amino-acids is also explicable in terms of the change in composition of the phases. Thus, in the phenol-water system, increase of temperature increases the miscibility and the rate of movement of the bands. In the collidine-water system the reverse is true. Further, the greater the difference between the working temperature and the critical solution temperature, the less sensitive will the rates be to change of temperature. However, though the absolute partition coefficients may be greatly changed, the ratios of the partition coefficients of the respective acids are almost unaltered.

There is an obvious advantage in working with unsubstituted amino-acids in that any substituent group, even though small, renders the physical properties of the derivatives more similar and hence increases the difficulties of separation. Martin and Synge and Gordon, Martin and Synge failed to separate the slower moving acids when acetylated, whereas all the acids are separable by the present technique. Moreover, selective losses associated with acetylation and extraction are obviated.

A considerable number of solvents has been tried. The relative positions of the amino-acids in the developed chromatogram depend upon the solvent used. Hence by development first in one direction with one solvent followed by development in a direction at right angles with another solvent, amino-acids (e.g., a drop of protein hydrolysate) placed near the corner of a sheet of paper becomes distributed in a pattern across the sheet to give a two-dimensional chromatogram characteristic of the pair of solvents used. Advantage is taken of the colour reaction with ninhydrin to reveal the positions of the amino-acids.

Experimental details follow.

The following selection is from page 2777 of *The Journal of the American Chemical Society 69*, 2777–2781 (1947).

The Separation of Rare Earths by Ion Exchange.
I. Cerium and Yttrium

F. H. SPEDDING, A. F. VOIGT, E. M. GLADROW AND N. R. SLEIGHT

For many years one of the most difficult processes in the field of chemistry has been the separation of the rare earths from each other into their pure states. Their chemical and physical properties are so similar that in general a single operation leads only to a partial separation or enrichment.

Ever since the beginning of the Manhattan Project there has been a constant demand for samples of rare earths of exceptional purity in gram amounts or greater. This demand arose for numerous reasons, but mainly because some of the rare earths are formed as fission fragments during fission of the heavy elements. It was highly desirable, therefore, to have a means of preparing pure rare earths so that their nuclear properties could be studied and also to allow a more thorough consideration of their chemical behavior. Their radioisotopes are less well understood than those of any other group of elements.

In general, the best means of separating these elements has been the well-known but laborious method of fractional crystallization as used by James and further developed in many laboratories. Exceptions are cerium with its quadrivalent state, and samarium, europium, and ytterbium with their di-valent states which do permit a means of separation from the normal trivalent rare earth ions.

A number of workers have reported studies on the application of chromatographic and ion exchange methods to the separation of the rare earths. While they obtained considerable enrichment their results were not sufficiently promising to lead to further intensive investigation or to the quantity production of pure rare earths. The history within the Manhattan District of the use of columns of Amberlite-type resins for the separation of fission products, both with and without the use of citric acid-ammonium citrate eluants at controlled pH, has been described elsewhere and will not be discussed here.

The present paper is the first of a series from this laboratory dealing with the successful separation of macro quantities of rare earths of spectrographic purity, by adsorption on Amberlite-type resins and subsequent elution with complexing agents such as citric acid-ammonium citrate solutions at controlled pH. This paper establishes that cerium and yttrium can be separated relatively rapidly by these methods on any desired scale.

The marked success of the process described depends on the fact that the rare earths form complexes with the citrate ions. If the pH is suitably adjusted, competition is set up for the rare earth ions between the citrate complexes and the active centers of the resin. Therefore, as the citrate solution washes the rare earths down the column, each rare earth is adsorbed and desorbed many times. Since the equilibrium constants for the rare earth citrate complexes vary slightly among the different rare earths, their rates of travel down the column differ sufficiently to lead to their separation. The repeated cycles in the columns effectively replace the thousands of individual operations required by the older methods for separating the rare earths and lead to a highly effective process analogous to the use of distillation columns.

Experimental details of the separations are then described.

SEPARATIONS OF PROTEINS BY SEDIMENTATION AND ELECTRO-PHORESIS. Because of the large size and the range of sizes among colloidal particles, they offered a particular problem in separation. Because of the biological importance of the proteins, which made up such a large number of natural colloidal systems, the challenge was even greater. Chemical methods did not give satisfactory results for such easily altered substances as the proteins, and even chromatography was not especially successful. Hence other physical methods had to be applied. The principle of flotation had been used for centuries to separate relatively coarse mixtures into fractions with particles of about the same size. It occurred to Svedberg that if sufficient gravitational force could be applied, even colloidal particles might be separated into fractions by sedimentation. His development of the ultracentrifuge, described in the first two selections that follow, was brilliantly successful.

An even more fundamental separation could be effected when the colloidal particles had varying electrical charges. Depending upon the rates of migration of ions in an electrical field, Tiselius was able to separate pure proteins or amino acids from their mixtures, as described in the third of the following selections. Both the ultracentrifuge and the electrophoretic method could also be applied to other complex mixtures of suitable substances.

The following selection is from pages 2910–2913 of *The Journal of the American Chemical Society 45*, 2910–2917 (1923).

Determination of the Size and Distribution of Size of Particle by Centrifugal Methods

THE SVEDBERG AND J. BURTON NICHOLS

In the determination of size and distribution of size of particle through gravity sedimentation by Oden's method one is limited to relatively coarsely grained sols of about 100 $\mu\mu$ radius or larger. Since this is due to the extremely slow rate of settling, if the effect of gravity be increased sols of true colloidal size might thus be determined. To this end we have employed centrifugal force, and since direct weighing becomes impracticable here we designed a special centrifuge so constructed that the sol may be observed as it is precipitated. Then for a uniform sol, size of particle may be determined by measuring the rate of movement outward of the boundary of the particles and applying a modified form of Stokes' law.

With the centrifuge the acceleration of the particle is no longer constant as in the case of gravity sedimentation but varies with the distance from the center.

Let a be the distance from the axis of rotation to the meniscus of the sol in the centrifuge tube. Then let x be the distance the boundary of the particles has moved in a given time t. Now consider the forces acting on a particle at the point x. The frictional force which tends to cause it to resist movement is $6\pi\eta r(dx/dt)$ where η is the viscosity of the liquid, r the radius of the particle considered to be a sphere, and dx/dt its velocity. But the centrifugal force applied to cause movement is $4/3\pi r^3(d_p - d_l)w^2(x + a)$, $(d_p - d_l)$ being the difference in density between the particles and the dispersion medium, w the angular viscosity, and $(x + a)$ the distance from the axis of rotation to the particle.

Equating and rearranging for integration

$$\int_0^t r^2 dt = \int_0^x \frac{9\eta}{2(d_p - d_l)w^2} \frac{dx}{x + a}$$

$$r^2 t = \frac{9\eta}{2(d_p - d_l)w^2} \ln\left(\frac{x + a}{a}\right)$$

$$r = \sqrt{\frac{9\eta \ln\left(\frac{x + a}{a}\right)}{2(d_p - d_l)w^2 t}} \tag{1}$$

Therefore by measuring the distance x which the boundary of the sol has moved out in a time t, and obtaining the speed of the centrifuge, it is possible to determine r.

Figure 1 shows the centrifuge devised. The rotor A is directly connected at B to a Dumore special 20,000 rpm motor C suspended in the heavy metal casing D and supported by a pivot bearing E. The machine is mounted on a large wooden base F, laminated to prevent warping, and several thicknesses of linoleum are glued on the top and bottom to absorb vibration.

The rotor is enclosed in a square metal box G for the purpose of protecting the tube from air currents and resulting temperature differences. Air may be blown through the box also in order to obtain constant temperature. The top is made removable so that the rotor may be adjusted when necessary.

The rotor consists of the central head H, horizontally cored I, to which are screwed the two arms J, also cored to correspond to the core of the head. These arms are closed at the outer end by screw-caps K to provide a means for changing the tubes L contained. In order to obtain vertical or horizontal illumination of the tubes, the arms are slotted M, top and bottom and on both sides.

The tubes used L, one for each arm, are made of a good resistance glass tubing such as Pyrex or Jena, sealed off smoothly at the outer end and closed at the inner end by paraffined corks. To prevent too much strain on the rounded portion a plastic substance is filled in the space between the tube and the cap K.

A thin metal disk N, of slightly greater diameter than the length of the rotor, attached to the head just below the arms, is slotted at O directly under the vertical slots in the arms and is fixed in position so that no relative motion of arms and disk will take place. This slotted disk therefore allows light to travel up through the box only when an arm is directly over the narrow beam of light employed for illumination.

Underneath the box is mounted a narrow plane mirror *P* for directing a uniform beam of light vertically through a slot *Q* in

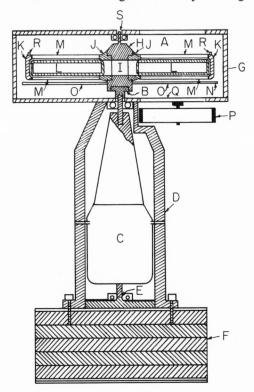

Fig. 1

the bottom of the box, of the same length as the slots in the arms, so that every time an arm passes over this slot a beam of light travels up through the slots in the arm and through a corresponding slot in the top of the box, where the image of the contents of the tube may be observed or photographed. There is also a slot in the side of the box at such a height that light reflected from the contents of the tubes also may be viewed or photographed.

The most difficult problem to solve was to provide a good means of balancing the rotor. This is essential, for when it is not in exact balance the vibrations tend to mix the colloid and vitiate the effect of the force applied. Several different methods were employed but none was sensitive enough. However, the sensitivity was finally obtained by inserting a hardened steel peg on each side of the head, in order to furnish a means of support for the rotor on knife edges. These rods are so situated that the center of gravity of the rotor lies just below the point of support, such arrangement giving maximum sensitivity. Then the end of each arm was threaded, and adjustable rings *R* gave us the means for varying the movement of the arms so that they would come to rest in a horizontal position.

Figure 2 gives a diagrammatic representation of the apparatus and the path of the beam of light up through the sol in the centrifuge

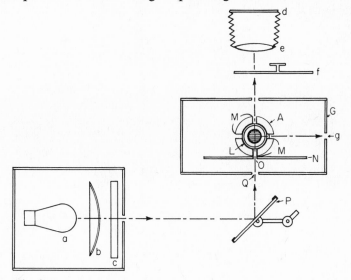

Fig. 2

tube to the photographic plate. In this case the section of the centrifuge box is at right angles to the view shown in Figure 1.

The practical use of the apparatus is then described.

The following selection is from pages 1–4 and 9–10 of *Chemical Reviews 14*, 1–15 (1934).

Sedimentation of Molecules in Centrifugal Fields
THE SVEDBERG

The usual methods for the determination of molecular weights in solution based upon the measurement of osmotic pressure, boiling point, or freezing point are, in principle, only procedures for counting the number of solute particles in the solution. If the concentration of the solute is known, the mean particle mass or molecular weight may be calculated. The mass of the individual particle or molecule does not influence the phenomenon studied. These classical methods, therefore, do not give any information about the weights or the different molecular species eventually present in the solution under investigation, but merely give us an average value of the molecular weight across all the species.

At the present time the means at our disposal for the measurement of individual molecular masses are very limited. The mass spectrograph allows of determination of the relation between electrical charge and mass of different molecular species in a beam of molecular rays. If the charge be known, the individual molecular mass may be calculated. This method, however, is possible only in the case of relatively simple molecules in gases at low pressures. The study of band spectra has furnished valuable information concerning moments of inertia and intermolecular distances, but this method, too, is restricted to gaseous systems containing molecules built up of only a few atoms.

The lack of a reliable method for the determination of molecular weights and especially for the molecular weight analysis of high molecular organic substances such as the proteins, the carbohydrates, the hydrocarbons, etc., has been a serious hindrance to research in those fields. When staying as a visiting professor at the University of Wisconsin ten years ago, the present writer tried to outline such a method. The technique was then developed in his laboratory at the University of Upsala. The procedure in question is based upon the measurement of the sedimentation of molecules in strong centrifugal fields.

The theory is fairly simple as long as we have to deal with electrically neutral molecules, e.g., proteins at the isoelectric point. Two different possibilities of measurement exist. We can determine the concentration gradient in a small column of solution exposed to the influence of the centrifugal field until equilibrium has been reached between sedimentation and diffusion (sedimentation equilibrium method). For each molecular species the following formula is valid:

$$M = \frac{2RT \ln (c_2/c_1)}{(1 - V\rho)\omega^2(x_2^2 - x_1^2)} \tag{1}$$

where
M = molecular weight,
R = gas constant,

T = absolute temperature,
V = partial specific volume of solute,
ρ = density of solvent,
x_2 and x_1 are distances to the center of rotation, and
ω = angular velocity

An inhomogeneity with regard to molecular weight shows up as a drift in the values with distance from the center of rotation. The absence of drift is therefore a reliable criterion that only one species of molecules is present in the solution. In the case of more than one species of solute molecules it is often possible, by choosing different intensities of the centrifugal field, to get one or the other component to predominate at the top or at the bottom of the column of solution.

A still sharper test of homogeneity, which at the same time enables us to find how many different kinds of molecules are present and to determine the sedimentation constants of the various molecular species present in the solution, consists in measuring the velocity of sedimentation of the molecules in a very strong centrifugal field. The sedimentation constant reduced to water of 20°C. is given by the formula:

$$S_{20°} = dx/dt \cdot 1/\omega^2 x \cdot \eta/\eta_0 \cdot \frac{(1 - V\rho_0)}{(1 - V\rho)} \qquad (2)$$

where dx/dt = observed sedimentation velocity,
ω = angular velocity,
x = distance from center of rotation,
η = viscosity of solvent,
η_0 = viscosity of water at 20° C.,
V = partial specific volume of solute,
ρ = density of solvent, and
ρ_0 = density of water at 20° C.

By combining a determination of sedimentation equilibrium and of sedimentation velocity we are able to obtain a measure of the deviation of the molecules from the spherical shape. The ratio

$$\frac{M(1 - V\rho)/S}{6\pi\eta N(3MV/4\pi N)^{\frac{1}{3}}} \qquad (3)$$

(where N is the Avogadro constant) ought to be unity if the molecules are spherical. A deviation from the spherical shape shows up as a value higher than unity for this ratio.

Certain complications are introduced if the sedimenting molecules are electrolytically dissociated. The sedimentation of the heavy part of the molecule is retarded because of the electrostatic attraction from the lighter ions. This effect may, however, be eliminated by the addition of a non-sedimenting electrolyte.

For the measurement of the sedimentation of molecules in centrifugal fields the following experimental problem has to be solved. A small column of liquid (height 4 to 12 mm., thickness 1 to 12 mm.) must be kept rotating at high speed for considerable time—during several hours in case of velocity runs and during days or even weeks in the case of sedimentation equilibrium runs. The distance from the center of rotation should not be less than, say, 50 mm. because of the higher accuracy of measurement in homogeneous centrifugal fields. The temperature in the column of solution should be constant or changing but very slowly. The latter condition is of vital importance. An unfavorable temperature distribution within the rotating solution creates convection currents which completely vitiate quantitative measurements. For the same reason evaporation from the surface of the liquid must be prevented. For sedimentation equilibrium measurements the height of the column of solution should not be more than 5 mm. because of the very long time required for the attainment of equilibrium in high columns. For sedimentation velocity determinations, on the other hand, the column should be as high as possible (not less than 10 mm.). The thickness of the layer of solution has to be chosen with regard to the concentration of the solution studied. Finally, the apparatus has to be built so as to permit of rapid and exact determinations of the concentration gradient in the solution while rotating at high speed.

The conditions just mentioned delimit the mechanical possibilities for the construction of the machinery (called ultracentrifuge) very much. For sedimentation equilibrium measurements on high molecular substances the centrifugal field need not exceed 10,000 times the force of gravity (corresponding to about 12,000 r.p.m. when the distance from the center of rotation is 50 mm.). In such cases, where the concentration gradient can be measured by taking photographs within a wave-length region of high light absorption, it is even possible to determine molecular weights down to about 500. On the other hand, by working at low speed (1500 r.p.m.) it is easy to measure molecular weights up to 5,000,000. The equilibrium method therefore allows us to master a large range with comparatively modest means.

A description of the apparatus used for this purpose at Upsala is given, and the author then proceeds to a description of the second method.

A detailed molecular weight analysis requires the determination of sedimentation velocity in very strong centrifugal fields (from 30,000 times the force of gravity and upwards to several hundred thousand). Here we meet with great experimental difficulties. In order to gain sufficient separation of the different molecular species during the run, the height of the rotating column of solution should not be too small. We have chosen 12 mm. as standard height. The use of optical methods for measuring the changes in concentration during centrifuging makes it necessary to enclose the solution in a transparent cell. Two circular plates of crystalline quartz, 18 mm. in diameter and 10 mm. thick, define the column of solution in the direction of observation. Between the quartz plates is an elastolite plate with a sectorial aperature of 4° forming bottom and sides of the cell for the liquid. Around the quartz and elastolite plates is a collar of elastolite. This aggregate is introduced into a duraluminum collar (outer diameter 26 mm.) threaded at the ends and kept together by guard rings of the same material Packings of very thin rubber membrane (0.06 mm.) are placed between the quartz plates and the elastolite plate. In order to delimit the light beam accurately, sector diaphragms of 2° are placed at the ends of the cell collar and fixed by means of two other guard rings. Cells of this construction withstand the action of a centrifugal field up to 400,000 times the force of gravity.

The rotor which carries the cell is shown in Fig. 6. It is made of

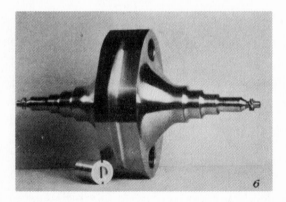

Fig. 6

chromium-nickel steel, is oval in shape (in order to lessen the strain), and has a diameter of 180 mm. across the cell holes. The thickness is 52 mm. at the periphery, and the weight 8.9 kg. The distance of the center of the cell holes from the axis of rotation is 65 mm. With a column of solution 12 mm. high the centrifugal force increases 20 per cent from top to bottom. When machining the rotor, two thin wings (total diameter 161 mm.) are left at right angles to the dia-meter bisecting the cell holes in order to prevent false light from reaching the photographic plate. Undue heating and temperature fluctuations are avoided by surrounding the rotor with a layer of hydrogen 1 mm. thick and of a pressure of about 25 mm. and outside of this with a heavy steel casing. In this way the friction is reduced very much and a bath of good heat-conducting properties is created. The bearings of the rotor are lubricated and cooled by oil of 2 kg. per cm^2 pressure. The driving agent is likewise oil acting on two small turbines (diameter 16 mm.), one on each end of the shaft of the rotor. By regulating the oil pressure from 1 to 16.5 kg. per cm.^{2} the speed range 5000 to 80,000 r.p.m. can be covered. The rotor shown in Fig. 6 was tested at 78,000 r.p.m. and has been run regularly at 75,000 r.p.m., corresponding to a centrifugal field 400,000 times gravity at the center of the cell. Figure 7 gives an axial diagrammatic section through the ultracentrifuge with a previous type of rotor, and Fig. 8 gives a picture of it with the upper part of

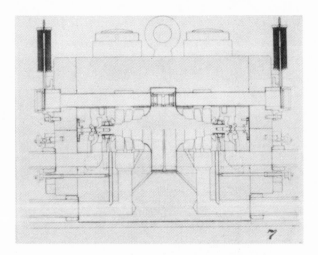

Fig. 7

the heavy steel casing lifted, laying bare the rotor and the turbine chambers. The cell with its sector diaphragm is in vertical position upside down. Behind the centrifuge is the lamp house and the light filters. The two halves of the thick steel casing are held together by bolts of chromium-nickel steel firmly anchored in a concrete foundation. This arrangement has proved an efficient protection in case of accident. Explosion of the rotor has occurred twice,

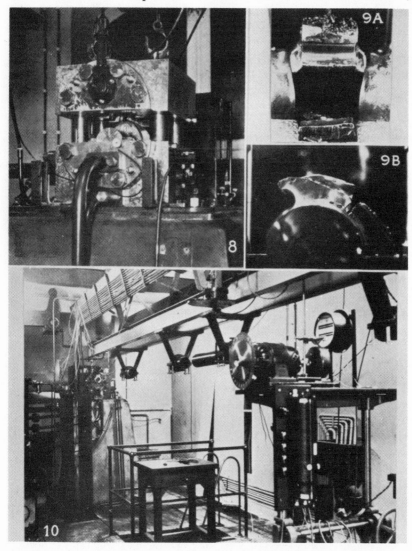

Fig. 8
Fig. 9A
Fig. 9B
Fig. 10

once from fatigue and another time because of flaw in the material. Pictures of the rotor and turbine chambers completely wrecked by such an explosion are shown in Fig. 9. Figure 10 gives a total view of the installation showing, from right to left, the stroboscope for measuring the speed, the camera, the centrifuge on its foundation, and the coolers. The compressor for delivery of pressure oil, together with the oil filters and vacuum pump, is mounted in a lower room, the entrance to which is seen in the middle of the picture. The switchboard with all the control instruments, such as voltmeters, ammeters, manometers, vacuum meters, resistance thermometers, thermocouples, etc., is to the left of the big room and is not shown in the picture. Two high-speed ultracentrifuge aggregates of this rather costly type are now available in the writer's laboratory, thanks to the generosity of the Rockefeller Foundation and the Nobel Foundation.

The first publication by Tiselius of his electrophoretic method was in his Inaugural Dissertation at Upsala in 1930. He described the method in detail before the Faraday Society in 1937.

The following selection is from pages 524–525, 526, and 527–530 of *Transactions of the Faraday Society 33*, 524–531 (1937).

A New Apparatus for Electrophoretic Analysis of Colloidal Mixtures

ARNE TISELIUS

In the course of earlier work on the electrophoretic migration of proteins in various buffer solutions (using a photographic-micro-photometric method to follow the migration), a detailed study was made of the different sources of error in electrophoretic measurements and the possibilities of their elimination. Special interest was devoted to the electrophoretic behavior of mixtures of proteins. It was found that the individual components in such mixtures do not usually mutually influence migration to any great extent, so that a partial separation is brought about by the current. From this we can derive conclusions as to the electrochemical homogeneity of a given colloidal solution, similar to those Svedberg derives from his ultracentrifuge molecular weight analysis. The importance of using physical methods for such a purpose is obvious:

the usual methods of fractionation of biocolloids (which are very unstable and very sensitive toward even quite mild chemical agents), are often of doubtful value. The procedure was exemplified both on artificial and on natural mixtures, and was also used for the purification of proteins. Figure 1 shows the apparatus used.

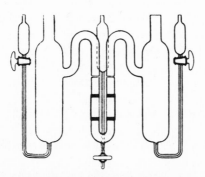

Fig. 1. Electrophoresis apparatus for the moving boundary method (Tiselius, 1930).

The value of electrophoretic fractionation and purification of mixtures of colloidal systems was first realized by Botho Schwerin, who described an experimental arrangement and some applications of the method in a number of patents from 1914 onwards. This work, of a preparative nature, was carried out in cells separated by permeable membranes. In addition to the author's work on proteins, quantitative investigations (free electrophoresis with reversible electrodes) on mixtures have been carried out recently by Theorell, especially on respiratory ferments, and by Bennhold on the serum proteins and their reactions with other substances. Theorell also describes an apparatus with membranes and reversible electrodes for the electrophoretic purification of larger volumes of material. Electrophoretic methods provide a means of characterising the often difficultly distinguishable high molecular substances by isoelectric points and by p_H-mobility relationships, so as to get some idea of the degree of their electrochemical homogeneity, and to detect and more or less completely fractionate the homogeneous components in a mixture. It may also be possible, if suitable precautions are taken, to determine the relative proportions, and to study the degree, if any, of mutual combination of the components; in these two applications the tendency of the components to exert a mutual influence on the migration may interfere. For quantitative interpretation the experiments must be carried out at a salt concentration considerably higher than is usually needed for the depression of the boundary disturbances discussed previously.

The migration in the electrophoresis tube may suitably be followed by optical observation of the boundaries, or by analytical determination of the change of the quantities of the components above and below fixed levels in the tube, as used extensively for biocolloids by Hardy, Michaelis, Landsteiner and Pauli, and later by Reiner, Engel and Pauli, and Theorell. Both methods have their advantages. Optical observation is particularly useful when the differently migrating substances have a similar chemical composition (*e.g.*, mixtures of proteins) which cannot be separately determined analytically. On the other hand, the analytical method alone can be used for the study of enzymes and other materials, when a measurement of activity is the only means for determining where the substance is in the tube. The apparatus for the latter method differs mainly in the provisions for sampling.

The apparatus now to be described is adapted for simultaneous use of both methods. Whichever method is being used, the modifications in the experimental arrangement resulting from the following considerations are of importance, especially in the study of mixtures and in work with media of high conductivity, and in electrophoretic fractionation.

Theoretical points to be considered in constructing the apparatus are discussed. The most significant of these is the following.

When both substances migrate in the same direction the possibility of sufficient separation is limited by the fact that long before the desired separation has been reached, both substances have migrated out of the electrophoresis tube. This is a somewhat serious limitation, since the absolute differences in mobilities are often very much larger at p_H regions where both components have mobilities of the same sign (*e.g.*, the serum proteins). Moreover, lack of solubility often prevents a choice of a p_H between the isoelectric points. For this reason we arranged for a slow and uniform movement of the solution in the electrophoresis tube at an exactly known rate and in a direction opposite to the migration, by slowly lifting a cylindrical glass tube by clockwork out of the liquid in one electrode tube during the electrophoresis. If the rate at which the tube is lifted is l cm. per hour, its cross-section area p cm.^{2}, the free surface of the liquid in each electrode tube Q cm.^{2}, and the cross-section area of the electrophoresis tube q cm.^{2} then a movement of a given level in this tube will take place, at a rate of $lpQ/q(2Q - p)$ cm. per hour. By suitably choosing l and p any desired rate can be obtained;

even in the narrow tubes used in our apparatus a rate of several centimetres per hour did not markedly blur the boundaries in the electrophoresis tube.

For fractionation purposes, this "compensation movement" is adjusted so that the observed boundary separating two fractions obtains a suitable "apparent mobility" and consequently, at the end of the run, the column of the solution can be cut off exactly at the right place (see below). . . .

Experimental Arrangement

(1) The thermostat is a well-insulated container taking about 100 *l* of water, and provided with double windows, between which are placed dishes with calcium chloride to prevent fog formation at the low temperature used. An Electrolux refrigeration unit of a maximum capacity of 100 kcal. per hour, but working at less than half-capacity, maintains the low temperature; the heat evolved in electrophoresis experiments usually does not exceed 20–30 kcal. per hour. Through a copper spiral wound around the evaporator of the refrigerator and connected to a similar spiral in the bath by rubber tubing, alcohol was circulated by a small pump, driven by the same motor as the stirrer. This maintained the bath automatically at $+0.1 - 0.2°$ C., even if the cooling effect varied within very wide limits. A compact layer of ice which is formed on the spiral in the bath is not removed by the stirring; if the cooling efiect is large the thickness of this layer increases, but this makes the conduction of the heat to the spiral less efficient, so that the evaporator temperature drops somewhat and the real cooling effect decreases and *vice versa*. The arrangement, providing a constant temperature just above zero, would seem useful for many laboratory purposes, for example, dialysis.

(2) The electrophoresis apparatus (Fig. 3), consisted of a central U-tube connected by thick rubber tubing with the large volume electrode vessels of which there were two pairs, one of about 2 litres capacity each for very difficult separations, the other of about 0.5 litre each. Reversible AgCl electrodes with saturated KCl were used as in the older apparatus, but of course the electrodes were given much larger surface. The volume of KCl in each tube was 25–100 c.c., it was allowed to form a layer at the bottom, running down through funnel tubes shortly before starting an experiment.

The U-tube, with an internal rectangular cross-section of 3 × 25 mm., was made of plain parallel glass plates, cemented together with acid-proof silicate cement; the curved walls of the U-shaped bottom part were cut from an ordinary cylindrical glass tube of the right diameter.

In order to follow the migration of any number of components analytically, the contents of the U-tube must be divided into at least two portions in one limb, preferably in both limbs. In most

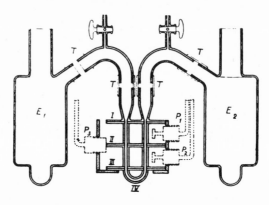

Fig. 3. Apparatus for electrophoretic analysis. E_1, E_2 represent the electrode tubes (the larger type), T rubber tubings; I, II, III, IV, the four U-tube sections, of which II and III can be moved with the pneumatic arrangement P_1, P_2, P_3.

previous constructions (Cohn, Michaelis, Landsteiner—Pauli, Reiner, Engel—Pauli), this has been done with stopcocks. Bennhold takes out samples with a capillary pipette. Theorell divides the U-tube into sections between which ebonite plates with circular holes are moved, there being as many as seven sections in each limb for isolating fractions migrating in the same direction. With the compensation device described above, no more than two sections are needed, even for this purpose. When working with high voltage, very good insulation is necessary to prevent leakage of current into the thermostat from the U-tube; our U-tube, therefore, consists of two equal sections, with one U-shaped bottom part, and one top part (for connection to the electrode tubes), all cemented to large (60 × 120 mm.) precision-ground glass plates, greased with a little vaseline thinned with paraffin oil. The arrangement resembles to a certain extent the diffusion apparatus of Cohen and Bruins. The four sections are held together in a metal stand with a slight pressure by means of rubber bands, so that they may be readily moved over each other. A movement of a little over 3 mm. of one section cuts it off completely from the other. The sections are moved by the pneumatic arrangement (shown in Fig. 3 dotted lines), connected by rubber tubing to a small metal air pressure pump of the type commonly used for filling burettes, etc. This arrangement avoids vibration since necessary operations can be made without touching the apparatus. To secure exact alignment, the sections are pressed against a plane metal plate (to the right in Fig. 3). When making a run, the two lower sections are filled with the colloid, the U-tube "closed" by pressing section III to the left, and the rest of the tube is then washed out with and finally filled with the buffer to be used, and connected to the electrode tubes. To save time, all solutions are kept in the cold room before filling the apparatus. The apparatus is left in the bath to attain constant temperature, after which the electrode vessels are leveled by connecting them for a few minutes through a tube between the two upper stopcocks. The clockwork to the compensation is then started, and the boundaries are made by moving section III back again, after which the current may be applied. If optical study of the boundaries is to be made right from the start, the compensation may be allowed to work for some time before the current is started, so that the boundaries are brought out into the region where they can be observed. However, this is not usually necessary, since the boundaries soon become visible in any event. If two components are observed, their rate of migration is estimated, and from this a rate of compensation chosen, so that a value corresponding to the arithmetic mean (the mobilities taken with their signs) will not move at all. Then one boundary will move downwards (relatively to the tube) at exactly the same speed as the other moves upwards, and at the end of the experiment, the two sections to the left will contain only one component, the two to the right only the other. In this way the separation capacity of the apparatus can be utilized to its full extent even though both components migrate very rapidly in the same direction. At the end of the experiment sections II and III are moved slightly to the left, the apparatus is taken out, the electrode tubes removed, and the contents of the sections can be pipetted out with capillary pipettes, without taking the sections apart. Each section holds 4 c.c. so that 8 c.c. of solution of each component can be obtained. In the larger apparatus, with 5 × 100 mm. cross-section, this volume will be increased to 100 c.c., but it will probably not take quite so high a voltage, on account of the wider tubes. If it is only desired to measure the mobilities it is not necessary to run the boundaries so far. The mobility can be determined by observation of the boundaries or by analysis of the contents of the sections in the usual way.

(3) Observation of the moving boundaries of colorless substances cannot be followed so readily by ultra-violet photography as in the

earlier apparatus, as this would necessitate the expense of using quartz both for the U-tube and for the large windows. The Töpler *"schlieren"* projection method has, however, been adopted with quite good results. In the usual arrangement a Dallmeyer objective of *f* about 60 cm. with large aperature (10 cm.) is placed as near to the apparatus as possible. A lamp and a diaphragm are placed at about 100 cm. distance, on the same side of the thermostat. The image of the diaphragm is thrown on the other side of the apparatus, at about 100 cm. from the window. Here a projection lens is placed, partially covered by a vertically movable screen with a sharp edge. Instead of the projection lens a camera objective can be used. . . .

This method has proved much superior to the earlier light absorption method, especially when studying mixtures. With one and the same cell thickness, moreover, any concentration can be used, instead of the very narrow limits of concentration which the earlier method permits. By suitable adjustment of the edge in front of the lens any gradient can be observed, and even very diffuse boundaries may be located accurately.

There are several ways in which the amounts of the different components present may be determined optically, if the boundaries are well separated, so that not only qualitative, but quantitative electrophoretic analysis may be effected. In the light absorption method the photographs were microphotometred, and the concentrations computed from the photometric diagrams; the same procedure can be applied to the photographs obtained by the present method. The concentrations are obtained by graphic integration of the curves obtained. The refractive index method originally suggested by the author and worked out by Lamm for use in the ultracentrifuge and diffusion measurements may also be applied for the same purpose. For measurement of the migration of the boundaries, however, the above method is much more convenient.

Examples of separation of various proteins by this apparatus are then given.

RADIOACTIVE TRACERS. Biochemists had always wished to know the location within the cell of some of the compounds that interested them, but the very nature of the living cell seemed to make it hopeless to follow substances through the body of an organism. When radioactive isotopes were discovered (p. 78), however, Hevesy realized that these could be used for just such localization. He first applied the principle in 1923 using the natural isotope of lead, and when artificial radioisotopes became available (p. 227), he utilized them in the same way. As the number of available radioisotopes increased, they were used by organic and inorganic chemists to follow the course of reactions and elucidate many reaction mechanisms.

The following selection is from pages 439–440 in *The Biochemical Journal 17*, 439–445 (1923).

The Absorption and Translocation of Lead by Plants. A Contribution to the Application of the Method of Radioactive Indicators in the Investigation of the Change of Substance in Plants

GEORGE HEVESY

The investigation of the absorption of lead by plants can be carried out quite simply by dipping them into a solution which contains a radioactive isotope of lead, and determining the radioactivity of the ash from various parts of the plant. In addition to its simplicity and the extraordinary rapidity with which the work can be carried out this method possesses the following advantages: — (*a*) By mixing suitable amounts of ordinary lead with the radioactive lead isotope, one can vary the lead concentration of the solution, as it were, between very wide limits. The assimilation of lead from a $N/1$ solution can be just as readily investigated as that from a solution many million times more dilute. (*b*) One can follow the change in localization of the lead taken up by the plant, and thence draw conclusions as to the nature of its combination.

The experiments described in this paper were so carried out, that the plants, which had been cultivated in a culture solution, were washed with distilled water, and then the roots were immersed from 1 to 48 hours in a solution containing a mixture of lead nitrate and thorium *B* nitrate. In most cases *Vicia Faba* (horse-bean) was used. After this period of immersion the individual parts of the plant were first well rinsed with distilled water, and then ignited, and the intensity of the radioactivity of the ash was determined by means of an electroscope. This latter magnitude gives directly the lead content of the ash and thus also that of the corresponding part of the plant, when we know the radioactivity and the lead content of the solution in which the plant has been immersed.

Thorium *B* is a transformation product of thorium emanation, and is obtained in a very simple manner. A piece of platinum foil is charged negatively to a potential of 110 volts, say, and suspended is a vessel containing the preparation (radio-thorium, thorium X, etc.) from which the thorium emanation is generated. Under these circumstances the thorium B collects on the platinum surface, and can be removed with the aid of a few drops of dilute nitric acid. The normality as regards lead of a solution (thorium B is an isotope of lead, *i.e.* a substance showing completely the chemical properties of lead) prepared in this way is about 10^{-12}, and if we wish to increase it we only need add to the solution a known amount of lead nitrate. For example, if we assume that we have prepared in this manner a 10^{-6} N solution of lead nitrate, and that after evaporating it to dryness it shows a radioactivity of 10,000 relative units, then each relative radioactive unit would correspond to an amount of 2.10^{-5} mg. of lead. We must of course take account of the fact that the material of the ash of the parts of the plants absorb part of the rays from the contained thorium B, but we can easily eliminate this disturbance by mixing the preparation used for comparison with the same quantity of ash as is contained in the sample the radioactivity of which we desire to know.

Experimental details are then reported.

The following selection is in *Nature 136*, 754–755 (1935).

Radioactive Indicators in the Study of Phosphorus Metabolism in Rats

O. CHIEWITZ AND G. HEVESY

Recent progress in the production of radioactive isotopes by neutron bombardment makes the radioactive isotope of phosphorus$_{15}$ P^{32} easily accessible. This isotope, which has a half-life value of 17 days, can be utilized as an indicator of inactive phosphorus in the same way that the radioactive isotopes of lead, bismuth and so on were formerly used as indicators of these elements. If, for example, we add active $_{15}P^{32}$ to 1 mgm. of inactive phosphorus in such quantity that the Geiger counter registers 1,000 impulses per minute, carry out with the phosphorus activated in this way any sort of chemical or biological reaction and then find that the product obtained gives 1 impulse per minute, we may conclude that 1/1,000 mgm. of the phosphorus originally introduced is present in the product investigated.

Rats were fed with a few milligrams of sodium phosphate containing $_{15}P^{32}$ as indicator. The radioactive phosphorus present in the urine and faeces was then investigated for a period of a month. The result is shown in Fig. 1, which shows the percentage of the

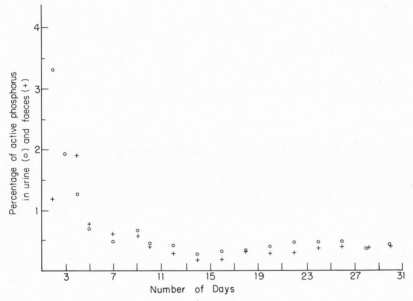

Fig. 1. (On the first day, 7.4 per cent of phosphorus was found in the faeces and 5 per cent in the urine.)

2 mgm. of phosphorus taken, found daily in the excrements. The rat was killed, and, after ignition, the phosphorus content of the different organs was investigated. The result of an experiment in which the rat was killed 22 days after being fed on active phosphorus is seen in the first column in Table 1. The largest part of the phosphorus taken in present in the bones, and the smallest in the kidneys. When, however, we take into account the very different weights of the different organs and calculate the phosphorus content of the latter per gram after drying, we obtain a very different picture, as seen from the second column in Table 1. The spleen, kidneys, and the brain are found to contain per gram most of the active phosphorus. During one of the experiments the rat produced six offspring on the seventh day, of which five were eaten by the mother; this caused a large increase in the active phosphorus content of the excreta in the following three days. The presence of 2 per cent of the 2 mgm.

active phosphorus taken by the mother was revealed by the analysis of the remaining offspring.

The active phosphorus content of the urine and faeces shows great fluctuations during the first few days after the intake of the preparation. Later, it becomes fairly constant; and we have obviously to

Table I

Distribution of the active phosphorus in the rat

	Percent	Percent per gm.
Urine	26.3	
Faeces	31.8	
Brain and medulla	0.5	14.7
Spleen and kidneys	0.2	18.2
Liver	1.7	13.9
Blood	0.4	1.8
Skeleton	24.8	2.8
Muscles and fat	17.4	7.4

deal with the excretion of phosphorus which has already been deposited for a while in the skeleton, the muscles, or other organs, and which has been displaced again. From our experiments, it follows that the average time which a phosphorus atom thus spends in the organism of a normally fed rat is about two months. This is also supported by the fact that rats killed about a month after the intake of phosphorus contain only about half the active phosphorus found in those killed after a week's time. This result strongly supports the view that the formation of the bones is a dynamic process, the bone continuously taking up phosphorus atoms which are partly or wholly lost again, and are replaced by other phosphorus atoms. In the case of an adult rat, about 30 per cent of the phosphorus atoms deposited in the skeleton were removed in the course of twenty days.

In another set of experiments we investigated the different parts of the skeleton. No conspicuous differences in the active phosphorus content could be found, with the exception of the teeth. The front teeth, which grow rapidly in rats, contained a larger part of the 2 mgm. phosphorus taken than the average of the whole skeleton, the ratio being about 10:1 in the case of the adult and 6:1 in that of half-adult rats, whereas the molar teeth took up less than the average per gram of the skeleton, the ratio being 1:2 in the most extreme case.

CRYSTAL STRUCTURE. In 1913 Max von Laue, in an attempt to prove that X-rays had an electromagnetic character, theorized that they could be diffracted by the lattice of a crystal. The introduction to his paper, given in the first selection that follows, illustrates his reasoning. His associates, Friedrich and Knipping, showed experimentally that his theory was correct. The Braggs, father and son, utilized this work to show that the location of atoms or groups in a crystal could be determined by this diffraction of X-rays and so worked out a practical method for determining the structure of a crystal lattice. The method, which they first applied to simple crystals like sodium chloride as shown in the second selection, was expanded and continued in determining the structures of a very large number of substances, both crystalline and amorphous.

The following selection is from pages 971–972 in *Annalen der Physik 41*, 971–988 (1913); a French translation was published in *Le Radium 10*, 47 (1913).

Interference Phenomena in Roentgen Rays

W. FRIEDRICH, P. KNIPPING, AND M. LAUE

Barkla's studies in recent years have shown that Roentgen rays undergo a dispersion in material substances which corresponds entirely to the dispersion of light in a turbid medium, but they also excite the emission in general from the atoms of substances of a spectrally homogeneous radiation (fluorescence radiation) which is exclusively characteristic of these substances.

On the other hand, even in 1850 Bravais introduced into crystallography the theory that the atoms in a crystal are arranged in a space lattice. If the Roentgen rays actually consist of electromagnetic waves, it can be supposed that the space lattice structure will give rise to interference phenomena from excitation of the atoms or an oscillation; and indeed, to interference phenomena of the same nature as in the optically known lattice spectrum. The constants of this lattice can easily be calculated from the molecular weight of the crystalline compound, its density, and the number of molecules per gram mole, as well as the crystallographic data. We find for it an order of magnitude of 10^{-8} cm., while the wave length of the Roentgen rays according to the deflection study of Walter and Pohl, and from the work of Sommerfeld and Koch, is on the order of magnitude of 10^{-9} cm. Of course, an important complication is that in the space lattice there is a triple periodicity, while in the optical lattice there is periodic repetition only in two directions (highest in the cross lattice).

Friedrich and Knipping, at my suggestion, have tested this idea experimentally. They will report on their investigations and results in the second part of this paper.

The following selection is in *Proceedings of the Royal Society* (*London*), *Series A, 88*, 428–438 (1913).

The Reflection of X-Rays by Crystals
W. H. BRAGG AND W. L. BRAGG

In a discussion of the Laue photographs it has been shown that they may conveniently be interpreted as due to the reflection of X-rays in such planes within the crystal as are rich in atoms. This leads at once to the attempt to use cleavage planes as mirrors, and it has been found that mica gives a reflected pencil from its cleavage plane strong enough to make a visible impression on a photographic plate in a few minutes' exposure. It has also been observed that the reflected pencil can be detected by the ionisation method.

For the purpose of examining more closely the reflection of X-rays in this manner we have used an apparatus resembling a spectrometer in form, an ionization chamber taking the place of the telescope. The collimeter is replaced by a lead block pierced by a hole which can be stopped down to slits of various widths. The revolving table in the centre carries the crystal. The ionization chamber is tubular, 15 cm. long and 5 cm. in diameter. It can be rotated about the axis of the instrument, to which its own axis is perpendicular. It is filled with sulphur dioxide in order to increase the ionization current: both air and methyl iodide have also been used occasionally to make sure that no special characteristics of the gas in the chamber affect the interpretation of the results. The ionization current is measured directly. A balance method has not been used as we have not found it possible to deflect a suitable portion of the primary rays into a balance chamber.

The face of the box containing the X-ray bulb is covered with a special shield of lead, 5.5 mm. thick; the general lead covering of the box is 1 mm. thick, which is not always enough to screen the chamber

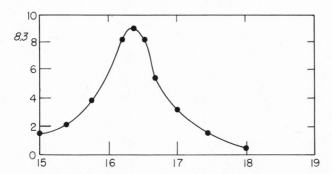

Fig. 1. Regular reflection from cleavage face of rock-salt, glancing angle 8.3°.

from penetrating X-rays that produce an effect comparable with the effect of the reflected rays. The circular end of the ionization chamber is also protected by lead. The slit through which the primary pencil of X-rays emerges from the box is 3.3 mm. long; its width has been 2 mm. for the rougher measurements and 0.75 mm. for the finer. Since the slit is 12 cm. from the anticathode, the emerging pencil has an angular width of about a third of a degree in the latter case. In the same way a slit 2 mm. wide and 5 mm. long admits the reflected pencil to the ionization chamber when preliminary measurements are being made, or when the whole effect is feeble; and this width can be cut down to 0.75 mm. when desired. The distance from either slit to the axis of the apparatus is 8 cm.

We have found it best to keep the bulb very "soft." The cathode stream has often been visible over its whole length.

As will be seen later, it is desirable to determine angles of incidence and reflection with great accuracy. This was not anticipated, and the circular scale was only divided into degrees, and was made too small. Nevertheless, it is possible to read tenths of a degree; a better and more open scale is now being put in.

Let us suppose that a crystal is placed on the revolving table so that the cleavage face passes through the axis of the instrument. Let the incident pencil fall on the face and make an angle θ with it; and let the crystal be kept fixed while the ionization chamber is revolved step by step through a series of angles including the double of θ, the ionization current being measured at each step. The results of such a set of measurements are shown in Fig. 1. In this case the crystal is rock-salt; and it has been placed so that the incident pencil makes an angle of 8.3°—as given by the apparatus—with the incident beam. The points marked in the figure show the result of setting the ionization chamber at various angles and measuring the current in each case. The maximum effect is not quite at 16.6°, but at a point somewhat less than 16.4°. The defect from the double angle is due in part to want of symmetry and accuracy of the apparatus; but not much of it is caused in this way. It is rather due to the difficulty of setting the crystal face exactly; sometimes this is much accentuated by "steps" on the face of the crystal. The error can be eliminated by swinging over the ionization chamber to the other side and taking corresponding observations, in a manner analogous to the method of finding the angle of a prism on the spectrometer.

The finer slits were used in obtaining this curve, and it may be inferred from the figure that the source of the X-rays is practically a point. For the width of the pencil from a point source by the time it reaches the slit of the ionisation chamber is $0.75 \times 28/12$, or 1.75 mm. The chamber slit being 0.75 mm. wide, the whole effect observed is comprised within a lateral movement of the chamber equal to $1.75 + 0.75$ or 2.50 mm. Since the chamber slit is 8 cm. from the axis of the apparatus this implies a rotation of the chamber through $(2.50 \times 180)/(\pi \times 80)$, or 1.78°. The figure shows that these limits are actually observed; the whole curve lies well within the range 15° to 18°. The source must therefore be nearly a point.

When the actual relation between the angles of the crystal mirror and the ionization chamber has been determined, the mirror and chamber may be swept together through an extended range, keeping the relation between the angles such that the chamber always shows the maximum current for each setting of the crystal. It is convenient to use the wide slits for a preliminary examination of this kind. When the effect is small the wide slits can alone be used. But in a number of cases it is possible to use the narrow slits in order to make a closer survey, and when this is done much more information can be obtained.

The curve in Fig. 2 shows the results of a sweeping movement of this kind, the crystal being iron pyrites. Curves for rock-salt are drawn in Figs. 3, I, and 3, II. It will be observed that there are peculiar and considerable variations in the intensity of the reflection at different angles. The three peaks marked A, B, and C are common to the curves of all crystals so far investigated, e.g., zinc blende, potassium ferrocyanide, potassium bichromate, quartz, calcite, and sodium ammonium tartrate. They are readily distinguishable by their invariant form, relative magnitudes, and spacings. Moreover, the absorption coefficients of the rays reflected at these separate angles do not vary with the nature of the crystal or the state of the bulb. It

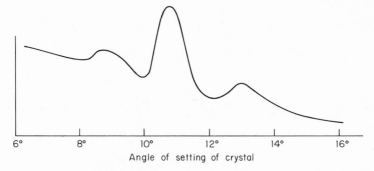

Fig. 2. Reflection from face (100) of iron pyrites, at varying angles of incidence. *Abscissa*—Angle of incidence of rays on crystal face. *Ordinate*—Strength of reflected beam, arbitrary scale.

happens that the actual angles of reflection of the three sets of rays are nearly the same for several crystals.

The use of the narrow slits permits a closer examination of these effects; but, of course, it takes much longer time to make, and more

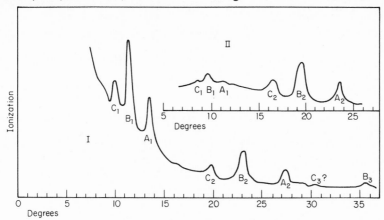

Fig. 3. Reflection (I) from face (100) and (II) from face (111) of rock-salt. The curves show the variation of strength of reflected beam with angle of incidence.

space to exhibit. The results for iron pyrites are shown in the series of curves of Fig. 4: a series in which each curve is obtained in the same way as the curve of Fig. 1, the crystal being set at some definite angle which is altered in going from curve to curve. The curves are arranged so that the vertical distances between the horizontal lines of reference of any pair is proportional to the difference in the angles of setting of the crystal in the two cases.

In comparing the curves at the different angles two principles must be borne in mind. In the first place, if there is a general reflection of rays throughout the whole range of the pencil which is emerging

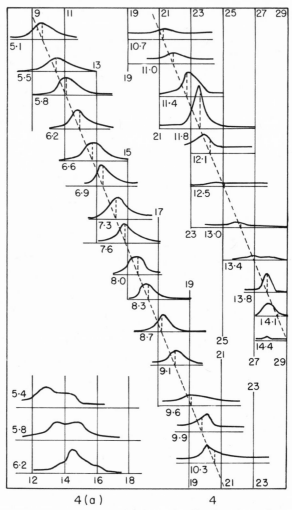

Fig. 4. Detailed examination of reflection from iron pyrites (100).

from the slit near the bulb, the curves show, as in Fig. 1, a maximum with similar slopes on each side of it. The maximum occurs at that setting of the chamber which is twice the angle of setting of the crystal or differs from it only by that constant error of setting to which allusion has already been made. The maximum slowly marches across the page as we go down the series of curves, and its progress is marked by the dotted line.

In the second place there is a special reflection which manifests its presence in a curious and most convenient way. It often happens that the rays emerging from the bulb slit and falling on the crystal contain a large preponderance of rays of a given quality which can only be reflected at a certain angle. This angle is very sharply defined: even our present and somewhat rough apparatus shows that it is limited to a very few minutes of arc in either direction. In this case the radiation which is reflected is not distributed generally over the whole range bounded by the edges of the bulb slit, which it will be remembered is about a third of a degree, but is confined to a select small portion of that range. When this is the case the position of the maximum does not change at all as the crystal is moved from setting to setting, so long as any of the radiation is reflected. For example, the curves for 13.4°, 13.8°, 14.1°, 14.4° show the existence of a special reflection of this kind which is always at its maximum when the chamber is set at 27.7°. The reason for this may be understood from Fig. 5.

Here O is the bulb slit, P the axis of the instrument, and Q the chamber slit. When the crystal face is in the position PR, let us say,

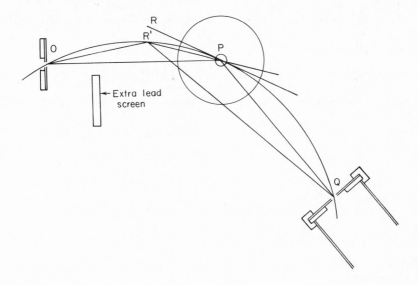

Fig. 5. Diagram of apparatus—O, bulb slit; P, axis of instrument; PR, PR′, two positions of crystal face; Q, slit of ionization chamber.

the ray OP strikes at the right angle for reflection, and is reflected along PQ. But when the crystal is turned to OR', the ray OP of the radiation of this quality which we are considering is not reflected at all. It is now the ray OR', where R' lies on the circle OPQ; for the angles made by OR' and QR' with PR' and the angles made by OP and QP with PR, are all equal to each other. The ray OR' is reflected along R'Q and still enters the ionisation chamber, though the latter has not been moved. When, therefore, we see a maximum persisting in the same angular position of the chamber for several successive positions of the crystal, we know that we have a case of this special reflection. There is a relatively large quantity of very homogeneous radiation of a certain kind present in the radiation from the bulb. The narrower we make the slits the more does it stand out, but the more difficult it is to find, if we do not know where to look for it.

It will be noticed how small the general reflection appears, in comparison with the special reflection between the angles (crystal settings) 12° and 14°. It is still smaller when the angle is reduced to 10.7°. At 10.3° there is enough of it to throw a hump on to one side of a peak of special reflection, and at 9.9° it has passed through, and thrown the hump upon the other side. Consideration of the whole series of curves shows that there are three strongly marked homogeneous pencils of sharply defined quality; they occur at (uncorrected chamber angles) 27.7°, 23.4°, and 20.0°. What we have called the general reflection may comprise many other definite pencils, but they are scarcely resolved at all in this series of curves. Their presence is, however, fairly obvious. A series of potassium ferrocyanide curves shows them much more clearly. Three of this series are shown in Fig. 4(a), and their peculiar forms indicate to what extent interpretation has yet to be carried.

When these homogeneous beams are isolated by the use of narrow slits, it is possible to determine their absorption coefficients in various substances. In the end, there is no doubt, this will be done with great accuracy; for the present, our results must only be looked on as provisional. They are, perhaps, right to 5 per cent; for many purposes this is quite sufficient. In the case of rock-salt we find the mass absorption coefficients in aluminium of A, B, and C to be 25.5, 18.8, and 10.6 respectively, the last being the most doubtful and probably too low. The absorption coefficient of the β-rays in Ag is 74, in Cu 140, in Ni 138; these values are approximate. We have made no exhaustive determination of the coefficients in the case of various crystals, but in a number of cases, all those tried, we have found them to be the same. There can be little doubt the three peaks are, in all cases, due to the same three sets of homogeneous rays, rays which do not change with the state of the bulb, but may well do so with the nature of the anticathode. It will be observed that the absorption coefficient of the least penetrating set is very nearly that found by Chapman for the characteristic radiation of platinum.

The angles at which the special reflections of these rays take place are not the same for all crystals, nor for all faces of the same crystal, as the table [I] shows. The angles can be determined with great

Table I

	A	B	C
Rock-salt, cube face {100}	27.3	23.1	19.9
Rock salt, face {111}	48.5	40.2	34.0
Potassium ferrocyanide	27.2	23.1	19.8
Calcite, cleavage plane {100}	25.4	21.6	—
Iron pyrites, cube face {100}	28.5	24.2	20.8
Zinc blende, cleavage face {110}	40.0 (approx.)	33.0	27.5 (approx.)
Potassium bichromate	22.4	19.8	—

accuracy; even with our rough apparatus they are probably within 1 per cent of the truth.

The readings for zinc blende and calcite are not corrected for errors of setting.

The difference in the case of the two faces of rock-salt suggested an attempt to find a repetition of the characteristic three peaks at multiples or sub multiples of those at which they were first observed. For the sines of 11.55 and 20.1 (half the angles of the chamber settings of the B peak in the two cases) are 0.200 and 0.344 respectively. These are very nearly in the ratio $1:\sqrt{3}$. If the effects are true diffraction effects such a relation might be expected. The {111} planes are further apart than the {100} planes in the ratio $2:\sqrt{3}$; the sines of the angles of special reflection should be in the inverse ratio, viz. $\sqrt{3}:2$. True, the sines of the angles have been increased in the ratio $1:\sqrt{3}$, instead of diminished in the ratio $2:\sqrt{3}$, but it is not at all unlikely that a spectrum in one case is being compared with a spectrum of higher or lower order in the other. We, therefore, made a search for other spectra and found them at once. In the case of rock-salt we found traces of a third. The full rock-salt curves are shown in Fig. 3 for the two kinds of face. The peaks first found are marked A_1, B_1, C_1, and their repetitions A_2, B_2, C_2; there is a trace of B_3 also. The corrected angular positions of B_1, B_2, B_3 are 23.1°, 47.3°, and 73.3°. The sines of the halves of these angles are 0.200, 0.401, and 0.597, and are very nearly in the proportion 1:2:3. The absorption coefficient of the rays at B_2 is the same as that of the rays at B_1.

In the case of the rock-salt section {111} a spectrum occurs at half the angles first found. This is shown in Fig. 3, II. It is not at all strongly marked, and the question at once arises as to why the second spectrum should be so much stronger than the first in this case and so much weaker in the case of the face {100}. A large amount of the general falling away of intensity at small angles, so obvious in curve II as compared with curve I, is undoubtedly due to the fact that the {111} face used was not extended enough to catch the whole pencil of rays from the bulb slit at so glancing an angle.

There can be little doubt as to the interpretation of these results. The three peaks A, B, and C represent three sets of homogeneous rays. Rays of a definite quality are reflected from a crystal when, and only when, the crystal is set at the right angle. This is really an alternative way of stating the original deduction of Laue. The three sets of rays are not manufactured in the crystal, because all their properties are independent of the nature of the crystal. An absorbing screen may be interposed with the same effect before or after the rays have struck the crystal. This was found by Moseley and Darwin, and we have verified it in the case of aluminium.

Since the reflection angle of each set of rays is so sharply defined, the waves must occur in trains of great length. A succession of irregularly spaced pulses could not give the observed effect. In the application of electromagnetic theory to monochromatic light on the one hand, and to homogeneous X-rays on the other, there is no difference to be considered beyond that of wave length.

These results do not really affect the use of the corpuscular theory of X-rays. The theory represents the facts of the transfer of energy from electron to X-ray and *vice versa*, and all the phenomena in which this transfer is the principal event. It can predict discoveries and interpret them. It is useful in its own field. The problem remains to discover how two hypotheses so different in appearance can be so closely linked together.

It is of great interest to attempt to find the exact wave-length of the rays to which these peaks correspond. On considering curve I, Fig. 3, it seems evident that the peaks A_1, B_1, C_1, A_2, B_2, C_2 are analogous to spectra of the first and second orders, because of the absence of intervening sets of peaks. The value of n in the equation

$$n\lambda = 2d \sin \theta$$

seems clear. The difficulty of assigning a definite wave-length to the rays arises when we attempt to determine the value of d, the distance of plane from plane.

There is strong evidence for supposing that the atoms of a cubic crystal like rock-salt, containing two elements of equal valency, are arranged parallel to the planes {100} in planes containing equal numbers of sodium and chlorine atoms. The atoms in any one plane are arranged in alternate rows of each element, diagonal to the cube axes, successive planes having these rows opposite ways. The question arises as to whether the value of d is to be taken as that between two successive planes, or two planes identical in all respects. The value of d in the one case is twice that in the other.

The centres of the atoms of sodium and chlorine, regarded for the time being as identical, are arranged in a point system, having as unit of its pattern a cube with a point at each corner and one at the centre of each cube face. The dimensions of this elementary cube can be found in the following way:

If the side of the cube is of length a, the volume associated with each point in the point system will be $\frac{1}{4}a^3$.

The mass of a hydrogen atom being 1.64×10^{-24} grm. and the density of rock-salt 2.17, we have

$$\frac{1}{\frac{1}{4}a^3} \frac{1}{2}(35.5 + 23) \times 1.64 \times 10^{-24} = 2.17$$

This gives

$$a = 4.45 \times 10^{-8}.$$

The distance between planes passing through atoms identical in all respects is this distance a. The wave-length, as calculated in this way, is

$$\lambda = 2a \sin \theta = 1.78 \times 10^{-8}$$

for the peak B.

But half-way between these planes which are identical in all respects are situated planes containing the same number of sodium and chlorine atoms, though the arrangement is not in all respects the same. Possibly this tends to make the odd spectra due to the first

lot of planes disappear, and, if this is the case, we must halve the
first estimate of the wave-length, and put

$$\lambda = 0.89 \times 10^{-8}.$$

The difference between these two values corresponds to taking as a
unit of the point system—

(1) The group 4 NaCl, the smallest complete unit of the crystal
pattern.

(2) The individual atom of either nature, associated with only
one eighth of the volume of the complete unit.

We have also examined the reflection from the {110} face of the
rock-salt, and have found the peaks situated at such angles as indicate
that the ratio of the distance between these parallel planes to the
distance between the planes parallel to the face (100) is as $1 : \sqrt{2}$.
Combined with the position of the peaks reflected from the (111)
face, this indicates that the point system which the diffracting centres
form has as element of its pattern that suggested above, a cube with
a point at each corner and one at the centre of each face. Of the
three elementary cubic face lattices, this is the only one in which the
distance between the (111) planes is greater than that between any
other of the planes of the system.

The wave-length as calculated from the reflection on the (110)
face of zinc blende agrees within the errors of experiment with that
calculated above.

The wave-lengths to be associated with the spots in the photographs taken by Laue of the diffraction of X-rays by crystals are
much smaller than these values. They belong to the region in which
we have found reflection to take place at all angles, a region in which
the peaks do not obviously occur. This agrees with the distribution of
intensity amongst the spots.

The experimental method can be applied to the analysis of the
radiation from any source of X-rays. It may, however, be able to
deal only with intense radiations. The three sets of rays issuing from
the bulb we have been using have angles of reflection whose sines are
0.236, 0.200, 0.173. The reciprocals of these are 4.24, 5, and 5.78.
The frequencies, and therefore, according to Planck, the corresponding quantum energies, are in arithmetical progression. In this there
is some hint of analogy with Rutherford's recent work on the energies
of the various types of β-ray from RaC.

Professor Barkla has lately communicated to the Physical Society
an account of certain experiments in which a diffuse pencil of X-rays,
when reflected on the cleavage plane of a crystal, acted on a photographic plate, producing a series of bands. The effect which we have

been describing is clearly identical in part with that which Professor Barkla has described. It is impossible, of course, to criticise a communication of which we have seen an abstract only. But it seems probable that the ionisation method can follow the details of the effect more closely than the photographic method has so far been able to do: and that in this way it is possible to distinguish between those bands which represent distinct sets of rays, and those which are repetitions of one and the same set.

Part II General and Physical Chemistry

ATOMIC AND MOLECULAR STRUCTURE

Until the chemist could understand the nature of the elements and of their combination into compounds, he was in no position to solve the fundamental problems of chemical change with which he was chiefly occupied. At the beginning of the twentieth century he knew almost all of the naturally occurring elements and hundreds of thousands of compounds formed from them, but he was still satisfied with the formal relationships of structural chemistry and the statistical approach of thermodynamics to affinity. He knew nothing of actual atomic or molecular structure. The discovery of radioactivity gave him the key to both.

It was necessary, nevertheless, to wait until the physicists had shown the nature of radioactivity before the chemist could profit from the discovery. At first the work on the electron and the electrical nature of the atom seemed to offer some hope that the old dualistic theory of Berzelius might be revived. A number of early and tentative attempts in this direction were not very successful. It was not until the work of Rutherford and his school had culminated in the Bohr theory of the atom that it became possible to produce a fruitful theory. After this, progress was rapid.

RADIOACTIVE DECAY SERIES. For the chemist, the first major result of the study of radioactivity came when it was realized that atoms were not, after all, hard, unchangeable particles. The discovery of radium and polonium in itself did not alter his ideas, but the unraveling of the nature of α- and β-rays did. This led to the work of Fajans and Soddy on the radioactive series and gave a new meaning to the periodic table.

Fajans and Soddy, working independently, established the fact that some elements could be converted into others in regular sequence, and that atomic weight was not the most fundamental property of an element. The discovery of isotopes (a term coined by Soddy) led to a drastic revision in thinking for all chemists. The next two selections show how these ideas were developed.

The following selection is from pages 423–430 and 432 in *Berichte der Deutschen Chemischen Gesellschaft 46*, 422–439 (1913).

Radioactive Transformations and the Periodic System of The Elements

KASIMIR FAJANS

The starting point for these considerations is the connection that I have established between the type of a radioactive transformation and the electrochemical character of the radio element being considered. It should be emphasized here that it is possible to divide all radioactive transformations into two classes: α-ray transformations in which a helium atom with a double positive charge is expelled; the atomic weight of the resulting element is thus smaller by the atomic weight of helium (3.99 or about 4.0) than that of its direct mother substance; and β-ray transformations, in which only an electron is emitted: thus, by such a transformation the atomic weight will not be altered; there is merely a rearrangement of the constituent components of the atoms.[1] This relationship now says that by an α-ray transformation the resulting product, electrochemically more positive, is lighter than its mother substance, while by a β-ray transformation exactly the opposite occurs, that is, the alteration product is electrochemically more negative than its mother substance. It can be shown that this relationship is valid for all transformations in which it can be tested, without exception. Since in the periodic system in a horizontal row, the electronegative character of the elements increases from left to right, we can express the

[1] One could object to this on the ground that since a β-particle, an electron, has mass (1/1800 of a hydrogen atom), then as a result of such a transformation a very small loss in atomic weight should occur. However, if we do not wish to make very complicated assumptions, we must assume that an outwardly neutral atom contains equal masses of positive and negative electricity. If it loses a negative electron by such a β-ray transformation, the resulting new atom will be positively charged and thus by the uptake of negative electricity from outside will again be brought quantitatively into the neutral state of the same composition as the mother substance.

opinion that in an α-ray transformation there results an element which belongs to a lower group of the same horizontal row of the periodic table, while in a β-ray transformation an element of a higher group (vertical row) results. This principle is also valid for all those cases in which the chemical nature of the elements considered is already known from a direct investigation (this is much more rarely possible than electrochemical characterization). The question still remains to be answered, by how many groups to the left (in α-ray transformation), or to the right (in β-ray transformation) this transition occurs. F. Soddy has already indicated as to this that in α-ray transformations in well-studied cases a transfer to the next second group is seen; thus, for example, from the fourth to the second, the sixth to the fourth, etc. I have accepted this Soddy rule as generally valid and will give a plausible meaning for it later. For the β-ray transformation I can show on the basis of several cases that we can assume a

Table I

$$
\overset{6}{\text{Ur I}} \overset{\alpha}{\to} \overset{4}{\text{Ur X}} \overset{\beta}{\to} \overset{(5)}{(\text{Ur X}_2)} \overset{\beta}{\to} \text{Ur II} \overset{\alpha}{\to} \overset{4}{\text{I}_0} \overset{\alpha}{\to} \overset{2}{\text{Ra}} \overset{\alpha}{\to} \overset{0}{\text{Ra Em}} \overset{\alpha}{\to} \overset{(6)}{\text{Ra A}} \overset{\alpha}{\to} \overset{(4)}{\text{Ra B}} \overset{\beta}{\to}
$$

5 × 10⁹ yrs   24.6 days   (10⁶ yrs) (10⁵ yrs) 2000 yrs 3.86 days 3 min   26.7 min

$$
\overset{(3)}{\text{Ra C}_2} \overset{\beta}{\to}
$$
$$
\overset{(5)}{} \overset{\alpha}{\nearrow} \quad 1.4\ \text{min}
$$
$$
\text{Ra C}_1
$$
19.5 min $\searrow^{\beta}$

$$
\overset{(6)}{\text{Ra C}'} \overset{\alpha}{\to} \overset{4}{\text{Ra D}} \overset{\beta}{\to} \overset{(5)}{\text{Ra E}} \overset{\beta}{\to} \overset{6}{\text{Ra F}} \overset{\alpha}{\to} \overset{4}{\text{Pb}}
$$
(10⁻⁶sec)   16 yrs   5 days   136 days

$$
\overset{4}{\text{Th}} \overset{\alpha}{\to} \overset{2}{\text{Mes Th I}} \overset{(\beta)}{\to} \overset{(3)}{\text{Mes Th II}} \overset{\beta}{\to} \overset{4}{\text{Rad Th}} \overset{\alpha}{\to} \overset{2}{\text{Th X}} \overset{\alpha}{\to} \overset{0}{\text{Th Em}} \overset{\alpha}{\to} \overset{(6)}{\text{Th A}} \overset{\alpha}{\to} \overset{4}{\text{Th B}} \overset{\beta}{\to}
$$
3 × 10¹⁰ yrs   5.5 yrs   6.2 hrs   2 yrs   3.7 days   58 sec   0.145 sec 10.6 hrs

$$
\overset{(3)}{\text{Th D}} \overset{\beta}{\to}
$$
$$
\overset{(5)}{} \overset{\alpha}{\nearrow} \quad 3.1\ \text{min}
$$
$$
\text{Th C}_1
$$
55 min $\searrow^{\beta}$

$$
\overset{(6)}{\text{Th C}_2} \overset{\alpha}{\to} \overset{(4)}{(\text{Th D}_2} \overset{\beta}{\to} \overset{5}{\text{Bi}} \overset{\alpha}{\to} \overset{3}{\text{Tl})}
$$
(10⁻¹¹ sec)

$$
\overset{(3)}{\text{Act D}} \overset{\beta}{\to}
$$
$$
\overset{(5)}{} \overset{\alpha}{\nearrow} \quad 4.7\ \text{min}
$$

$$
\text{Act} \overset{\beta}{\to} \overset{4}{\text{Rad Act}} \overset{\alpha}{\to} \overset{2}{\text{Act X}} \overset{\alpha}{\to} \overset{0}{\text{Act Em}} \overset{\alpha}{\to} \overset{(6)}{\text{Act A}} \overset{\alpha}{\to} \overset{(4)}{\text{Act B}} \overset{\beta}{\to} \overset{(5)}{\text{Act C}} \overset{\alpha}{\to}
$$
19.5 days 10.2 days   3.9 sec   0.002 sec   36.1 min   2.15 min

jump of only one group, and this principle is also accepted as generally valid. Since for several radioactive elements, the chemical character has already been known with assurance, with the aid of these two rules we can give the alteration of the groups for α- and β-ray transformations for all known radioelements so as to tell to which group of the periodic table they belong. The results obtained in this way are given in the following tables. The first table [Table I] contains the three known radioactive series (uranium-radium, thorium, and actinium series) in which the genetic relation of the individual products appears. The letters α and β indicate the type of transformation, the times under the symbols of the elements show their half-lives, while the upper numbers give the group in the periodic system to which the elements belong; the numbers in parentheses were derived in the above way. The table also shows the course of some transformations so arranged that here they have the positions most likely on the basis of the new rule.[1]

It should now be remarked that, beginning with ionium, radiothorium, and radioactinium, the transformations in the three series take place in a completely analogous manner, and that the corresponding members of the three series from the radioactive viewpoint also agree completely in chemical and radioactive respects. The groups to which the short-lived products of the radium series belong will be found by following the genetic series to the left, starting from radium D. Thus, it is known that RaD belongs in the fourth group. The results obtained in this way should be applied to the analogous products of the other series, and the result for ThB agrees completely with experience.

The two arrows from RaC_1 and ThC_1 express the fact, first observed by the author, that these products undergo two different transformations in which one part of the atoms is disintegrated in one way, the other in another. In this case we speak of a branching

[1] An extension of the electrochemical considerations with reference to the emanations has indicated that between radium, ThX and ActX on the one hand, and the three emanations on the other, the existence of alkali elements is to be assumed, for which the provisory designations RaX, ThX_2, and $ActX_2$ will be used. However, such an assumption is in contradiction to the rule of the alteration of groups in the transformations, for then there would be in the transformation $Ra \xrightarrow{\alpha} RaX \xrightarrow{\beta} Em$ a passage of only one group to the left by an α-ray transformation and a similar transformation by a β-ray passage. However, this assumption cannot be considered correct. Even though the electrochemical relation would not be affected, it must be concluded that the extension of the idea of electrochemical behavior is not applicable to the noble gases. As concerns the question of a radioactive alkali metal with atomic weight near 220, there must be for its existence a corresponding free place in the periodic system. The genetic connection with the radioactive series can be explained by the assumption of a branching in radium, ThX and ActX. This question will be tested experimentally.

of the series. Such a branching will play a role in what follows for the interpretation of the periodic system.

Attention should be directed to one point: the fact that the three radioactive series are so extensively analogous shows clearly that the sequence in which the transformations of the elements in the groups (vertical rows) of the periodic system occurs in the cases already known to us is the same. We can already suspect from this fact that the periodic character of the transformations forms the basis of the periodic law. Thus, if we consider the uranium-radium-lead series, the periodic character of the transformations becomes clear: they pass through the groups

$$6\ 4\ 5\ 6\ 4\ 2\ \overline{0\ 6\ 4\ 5\ 6\ 4}\ 5\ 6\ 4$$

The series 6 4 5 6 4 is thus repeated three times.

In [Table II] all the radioactive elements are arranged according to decreasing atomic weight in the groups to which they belong. For calculation of the atomic weights we use as the basis the atomic weight of uranium (UrI) = 238.5 and that of thorium 232.4; the others are calculated on the assumption that in an α-ray transformation the atomic weight is decreased by 4 and that in a β-ray transformation no change in atomic weight occurs. The atomic weight of actinium and its transformation products is still unknown. The values given in the tables have only a hypothetical character. In this work they will be derived from the atomic weight of uranium on the basis of the assumption made probable by the new rule of a sort of relation of the uranium-radium series with the actinium series. It is also still uncertain whether actinium belongs in the second or third group of the periodic system.

It happens that in this table places that are already occupied in the periodic system are here occupied by several elements. If we compare the chemical behavior of the elements which occupy these same positions it appears that this is much more similar than for that of any other elements. *Such elements cannot be separated from each other either by chemical methods or by crystallization.* The similarity here is thus much greater than among the rare earths. There is much more trouble in separating ionium from thorium, or radium D from lead, or mesothorium I from radium, and actually it would be meaningless to obtain a separation. If we consider all these elements as separate individuals it is only because of their radioactive properties such as the different life periods, the different rays, and the genetic relations. *They are not separable by the usual chemical methods.* This fact is of fundamental significance for the arrangement of the

Table II

0	I	II	III	IV	V	VI
	Au 197.2					
		Hg 200.6				
			Tl 204.4			
			Act D 206.5	Pb 206.5		
			Th D 208.4	Th D₂ 208.4	Bi 208.4	
			RaC₂ 210.5	RaD 210.5	RaE 210.5	Ra F 210.5
				Act B 210.5	Act C 210.5	Th C₂ 212.4
				Th B 212.4	Th C₁ 212.4	Ra C 214.5
				Ra B 214.5	Ra C 214.5	Act A 214.5
						Th A 216.4
						Ra A 218.5
Act Em 218.5	(Act X₂) 218.5					
Th Em 220.4	(Th X₂) 220.4					
Ra Em 222.5	(Ra X) 222.5	Act X 222.5				
		Th X 224.4				
		Ra 226.5	Act 226.5	Rad Act 226.5		
		Mes Th I 228.4	Mes Th II 228.4	Rad Th 228.4		
				Io 230.5		
				Th 232.4		
				Ur X 234.5	(Ur X₂) 234.5	Ur II 234.5
						Ur I 238.5

Table III

0	I	II	III	IV	V	VI
	Au 197.2	Hg 200.6	Tl 204.0	Pb 207.1	Bi 208.0	Pol 210.5
	(RaX) 222.5	Ra 226.5	Mes Th II 228.4	Th 232.4	$(Ur\ X_2)$ 234.5	Ur I 238.5
Ra Em 222.5						

radioelements in the general periodic system. In order to arrange the last two horizontal rows properly by analogy with the others we must naturally proceed in the same way as for the other elements. Thus, only chemical methods can be used. However, this would give us only one element from a mixture of such elements in a group of the same horizontal row, and so it is that *only one place in the Mendeleev system can, in fact, be assigned to this complex element.* We must therefore answer only the question of which atomic weight should be ascribed to this complex element. Here also we must use experimental methods that we use for the ordinary elements, that is, the result of direct atomic weight determinations of this complex element isolated from a mineral chosen from the suitable system. The resulting value will depend on the mass ratio in which the individual components of this complex are combined. If the radioactive substances are in the stationary state, the individual products will be present in so much the greater amount, the longer-lived they are. If, however, one of the elements of such a group is much longer-lived than another, we can simply take its atomic weight as the one to be used, or else choose a corresponding intermediate value. The first procedure is exact enough for all the radioactive elements. If we proceed in this way, we get the arrangement of Table III for the two last rows of the periodic system.

The previously empty spaces in the 0, I, III, and V groups of the last row and in the sixth group of the next row are occupied by short-lived (still partly hypothetical) elements, which explains completely why they have not been discovered by ordinary chemical methods. The places in groups II, IV, and VI of the last row belong to known elements.

II. The End Products of the Transformation Series

The consequences that result from the places occupied by bismuth, lead, and thallium are of especially great importance. It is practically certain that lead is the end product of the radium series and indeed the direct transformation product of RaF (polonium). Besides lead, for which the theoretical atomic weight from uranium is calculated at 206.5, and which with other very short-lived elements is in the fourth group of the next row down according to the new rule, we must also assume the existence of ThD_2, whose atomic weight should be 208.4. This results from the fact that ThC_2, which according to the new rule belongs in the sixth group, undergoes an α-ray transformation and thus must yield an element of the fourth group. Since the existence of such an element is not recognizable by radioactive means, we must conclude that it is very long-lived. Then its chemical properties will be those of the lead obtained from uranium minerals since it belongs to the same group of the same horizontal row. It will thus appear to us as lead. However, there will be an apparent difference between the two leads: the atomic weight of one differs from that of the other by two full units. We must therefore obtain a different value for the atomic weight of lead from thorium-free uranium minerals than for lead from uranium-free thorium minerals. If ordinary lead is a mixture of these two types of lead, this would explain why the experimentally determined atomic weight of lead, 207.1, is greater than that calculated from the atomic weight of uranium on the basis of the genetic relationship, 206.5.

Similar considerations are applied to bismuth and thallium.

The determination of the atomic weights of lead, bismuth, and thallium from different sources would be of the very greatest significance for our understanding of the elements.

The following selection is in *Chemical News 107*, 97–99 (1913).

The Radio-Elements and the Periodic Law

FREDERICK SODDY

In the paper in which I proved that the two radio-elements mesothorium I and radium are non-separable by chemical processes, and by fractional crystallization of the chlorides, although the atomic weight of the two elements differs by about two units, it was pointed out that some of the common elements might also be mixtures of non-separable elements of different atomic weight in constant proportions. In a recent book (*Chemistry of the Radio-elements*, p. 30) I stated the rule that held good in several cases, that when the α-particle was expelled the atom passed from a family of even number in the Periodic Table to the next lower-numbered even family, the family of odd number being always missed. Further, in the changes in which the α-particle was not expelled the atom in several cases reverted to its original group, resulting in a curious alternation of properties as the series proceeds. Now, when this occurs, an element of the fourth family, for example, expelling an α-particle and becoming a member of the second family, which after further changes reverts to the fourth family, the two representatives of the fourth family so resulting are not merely similar in chemical properties. They are non-separable by any known process. This applies not merely to the disintegration products of one series, but to all the products. Thus, in the fourth group, thorium, uranium X, ionium, radio-thorium, radio-actinium are all chemically non-separable, though they result from three separate series, and the calculated atomic weight varies from 234 to 228.

I suggested to my demonstrator, Mr. Alexander Fleck, that he should make a systematic investigation of as many of the radio-elements as possible, the chemical nature of which remained indefinite, and the first part of his results has recently been communicated to the Chemical Society. As the result of this work, at the present time it is possible to state or predict the chemical nature of every known member of the disintegration series, and to bring these series from end to end under a few general laws of the type described, which throw a flood of new light on the nature of the Periodic Law. The lacunae that still remain to be filled up between uranium and ionium, owing to the existence in this part of products with periods of the order of millions of years, can be discussed in a much narrower way in consequence.

In a paper published by A. S. Russell recently, some of these generalizations have already been dealt with. Mr. Russell put forward a corollary to my rule for the α-particle which he had previously communicated to me privately in a letter in October, 1912, and which has since been strikingly verified by some of Mr. Fleck's results. Mr. Russell's rule refers to the β-ray and rayless changes, and is that when a β-ray or rayless change occurs the atom changes in chemical nature so as to pass into the family in the Periodic Table next higher in number. That is, the passage in these cases is always from an even to an odd, or from an odd to an even-numbered family. G. von Hevesy, who has also been working in Prof. Rutherford's laboratory on the valency of the disintegration products, has put forward very similar views, the difference being that the effect of the β-ray change is considered by him to be the opposite or "polar" to that of the α-ray change, the valency increasing by two after a β-ray change.

The same questions are also very clearly discussed by K. Fajans, who has been connected with the development of our knowledge in the branch series, but his paper did not come to hand until after this paper was drafted. He takes the view here advocated that the Periodic Law is the expression of the periodic character of radio-active changes, and anticipates some of the other points dealt with in this paper.

There is no doubt that Mr. Russell's corollary to my α-ray rule is correct, and I have adopted it just as he has put it forward, but it is possible from Mr. Fleck's results still to learn a good deal that is quite definite as to the nature of radio-active change.

In the first place let us consider the radium series from the emanation to the ultimate products with the branch series that occurs at the C-member. These branch series are now fairly clear owing to the work of Barratt, Marsden, and Darwin in the thorium series, and Makower and Fajans in the radium series, and as I have discussed them fully from the standpoint of the theory of multiple disintegration in the "Annual Report on Radio-activity for 1912" I need not further deal with them here.

$$
\begin{array}{ccccc}
& C' & D & E & F & G \\
\end{array}
$$

$$
Em \xrightarrow{\alpha} A \xrightarrow{\alpha} B \xrightarrow{\beta} C \overset{\beta\nearrow}{\underset{\alpha\searrow}{}} VI \xrightarrow{\alpha} IV \xrightarrow{\beta} V \xrightarrow{\beta} VI \xrightarrow{\alpha} IV
$$

$$
\begin{array}{ccccccc}
0 & VI & IV & V & C_2 & & ? \\
& & & & III & & IV
\end{array}
$$

Radium Series

Apart from the definite recognition of polonium (RaF) as the homologue of tellurium and of radium D as non-separable from lead, there was practically nothing known of the chemistry of the other members. From von Lerch's rule and the easy deposition on metals before the phenomenon had been recently investigated from the electrochemical standpoint by v. Hevesy, the impression had become general that they might be allied to the noble metals.

From Fleck's results the series runs:—A, unknown; B, lead; C, bismuth; C', unknown; D, lead, E, bismuth; F, polonium; G, lead. The known members are in accord with the rule about the expulsion of α- and β-particles, and if we extend the rule to the members the chemistry of which is still unknown, it gives for the members of the families of the successive members:—A, VI; B, IV; C, V; C', VI; D, IV; E, V; F, VI; G, IV. Now, applying the rule that when similar groups recur the elements are not merely similar, but nonseparable, we can predict that in chemical behavior the two unplaced substances RaA and RaC' will be non-separable from polonium. The prediction with regard to C' is unverifiable, as the period of this body is estimated to be only 10^{-6} sec. But with regard to RaA it should be possible to test it, and this is now being done. As regards the branch series, which is difficult to investigate, as only some three out of 10,000 of the atoms choose this route, it may be predicted that RaC_2 is in the third family, and will prove to be nonseparable from thallium, as will later be discussed. The end-product of the branch is again lead. The atomic weight of the two end-products, both non-separable from lead, are about 206 and 210 respectively.

The same reasoning is applied to the thorium and actinium series.

These results prove that almost every vacant place in the Periodic Table between thallium and uranium is crowded with non-separable elements of atomic weight varying over several units, and leads inevitably to the presumption that the same may be true in other parts of the table. As previously pointed out, nothing further is necessary to explain the failure of all attempts to obtain numerical relations between the atomic weights. The view that the atomic mass is a real constant fixing all the chemical and physical properties of the elements is combatted most definitely by the fact that after the α-particle of mass 4 is expelled the members revert later to the original chemical type.

Finally, it may be predicted that *all* the end-products, probably six in number of the three series, with calculated atomic weights varying from 210 to 206, should be non-separable from lead; that is, should be "lead," the element that appears in the International List with the atomic weight 207.1. I should mention that Mr. Russell a year ago told me that he believed that the discrepancy between this value and that calculated (206.0) from the atomic weight of radium by the subtraction of five α-particles was due to the end-product of radium not being lead, but an element non-separable from it. It appears from the foregoing that all the end-products are probably non-separable from lead, and that "lead" is actually such a mixture as formerly, I supposed, might exist among the inactive elements.

If we suppose that all the lead in the world is produced as the end-products in the three disintegration series in constant proportion, the found atomic weight, 207.1, indicates that about half of it may result in that of thorium and the other half in that of uranium. It is, however, hardly profitable to go further in detail until the constancy of the atomic weight of lead from a variety of radio-active minerals has been experimentally tested.

ISOTOPES. It was one thing to work out the theory of radioactive decay and to show that this led inevitably to the concept of isotopes. It was another matter, but an essential one for the chemist, to prove that isotopes existed. This proof came with the experimental verification of the prediction that lead isotopes of differing atomic weights must exist. The periodic table had been founded on the idea of the basic nature of atomic weight, in spite of the contradictions in certain cases. A vast amount of work had been done in refining analytical methods so that the highest degree of accuracy could be attained in determining atomic weights. Chemists felt such confidence in the results of these methods that they based their whole science upon them. Now the same methods were applied by the master analysts of the time to show that something still more fundamental must exist.

The papers of Richards and Hönigschmid that follow proved the existence of lead isotopes and changed the course of chemical thinking. However, the concept of these isotopes was connected with the theory of radioactivity, and so it was possible for a time to consider that here was a special case. The work of Aston, using his newly developed mass spectrograph, showed the generality of isotopes when he found that neon was a mixture. Soon more and more isotope mixtures were discovered. The most spectacular discovery in the eyes of contemporary chemists was Urey's finding that even the simplest element, hydrogen, also had an isotope, and in this case the atomic weight was double that of ordinary hydrogen. Apart from its theoretical interest, this heavy hydrogen, or deuterium as it was soon named, could be used to label compounds in much the same way as the radioactive isotopes (p. 48). An example of such use as a label is seen in the work of Schoenheimer (p. 346).

The next four selections illustrate these developments in the chemistry of isotopes.

The following selection is from pages 1329–1331, 1339, and 1342 in *The Journal of the American Chemical Society 36*, 1329–1344 (1914).

The Atomic Weight of Lead of Radioactive Origin

THEODORE W. RICHARDS AND MAX E. LEMBERT

It has been pointed out by many of the workers upon radioactivity, especially by Boltwood, Ramsay, Rutherford, and Fajans, that the most conclusive test concerning the recent theory of the degeneration of radioactive elements is to be found in the determination of the atomic weights. If each α-transformation involves the loss of an atom of helium and nothing else which is weighable, the atomic weight of the product should be just 3.99 less than that of the original substance, because 3.99 is the atomic weight of helium evolved during the α-transformation. Thus, if radium has an atomic weight of 225.97, its emanation ("niton") should have an atomic weight of 221.98, radium D (which is supposed to involve three more α-transformations) should be 210.01; and radium G (yet another α-transformation) should be 206.02.

Still more recently, a further theory, which has been independently proposed by Fajans, and by Soddy, indicates that some of the places in the periodic table, corresponding to high atomic weights, should perhaps each include several elements, different in atomic weight but very similar in other properties. Thus, in the place which we usually assign to lead, we should expect to find a mixture of ordinary lead, radium B, D, and G, and perhaps, also at least one other radioactive product from thorium and one from actinium. These different substances, according to the hypothesis, should have identical spectra and be inseparable by chemical means, but, coming from different sources, they should have different atomic weights. The theory supposes that each α-transformation involves a loss of valence of two, and each β-transformation a gain of valence of one. The β-transformation involves no change of weight. Thus radium D (supposed to have an atomic weight of 210) after two β- and one α-transformations returns again as radium G to the same place in the periodic system with an atomic weight of only 206. This place is that assigned to lead (which some suppose to be primarily radium G), the only one of the radium series possessed of a long life and not highly radioactive.

The problem is one capable of a decisive gravimetric test; specimens of lead, consisting of different mixtures, obtained from different sources, should have different atomic weights. On the generous suggestion of Dr. Fajans this matter was taken up in the autumn of 1913 at Harvard.[1] In order to glean as much knowledge as was within reach, we have endeavored to obtain as many different samples of radioactive lead as possible and to determine the atomic weights of the possibly composite element by precisely comparable methods, so as to discover if any variation might exist in the chemical equivalents of the different products.

It is a pleasure, at the outset, to express our deep gratitude to many workers in radioactivity who have furnished us with material. Without this general coöperation, it would not have been possible for us to accomplish anything in so short a time, and we cannot express too highly our appreciation.

[1] Mr. Max E. Lembert, Dipl. Ing., a pupil of Dr. Fajans, was sent by him and the Technische Hochschule of Karlsruhe, with the support of Professor Bredig, to Harvard University especially for this purpose. Sir William Ramsay, also, at about the same time, had urged on behalf of Dr. Soddy that the atomic weight of radioactive lead should be studied in the Wolcott Gibbs Memorial Laboratory. It is needless to say that the opportunity was welcomed; indeed, the matter would have been taken up here before, except for a fear of trespassing upon a field which might properly be considered as belonging to the proposers of the theory. A brief announcement of the work was made by Dr. Fajans at the meeting of the Bunsen Gesellschaft in Leipzig on May 21st, and a brief notice was published in *Science* on June 5, 1914.—T.W.R.

In brief, the method of analysis was essentially similar to that used so successfully by Baxter and Wilson in their work upon the atomic weight of ordinary lead. The chloride was in each case prepared in a state of great purity by recrystallization in quartz and platinum vessels, after extensive preliminary treatment to eliminate foreign substances. This chloride was carefully dried in a desiccator and heated to fusion in a stream of hydrochloric acid gas and nitrogen, in the quartz tube of the well-known bottling apparatus which has served in so many similar cases. The lead chloride was then dissolved in much water, and the chlorine precipitated by silver nitrate. Both the weight of silver required and the weight of the precipitate were determined in the usual Harvard fashion.

As a further check upon the work, control analyses giving the atomic weight of ordinary lead were carried out in precisely the same way. These yielded essentially the same value as that found by Baxter and Wilson, and more recently, by Baxter and Grover in work as yet unpublished.

The outcome was striking. There can be no question that the radioactive samples contain another element having an atomic weight so much lower than that of ordinary lead as to admit of no explanation through analytical error, and yet so nearly like ordinary lead as not to have been separated from it by any of the rather elaborate processes to which we had subjected the various samples.

Details of the preparation of reagents and carrying out the analyses are then given.

Thus the final analysis yielded results essentially like the preliminary ones. The situation will become clearer if the results are all collected and averaged in a summarized table (V) giving the values of the atomic weight corresponding to each kind of lead.

Table V

Final values found for atomic weight of lead
from different sources

Lead from North Carolina uraninite (Sample R)	206.40
Lead from Joachimsthal pitchblende (Sample I, K)	206.57
Lead from Colorado carnotite (Samples D and P)	206.59
Lead from Ceylonese thorianite (Samples H, M)	206.82
Lead from English pitchblende (Sample G)	206.86
Common lead	207.15

The result is amazing. Evidently then the chemical equivalents of these different specimens are markedly different from one another. Because the method of analysis was the same in each case, one cannot help thinking that there is a real variation in the chemical equivalents of these samples of lead. Either a large amount of some element having a chemical equivalent nearly as great as lead, or a small amount of an element having a low chemical equivalent, must be present, mixed with the substance which we ordinarily call lead. The fact that all the analyses were carried out by the same method, and that each sample gives consistent results, seems to exclude the effect of analytical error. The nature of the admixture it would be perhaps premature to decide. Clearly it has reactions very much like those of lead, if not exactly identical; for the various processes to which our material was subjected would have eliminated any element widely different. Moreover, the fact that protracted purification had no effect on the atomic weight of any one sample is evidence in the same direction. . . .

That lead should be composed of a mixture of substances of different origin but similar properties is, after all, possibly not so revolutionary a proposition as might appear at first sight. Rare earths are often very similar in properties, and large amounts of material and very patient fractionation are necessary to separate them. Why should not the same thing be true of several of the commoner elements? The only practical difference besides the presence of radioactivity seems to lie in the fact that in the present case the intruders produce no obvious change in the ultra-violet spectrum. But if all lead is a mixture, this might be expected.

The paper closes with speculation on possible variations in the other elements.

The following selection is in *Comptes Rendus Hebdomadaires des Séances de l'Académie des Sciences 158*, 1796–1798 (1914).

The Atomic Weight of Lead from Pitchblende

O. HÖNIGSCHMID AND MLLE. ST.-HOROVITZ

Recent theories indicate that the final product of disintegration in the series uranium-radium, designated by the name *radium G*, should be an element *isotopic* with lead, that is to say, inseparable from it by a chemical method, though possessing a different atomic weight.

Passage from uranium to radium occurs by disengaging three α-particles; and from radium to radium G by disengaging five particles. According to the determination of one of us, U-Ra $= 238.18 - 225.97 = 12.21$, which gives for the emission of an α-particle a decrease of 4.07. The atomic weight of radium G should then be $225.97 - 5 \times 4.07 = 205.62$.

Since the purest pitchblende, with 60% U_3O_8, also contains 2 to 3 per cent lead, it is possible that at least a part of this lead would be radium G; the atomic weight of lead extracted from pitchblende should be below that of ordinary lead by an amount corresponding to its content of radium G.

The lead chloride coming from the residues of treating pitchblende for the preparation of radium salts has been put at our disposal by the Academy of Sciences in Vienna. This chloride was first dissolved by ammonium acetate, then precipitated as the sulfate. The sulfate, washed and redissolved in ammonium acetate, was transformed into the sulfide and then into the nitrate. The nitrate was crystallized by solution in hot water and precipitation with concentrated nitric acid, the small crystals being dried each time by centrifuging in a platinum apparatus. The purified nitrate was again transformed into the chloride and this was redissolved similarly in a saturated solution of hydrochloric acid gas in a silica vessel, followed by precipitation with water. Finally the chloride was fractionated by new crystallizations from pure water.

The resulting product had all the evidences of purity that could be required in a lead chloride intended for the determination of atomic weight.

The analysis of this chloride was carried out by the two methods used by Baxter for the determination of the atomic weight actually accepted for lead; one exclusively gravimetric, the other based on the use of nephelometry.

The following results were obtained: in a series of 6 experiments, where the weight of $PbCl_2$ varied from 1.97691 g. to 3.33164 g., the determination of the ratio of $PbCl_2$ to 2 AgCl gave for the atomic weight of lead values varying from 206.719 to 206.749, of which the mean was 206.732. Another series of 3 experiments, where the weight of $PbCl_2$ varied from 3.22459 g. to 3.49447 g., gave by direct determination of the ratio of $PbCl_2$ to 2 AgCl atomic weights varying from 206.730 to 206.748, of which the mean was 206.741.

The mean of these two means gives for the atomic weight of lead extracted from pitchblende a value of 206.736, 0.4 below the atomic weight of ordinary lead.

It is possible that a lead with still lower atomic weight could be extracted from pitchblende free from isolated fragments of blende. Studies are in progress in this direction.

The determinations which are the object of the present memoir have been reported to the Congress of the Bunsen Gesellschaft at Leipzig on May 23, 1914, and to the German Chemical Society in Berlin. They confirm the theory relative to the existence of elements that possess identical chemical properties with different atomic weights.

Similar results have recently been reported to the Academy by M. Curie. They are in accord with the preceding.

The following selection is in *The London, Edinburgh and Dublin Philosophical Magazine* [6] *39*, 449–455 (1920).

The Constitution of Atmospheric Neon

F. W. ASTON

In periodic tables of the elements arranged in order of their atomic weights the part lying between Fluorine on the one hand and Sodium on the other is of considerable interest.

Soon after the discovery of argon and while the monatomic nature of its molecule was still under discussion, Emerson Reynolds, in a letter to *Nature* (March 21, 1895), described a particular periodic diagram which he had used with advantage. In this letter, referring to the occurrence of the groups Fe, Ni, Co: Ru, Rh, Pd: and Os, Ir, Pt, the following passage occurs:

". . . the distribution of the triplets throughout the whole of the best known elements is so nearly regular that it is difficult to avoid the inference that three elements should also be found in the symmetrical position between 19 and 23, *i.e.*, between F and Na, . . . of which argon may be one. . . ."

In 1898 neon was isolated from the atmosphere, in which it occurs to the extent of .00123 per cent by volume, by Ramsay and Travers, and was accepted as an elementary monatomic gas of the helium group. Its density was measured with extreme care by Watson, and found to correspond with an atomic weight 20.200 ($0 = 16$), making it the lightest element to diverge from the whole number rule in an unmistakable manner.

Neon has many very remarkable properties, its compressibility, viscosity and dielectric cohesion are all abnormal; but the first suggestion that it might be a mixture was the observation in 1912 by Sir J. J. Thomson of a faint but unmistakable parabola at a position corresponding roughly to an atomic weight 22, in addition to the expected one at 20, in positive ray photographs, whenever neon was present in the discharge bulb (*v. Rays of Positive Electricity*, p. 112). The first plate which showed this was obtained from a sample of the lighter constituents of air supplied by Sir James Dewar; other specimens of impure neon gave a similar result. So also did a portion of the gas used by Watson, in the atomic weight determinations, which fact, together with the complete invisibility of any parabola at 22 on hundreds of plates where neon was known to be absent, was very strong evidence that the line was ascribable to neon and to neon alone.

The facts led the author to undertake a searching investigation on the constitution of the gas by two distinct lines of attack, firstly attempts at separation, secondly accumulation of the evidence obtainable by positive rays.

A short section follows which shows that fractional distillation and fractional diffusion do not cause separation of neon.

Evidence of Positive Rays

This is available on three distinct counts: the character of the lines, their position and their intensity.

Character of the parabolas. Plate VIII shows a dark and a light print taken from a negative obtained in 1913 by Thomson's method of analysis from a gas containing a large percentage of neon. The line due to the lighter constituent which will be called Ne^{α} can easily be recognized as the brightest on the plate, the Ne^{β}, *i.e.* 22, line being the fainter one immediately below it. It can easily be seen that the latter possesses characteristics identical in all but intensity with those of the former. As has already been pointed out (*Rays of Positive Electricity*, p. 111) the prolongation of the lines toward the vertical axis indicates that the particles causing them are capable of carrying more than one charge; multiple charges not occurring on molecules but only on atoms, one is led to infer that both lines are due to elements.

Position of the parabolas. Measurements of plates obtained in this way indicated that it was probable that the lighter constituent did not correspond in mass with the accepted atomic weight of 20.2, but the accuracy was not sufficient to make this certain.

Intensity of the parabolas. The relative intensity of the Ne$^\alpha$ and Ne$^\beta$ parabolas obtained from atmospheric neon untreated by diffusion has been estimated by three different observers as about 10 to 1. Its apparent invariability is corroborative evidence against the possibility of the 22 line being due to the presence of other gases in the discharge-bulb.

It will be seen that although by Thomson's system of analysis the presence of two isotopes in atmospheric neon was indicated by

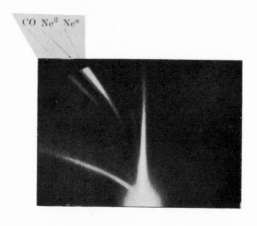

Plate VIII

several lines of reasoning, none of them can be regarded as quite conclusive, and it was realized that, failing separation, the most satisfactory proof would be afforded by measurements of atomic weight so accurate as to prove beyond dispute that neither constituent corresponded with the accepted atomic weight of atmospheric neon.

Evidence of the Positive Ray Spectrograph

The "mass-spectra" yielded by the new method of positive ray analysis recently described supply these measurements in an entirely satisfactory manner. Plate IX, A, B, C, D, are prints from negatives obtained by means of this apparatus. Each contains a number of spectra taken with different electric and magnetic fields; the following table [I] of values of P, the potential between the electrostatic plates

Table I

	A					B				
	1	2	3	4	5	1	2	3	4	5
P =	240	240	240	320	320	320	320	360	240	240
I =	.130	.450	.600	.600	.800	.351	.600	.600	.600	.173
T =	4	10	10	10	10	15	15	15	15	4

	C						D					
	1	2	3	4	5	6	1	2	3	4	5	6
P =	240	240	280	320	360	360	320	320	320	320	320	320
I =	.380	.550	.550	.550	.550	.700	.482	.520	.554	.606	.701	.798
T =	15	15	15	15	15	10	10	10	10	10	10	10

in volts, I, the current passing through the magnet in amperes, and T, the time of exposure in minutes, is given for reference:

On the left of each spectrum can be seen the small circular dot photographed on the plate just before or during the exposure; this is used as a register spot for measuring purposes.

Plate A was taken with carbon monoxide. That is to say, the vacuum in the discharge-tube was maintained by continual pumping with a Gaede rotating mercury pump against a small leak of CO. It must be understood that this does not imply that the contents of the discharge-bulb were pure CO, since the use of tap-grease and wax joints necessitates the presence of hydrocarbons, etc., but at least one can be certain that the quantity of neon present was negligible as none had yet been put into the apparatus. The electric deflexion is away from the register spot, the magnetic towards it, so that the heavier masses are to the right of lighter ones.

Spectrum A I. was taken with a very small magnetic field showing the lines due to the hydrogen atom and molecule. In A II. the field has been increased and a group of five lines are seen. These, which

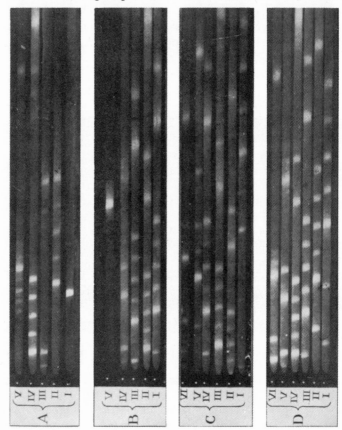

Plate IX

may be called the C_1 group, are 12-C, 13-CH, 14-CH_2 (or N), 15-CH_3, 16-CH_4 (or O). They are important lines of reference and are certainly of the relative masses given above to the order of accuracy (one-tenth per cent) claimed in the present experiment.

In A IV. the deflexion has been still further increased and a new group of lines, the C_2 group 24, 25, 26, 27, 28, 29, 30 containing the strong reference line of CO (or C_2H_4), have come into view.

In A III. of the C_1 group only 15 and 16 are visible, and in A V. the C_2 group has moved to the left and the strong line 44, CO_2 is seen to the right.

Plate B was taken with CO to which about 20 per cent of atmospheric neon had been added. Considering the spectrum B III. it will be seen that four unmistakably new lines have made their appearance, one pair between the C_1 and C_2 groups, another weaker pair to the left of the C_1 group. The first pair are $(Ne^\alpha)^+$ 20 and $(Ne^\beta)^+$ 22 singly charged, the second pair are the same atoms with double charges $10(Ne^\alpha)^{++}$ and $11(Ne^\beta)^{++}$ respectively. The other spectra consist of lines already mentioned brought into different positions to increase the convenience and accuracy of comparison and, in addition, there are on C I two other valuable reference lines, O^{++} apparent mass 8, and on the extreme left just visible C^{++} apparent mass 6.

Method of Comparing Masses

It will be noticed that although the lines are broad (the best focus was only obtained by a series of trials after these results were completed) their edges, particularly their left-hand edges, are remarkably sharp, so that measurements of a reasonably good line from the register spot repeat to a twentieth of a millemetre with certainty. Hence for accurate determination of unknown lines only two assumptions need be made. Firstly, that the masses of the reference lines are known, and secondly that, whatever the function connecting displacement with mass, any two positions on the spectrum being taken, the *ratio* of any two masses giving lines in these positions will be constant. This being so, by moving a group of reference lines into overlapping positions along the spectrum it is clear that the whole length can be plotted out and calibrated.

Fortunately there is an easy method of testing both these assumptions, for although it is impossible to measure the magnetic field to one-tenth per cent, it can be kept constant to that accuracy while the electric field is altered by a known ratio. But, for constant deflexions, $mv^2 \propto X$ and $mv \propto H = $ const. Therefore $m \propto X^{-1}$, so that, to take a typical case, the position occupied by carbon with a field of 320 volts should be exactly coincident with the position occupied by oxygen with 240 volts when the magnetic field is constant. Over the range of fields used in the case of neon, all such coincidences when expected have been found to occur within the error of experiment whatever the position on the plate.

For some reason, by no means obvious, connected with the geometry of the apparatus, the relation between displacement and mass is very nearly linear, a fact which lightens the labour and increases the accuracy of calibration very considerably.

Numerical Results

In the case of plate B the masses of the neon lines were estimated by carefully drawing the calibration curve representing the relation between displacement and mass by means of the known lines 12, 13, 14, 15, 16 checked by that at 28.

With plate D another mode of procedure was adopted. A linear relation was assumed and a table of corrections made by means of reference lines, which correction when subtracted from the observed displacement gave an exactly linear relation with mass. A correction-curve (apparently parabolic) was drawn, from which the appropriate corrections for any displacements could be written down and the masses corresponding to those displacements obtained by a simple proportion. The accompanying table [II] gives the results.

Table II

$(Ne^{\alpha})^{++}$	$(Ne^{\beta})^{++}$	$(Ne^{\alpha})^{+}$	$(Ne^{\beta})^{+}$
	Plate B		
9.98	11.00	20.00	20.00
10.02	10.99	19.95	22.01
10.00	10.99 (5)	19.97 (5)	22.00 (5)
	Plate D		
10.01	11.06	20.00	21.90
9.98	10.98	19.98	22.10
9.98	11.01	20.00	22.03
—	—	19.90	21.98
9.99	11.01	19.97	22.00 (5)

The method of measurement combined with a slight halation of the plate tends to make the edge of bright lines appear a little too near the register spot. This is enough to account for the reading of the very bright Ne^+ line giving a mass a little too low. The above figures therefore can be accepted as fairly conclusive evidence that Atmospheric Neon contains two isotopes of atomic weights 20.00 and 22.00 respectively to an accuracy of about one-tenth per cent.

In order to give the accepted density, the quantities required are 90 per cent and 10 per cent, which is in good agreement with the estimated intensity of the lines.

Possibility of a Third Isotope

On the clearest spectra obtained with neon there are distinct indications of a line corresponding to an isotope of mass 21. This line is extremely faint, so that if this constituent exists its proportion would be very small, probably well under 1 per cent, and it would not affect the density appreciably. Attempts to bring this line out more distinctly by longer exposures have not succeeded owing to the fogging from the strong neighbouring lines, but it is intended to return to this point when further improvements of the method give hope of more extensive results. This matter is interesting in connexion with the suggestion by Emerson Reynolds already quoted.[1]

The following selection is in *The Physical Review 39*, 164–165 (1932).

A Hydrogen Isotope of Mass 2

HAROLD C. UREY, F. G. BRICKWEDDE, AND G. M. MURPHY

The proton-electron plot of known atomic nuclei shows some rather marked regularities among atoms of lower atomic number. Up to O^{16} a simple step-wise figure appears into which the nuclear species H^2, H^3 and He^5 could be fitted very nicely. Birge and Menzel have shown that the discrepancy between the chemical atomic weight of hydrogen and Aston's value by the mass spectrograph could be accounted for by the assumption of a hydrogen isotope of mass 2 present to the extent of 1 part in 4500 parts of hydrogen of mass 1.

It is possible to calculate with confidence the vapor pressures of the pure substances H^1H^1, H^1H^2, H^1H^3, in equilibrium with the

[1] Though at the time this was made isotopes were not thought of, and the modern idea of atomic numbers has since precluded the possibility of three distinct elements.

pure solid phases. It is only necessary to assume that in the Debye theory of the solid state, θ is inversely proportional to the square root of the masses of these molecules and that the rotational and vibrational energies of the molecules do not change in the process of vaporization. These assumptions are in accord with well-established experimental evidence. We find that the vapor pressures for these three molecules in equilibrium with their solids should be in the ratio of $P_{11}:P_{12}:P_{13} = 1:0.37:0.29$. The theory of the liquid state is not so well understood but it seems reasonable to believe that the differences in vapor pressure of these molecules in equilibrium with their liquids should be rather large and should make possible a rapid concentration of the heavier isotopes, if they exist, in the residue from the simple evaporation of liquid hydrogen near its triple point.

Accordingly two samples of hydrogen were prepared by evaporating large quantities of liquid hydrogen and collecting the gas which evaporated from the last fraction of the last cubic centimeter. The first sample was collected from the end portion of six liters of liquid evaporated at atmospheric pressure, and the second sample from four liters evaporated at a pressure only a few millimeters above the triple point. The process of liquefaction has probably no effect in changing the concentration of the isotopes since no appreciable change was observed in the sample evaporated at atmospheric pressure.

These samples were investigated for the atomic spectra of H^2 and H^3 in a hydrogen discharge tube run in Wood's so-called "black stage" by using the second order of a 21-foot grating with a dispersion of 1.31 A per mm. With the sample evaporated at the boiling point no concentration so high as had been estimated was detected. We then increased the exposures so that the ratio of the time of exposure to the minimum required to get the H^1 lines on our plates was about 4500:1. Under these conditions we found in this sample as well as in ordinary hydrogen faint lines at the calculated positions for the lines of H^2 accompanying H_β, H_γ, H_σ. These lines do not agree in wave-length with any molecular lines reported in the literature. However they were so weak that it was difficult to be sure that they were not ghosts of the strongly over-exposed atomic lines.

The sample of hydrogen evaporated near the triple point shows these lines greatly enhanced, relative to the lines of H^1, over both those of ordinary hydrogen and of the first sample. The relative intensities can be judged by the number and intensity of the symmetrical ghosts on the plates. The wave-lengths of the H^2 lines appearing on these plates could be easily measured within about 0.02 A. The following table gives the mean of the observed displacements of these lines from those of H^1 and the calculated displacements:

Line	H_α	H_β	H_γ	H_δ
$\Delta\lambda_{calc.}$	1.793	1.326	1.185	1.119
$\Delta\lambda_{obs.}$ ordinary hydrogen	—	1.346	1.206	1.145
1st sample	—	1.330	1.199	1.103
2nd sample	1.820	1.315	1.176	—

The H^2 lines are broad, as is to be expected for close unresolved doublets, but they are not as broad and diffuse as the H^1 lines, probably due to the smaller Döppler broadening. Although their intensities relative to the ghosts of the respective H^1 lines appear nearly constant for any one sample of hydrogen, they are not ghosts, for their intensities relative to the known ghosts are not the same in the case of ordinary hydrogen and of the 1st sample as they are in the case of the second sample. They are not molecular lines for they do not appear on a plate taken with the discharge tube in the "white stage" with the molecular spectrum enhanced ($H_\gamma{}^2$ was found as a slight irregularity on a microphotometer curve of this plate). Finally the $H_\alpha{}^2$ line is resolved into a doublet with a separation of about 0.16 A in agreement with the observed separation of the $H_\alpha{}^1$ line.

The relative abundance in ordinary hydrogen, judging from relative minimum exposure time is about 1:4000, or less, in agreement with Birge and Menzel's estimate. A similar estimate of the abundance in the second sample indicated a concentration of about 1 in 800. Thus an appreciable fractionation has been secured as expected from theory.

No evidence for H^3 has been secured, but its lines would fail on regions of our plates where the halation is bad.

The distillation was carried out at the Bureau of Standards by one of us (F. G. B.) who is continuing the fractionation to secure more highly concentrated samples. The spectroscopic work was done at Columbia University by the other two (H. C. U. and G. M. M.) who are working on the molecular spectrum.

MOLECULAR STRUCTURE. After the Bohr picture of the atom had been accepted, it became possible to return to the old problem of the actual nature of valence forces. The chief reason for the downfall of the Berzelius dualistic theory had been its inability to explain the nature of the bonds in organic compounds. Now the theory was revived and extended to account for all types of bonds.

The first successful application of the new electron theory of atomic structure was made by Kossel, who explained the nature of inorganic, polar bonds. A similar explanation was offered by G. N. Lewis at about the same time, and he extended and theory to nonpolar bonds, or covalent links, as they came to be called. Langmuir further developed this aspect of the theory. The work of Kossel, Lewis, and Langmuir, illustrated in the three selections that follow, laid the foundations for all later theories of molecular structure. The development of the electron theory of structure has been extensively reviewed by G. V. Bykov (*Chymia 10*, 199–253, 1965).

The following selection is from pages 229–230 and 234–241 in *Annalen der Physik 49*, 229–362 (1916).

Molecule Formation as a Question of Atomic Structure

W. KOSSEL

The periodicity of behavior which previously had been considered as the most important characteristic of the series of elements and the basis of all studies of atomic structure has been pushed strongly into the background by the results obtained in recent years. Since Lenard's discovery that cathode ray absorption follows mass, it has been discovered for the first time that there is a unity of matter toward electrical phenomena, and the number of such facts has constantly grown, until finally the laws of Röntgen ray spectra have established in the clearest manner that among the elements there is a continuous series of structures of the same type, in which the identical type of alterations of dimensions occurs from step to step. Therefore there have been more and more studies which approach a concept of treating chemical behavior so that only the constituents of this unitary building material are everywhere involved and all ad hoc assumptions of special types are avoided; in this view the periodic phenomena reflect only an alteration in the order of the outermost of the constituents mentioned. The present work is devoted to this theme, since it considers the question of how simple may be the major features of molecule formation that can be described, and what assumptions will be necessarily required.

The result is that remarkably few special assumptions are necessary at first for a description of the basic facts that can give the behavior of compounds that have polar characteristics. Since the overwhelming majority of the compounds of inorganic chemistry of a wide variety of elements have a polar character, there is a corresponding reduction in the number of compounds of special, individual elements that must at first have specific assumptions, and thus need special treatment. Such compounds lie among the homopolar compounds of other elements, especially in the realm of carbon compounds, concerning which Stark's special picture of electron arrangements has already given such outstanding results, and where the special requirements are obviously already beginning to be worked out in the structure of the diamond.

A summary of the organization of the rest of the paper is then given.

Basic Assumptions. In what follows we will not use any of the previous proposals as expressed in individual atomic models; rather we will employ only such general assumptions as seem to be experimentally well grounded. We will therefore naturally begin with well-known ideas.

We envisage the method of molecule formation as the coming together of the electron structures of different atoms. We will thus generalize the ideas which Helmholz in his time developed concerning electrical elementary quanta. In electrolytic dissociation we are acquainted with separation of molecules in which the number of elementary quanta agrees with the number of valence units passed from one component to the other, as chemical experience shows. Since the freely moving elementary quantum is known to have only a negative charge, the exchange of charges will occur especially here; the passing of an electron will be assumed, while the positive charge, whose structure for the moment will be left open, remains in the mass of the atom. The number of available electrons in the atom and the conditions under which it is possible for them to leave the atom will be the factors that determine the chemical behavior of the atom. As to what first sets the total number of electrons in the atom, we accept van den Broek's hypothesis that makes this equal to the order number of the elements in the periodic table. This assumption seems necessary to satisfy the results of the studies on Röntgen ray scattering and especially the exact results that have been obtained for the relative number of electrons from the interaction of various kinds of atoms in interference in crystals; we assume that a more accurate formulation of the theory, which today is somewhat incomplete, will not bring about any very fundamental changes in the results. Since, as it seems, never more than eight valence units are active in an atom, in most cases we must deal with the exchange of only a small portion of the electrons present, and so the question arises, how to consider the order of the electrons in the atom so as to understand why only a definitely determined number of them can enter into an exchange. It is generally accepted, to be sure, that the electro-static forces and the electromagnetic forces that they overcome are modified for all the electrons of an atom by the approach of another atom. Experience has already shown, however, that this action, as judged from the emission frequencies, is of a completely different order of magnitude for different electrons. We are forced to assume that the conditions by which the frequency is determined for some of the electrons of a heavy atom entering a molecular union are altered only very slightly, while for others (emitting the "optical frequencies") the conditions are fundamentally changed. It is required as much from the valence properties as from emission that each element must have a determined atomic structure whose various electrons are approachable from the outside and able to be affected in different degree. The simplest picture is given when we assign to the interior of the atom those electrons that are not affected and whose high frequency in any case is related to some sort of strong binding (quasi-elastic or quantum holding), while the valence electrons and those active at optical frequencies are more loosely bound and can be affected; these are considered to be lying on the surface of the atoms.

On the basis that we have reviewed, we thus conceive of the valence properties as an expression of the behavior of the outermost electrons of the atom, and henceforth we will follow them through a series of elements from below upwards.

According to the van den Broek assumption, each successive element will contain one more electron and one more elementary quantity of positive charge than the previous one. This is primarily shown by the fact of the periodic changes of the valence number so that as the elements pass from lower to higher weight the configuration is not altered uniformly (also perhaps not if the newly arriving electrons are assumed to add on singly to the structure already formed arranged on a spiral). In the course of a regular change we are much more likely to come to a configuration in which the number of electrons capable of valence activity is repeated, and also some in which practically no tendency to exchange exists, the noble gases, among others. In order to come closer to the assumption now becoming necessary, we will at first confine ourselves to the region of the two short periods and the beginning of the first long one; the region from He to Ti. Here, after eight element positions there is repetition of the same chemical properties and the same valence maxima. After addition of eight electrons, we once more get the same surface order for the atoms. The continuity with which the K-frequency in the whole periodic system depends on the unit number (the number of the element in the periodic system) shows that the periodicity found in the sequence in no way extends to the whole electron structure, but is limited to the surface. Accordingly, we can follow up the simplest idea that suggests itself: the order of the inner electrons remains unchanged in the elements that follow each other, always similar in each element and only changing its size through the continuous increase of the charge, which corresponds to the same increase in characteristic frequencies. The electrons that come anew in the sequence of atomic weights will always add to the outside and their order will be such that the observed periodicity results from the fact of their approach from outside. This leads to the suggestion that these electrons that are newly added are arranged in concentric rings, or shells, in which (perhaps because of conditions of stability that we will not discuss) only a definite number of electrons, here eight, can find places. If a ring or shell is completed, the next element must begin a new one; the number of electrons approaching entirely from outside again increases from element to element and thus the chemical character is repeated by building a new shell.

In order to test these ideas more fully, we now ask in which column of the periodic table we must seek the elements in which a new shell from some electron lying outside is begun. This can be seen from strictly chemical considerations. The characteristic of the alkali metals always to give up electrons with great ease—for example, to show greater "emissivity" for electrons when there is more violent heat motion in the surroundings—suggests to us that in them an electron is bound especially loosely and is exposed to outside influences; this suggests that in the area of the periodic system discussed above we can consider, on the basis of experimental evidence, that Na and K are elements in which, outside the completed shell, the first electron of the new shell is located. To the preceding elements Ne and Ar we must then logically ascribe an atomic structure in which a shell or a ring of electrons is completely closed, while the preceding Fl and Cl lack one electron in theirs. Now we know that these last, the halogens, are elements that whenever possible seek to acquire electrons: they have, we might say, "a high affinity for free electrons." It appears, then, that the configuration of the outer electrons reached in the noble gases can be considered somewhat analogous to an equilibrium state. Not only do the noble gases themselves lack an inclination to take up electrons ("no affinity for free electrons") or to give them up (they have the highest splitting tension yet measured), but also the neighboring configurations endeavor, by giving up or taking on electrons, to form systems of the same total number of electrons as the noble gases. The configurations they form are thus not only exceptionally stable themselves, resisting all changes, but also are the prototypes of the configurations that the neighboring systems, which have only a slightly different normal number of electrons or few different positive charges, form preferentially by electron exchange with the surroundings. In the picture of the arrangement of shells that we will finally use we will assume as the most natural idea that the foreign electron in a halogen atom thus serves to close an almost completed shell.

On the basis of the behavior of the elements adjacent to the noble gases, we will proceed further experimentally. On the one hand, we assume that throughout an atom those electrons that lie outside the last completed shell are given up considerably more easily than those which belong to it. On the other hand, we assume that generally atoms whose number of electrons approaches that of a noble gas (the completion of a shell) have a tendency to add as many foreign electrons as will give the "stable" form of the noble gas. Since the number of electrons of the neutral atom agrees with the position in the sequence of atomic weights (reported as already known in part from the Röntgen ray spectra), we find that the number of electrons that can be taken up or given off also has a simple relation to this position. To the halogens, which stand immediately before the noble gases, we ascribe the ability to bind *one* electron; the elements of the preceding sixth column of the system, O and S, for example, must correspondingly take up two electrons to reach the number of a noble gas, the next preceding N and P must take up three, and so on. The tendency for such addition seems to decrease with increasing distance from the noble gases. On the other side of the noble gases we find analogously the opposite function of the atoms; the most electropositive, most easily losing electron elements are the alkali metals; they are followed with decreasing tendency to give up electrons by the alkaline earths, which already have two more electrons than the noble gases. Consequently here we go through a series: the elements of column III, B and Al, have three electrons that easily separate; those of column IV, four; those of VII, seven; until finally in the eighth element, the next noble gas, the new ring is closed. Obviously we agree completely here with Drude's results, which showed that the number of loosely bound electrons which give dispersion agrees excellently with the Abegg valence theory provided we indicate each possible valence position as a detachable electron. We now turn to a consideration of the evidence from valence. In the physical processes on which we based our previous considerations we obviously only very rarely considered such a great accumulation as would correspond to maximum loss of electrons by the halogens.

We now must show that the electron exchange which leads to chemical molecule formation is as useful for our expanded picture.

Molecule Formation. Up to this time we have generally considered electron exchange of the individual atoms with their surroundings; now we will consider the consequences when more atom systems (at least two) are brought together, when we find that they have opposite tendencies in the exchange process. For instance, if a halogen atom comes together with an alkali metal atom, we find for both atoms the opportunity for the tendency that they follow as free atoms: the alkali metal gives up the farthest outlying electron, as in a flame, and the halogen takes it up to close its ring. Both now adhere to each other electrostatically, since the halogen system as a whole is negatively charged, and the alkali positively charged. These charges appear separately if the molecule is brought into a medium of high dielectric constant so that the electrostatic attractive force is weakened. If it becomes too slight to maintain an equilibrium under the shock of thermal agitation, the system separates in terms of its present situation: the halogen retains its abnormal electron as an anion, the alkali metal shows an excess of positive charge. Both have completely lost the chemical properties that they show as neutral atoms, since they have satisfied their characteristic tendencies. This fact is necessarily connected with their structures. The fact that perhaps a potassium ion does not behave in water like a neutral potassium atom, that a solution of chloride does not show the properties of a water solution of chlorine gas, always occurs because here the atoms are charged, which must basically change their properties. This change follows directly from the fact that the atoms have given up their characteristic activities of reaction. This behavior necessarily follows: the K^+ ion has completely lost its specific chemical activity with the loss of the cause of this activity, the outer electron; the Cl^- ion has obtained what it otherwise always tends to acquire; both reach their structures because of these directing and attracting forces and the tendency to electron exchange of these elements. We will return later to ion formation (Part II); here we have elucidated the manner of chemical bonding by the ideas we have introduced and further expanded. The two atoms that are bound as a result of passage of their elementary charges have been monovalent and polar in two different ways: the halogen attracts one electron into its system to build a stable configuration; the alkali metal gives one up readily. It is essential for our theory that in processes like this, as we often find today, each valence position as seen chemically has a "valence electron" arranged on the atom, but the specific *negative* valence position, that on the halogen in our case, is perhaps to be considered as a "free place" with respect to the element following in the periodic system, which the atom strives to fill up. We continue with the cases which at least are similar and which occur in the overwhelming majority of inorganic compounds where there is necessary a polarity of function shown in the atoms as valence; this reminds us of the experimental material which Abegg obtained from his comprehensive study from the purely chemical side and which has likewise interpreted valence as a polar function.

Further applications to other elements are then made.

The following selection is from pages 763, 767–768, and 774–779 in *The Journal of the American Chemical Society 38*, 762–785 (1916).

The Atom and the Molecule

GILBERT N. LEWIS

To enable us to appreciate the importance and the usefulness of a distinction between polar and nonpolar types of chemical molecules no hypotheses are necessary, but in a more minute examination of the nature of such a distribution some theory of atomic structure is indispensable. Such a theory I have employed for a number of years in the interpretation of chemical phenomena, but it has not hitherto been published. I shall present this theory briefly in the present paper, for, while it bears much resemblance to some current theories of the atom, it shows some radical points of departure from them. As an introduction it will be desirable to review the characteristics of polar and nonpolar compounds.

A detailed comparison is then made of the properties of polar and nonpolar compounds to show that it is the strength with which atoms are held together in molecules that accounts for the observed differences.

The Cubical Atom

A number of years ago, to account for the striking fact which has become known as Abegg's law of valence and countervalence, and according to which the total difference between the maximum negative and positive valences or polar numbers of an element is frequently eight and is in no case more than eight, I designed what may be called the theory of the cubical atom. This theory, while it has become familiar to a number of my colleagues, has never been published, partly because it was in many respects incomplete.

Although many of these elements of incompleteness remain, and although the theory lacks today much of the novelty which it originally possessed, it seems to me more probable intrinsically than some of the other theories of atomic structure which have been proposed, and I cannot discuss more fully the nature of the differences between polar and nonpolar compounds without a brief discussion of this theory.

The pictures of atomic structure which are reproduced in Fig. 2[1] and in which the circles represent the electrons in the outer shell of

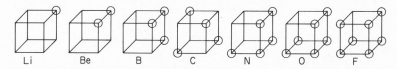

Fig. 2

the neutral atom, were designed to explain a number of important laws of chemical behavior with the aid of the following postulates:

1. In every atom is an essential *kernel* which remains unaltered in all ordinary chemical changes, and which possesses an excess of positive charges corresponding in number to the ordinal number of the group in the periodic table to which the element belongs.

2. The atom is composed of the kernel and an *outer atom* or *shell* which in the case of the neutral atom, contains negative electrons equal in number to the excess of positive charges of the kernel, but the number of electrons in the shell may vary during chemical change between 0 and 8.

3. The atom tends to hold an even number of electrons in the shell, and especially to hold eight electrons which are normally arranged symmetrically at the eight corners of a cube.[2]

4. Two atomic shells are mutually interpenetrable.

5. Electrons may ordinarily pass with readiness from one position in the outer shell to another. Nevertheless they are held in position by more or less rigid constraints, and these positions and magnitude

[1] These figures are taken from a memorandum dated March 28, 1902; together with the models are notes concerning different types of chemical compounds; the various possible arrangements of electrons in the outer atom and the possibility of intra-atomic isomerism; the relationship between symmetrical structure and atomic volume; and certain speculations as to the structure of the helium atom which we shall see were probably partly incorrect. The date of origin of this theory is mentioned not with the purpose of claiming any sort of priority with respect to those portions which overlap existing theories, but because the fact that similar theories have been developed independently adds to the probability that all possess some characteristic of fundamental reality.

[2] We shall see later the advisability of modifying this assumption of the cubic arrangement of the fundamental group of eight electrons.

of the constraints are determined by the nature of the atom and of such other atoms as are combined with it.

6. Electric forces between particles which are very close together do not obey the simple law of inverse squares which holds at greater distances.

These postulates are explained in detail. The author represents the kernel of the atom by the boldfaced symbol of the element. He next applies the postulates to the structure of molecules.

Molecular Structure

I shall now attempt to show how, by a single type of chemical combination, we may explain the widely varying phenomena of chemical change. With the original assumption of Helmholtz, which has been used by some authors under the name of the electron theory of valence, and according to which a given electron either does or does not pass completely from one atom to another, it is possible to give a very satisfactory explanation of compounds which are of distinctly polar type, but the method becomes less and less satisfactory as we approach the nonpolar type. Great as the difference is between the typical polar and nonpolar substances, we may show how a single molecule may, according to its environment, pass from the extreme polar to the extreme nonpolar form, not *per saltum*, but by imperceptible gradations, as soon as we admit that an electron may be the common property of two atomic shells.

Let us consider first the very polar compounds. Here we find elements with but few electrons in their shells tending to give up these electrons altogether to form positive ions, and elements which already possess a number of electrons tending to increase this number to form the group of eight. Thus Na^+ and Ca^{++} are kernels without a shell, while chloride ion, sulfide ion, nitride ion (as in fused nitrides) may each be represented by an atom having in the shell eight electrons at the corners of a cube.

As an introduction to the study of substances of slightly polar type we may consider the halogens. In Fig. 3 I have attempted to show the different forms of the iodine molecule I_2. *A* represents the

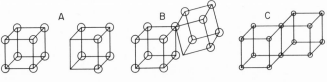

Fig. 3

molecule as completely ionized, as it undoubtedly is to a measurable extent in liquid iodine. Without ionization we may still have one of the electrons of one atom fitting into the outer shell of the second atom, thus completing its group of eight as in *B*. But at the same time an electron of the second atom may fit into the shell of the first, thus satisfying both groups of eight and giving the form *C* which is the predominant and characteristic structure of the halogens. Now, notwithstanding the symmetry of the form *C*, if the two atoms are for any reason tending to separate, the two common electrons may cling more firmly sometimes to one of the atoms, sometimes to the other, thus producing some dissymmetry in the molecule as a whole, and one atom will have a slight excess of positive charge, the other of negative. This separation of the charges and the consequent increase in the polar character of the molecule will increase as the atoms become separated to a greater distance until complete ionization results.[1] Thus between the perfectly symmetrical and nonpolar molecule *C* and the completely polar and ionized molecule represented by *A* there will be an infinity of positions representing a greater or lesser degree of polarity. Now in a substance like liquid iodine it must not be assumed that all of the molecules are in the same state, but rather that some are highly polar, some almost nonpolar, and others represent all gradations between the two. When we find that iodine in different environments shows different degrees of polarity, it means merely that in one medium there is a larger percentage of the more polar forms. So bromine, although represented by an entirely similar formula, is less polar than iodine. In other words, in the average molecule the separation of the charge is less than in the case of iodine. Chlorine and fluorine are less polar than either and can be regarded as composed almost completely of molecules of the form *C*.

I wish to emphasize once more the meaning that must be ascribed to the term tautomerism. In the simplest case where we deal with a single tautomeric change we speak of the two tautomers and sometimes write definite formulae to express the two. But we must not assume that all of the molecules of the substance possess either one structure or the other, but rather that these forms represent the two limiting types, and that the individual molecules range all the way from one limit to the other. In certain cases where the majority of molecules lie very near to one limit or to the other, it is very convenient and desirable to attempt to express the percentage of the molecules belonging to one or to the other tautomeric form; but in a case where

[1] When the separation occurs in a nonpolar environment the atoms may separate in such a way that each retains one of the two common electrons, as in the thermal dissociation of iodine gas.

the majority of molecules lie in the intermediate range and relatively few in the immediate neighborhood of the two limiting forms, such a calculation loses most of its significance.

With the halogens it is a matter of chance as to which of the atoms acquires a positive and which a negative charge, but in the case of a binary compound composed of different elements the atoms of one element will be positive in most, though not necessarily all, of the molecules. Thus in Br_2 the bromine atom is as often positive as negative, but in BrCl it will be usually positive and in IBr usually negative, although in all these substances which are not very polar the separation of charges in the molecule will be slight, whereas in the metallic halides the separation is nearly complete and the halogen atoms acquire almost complete possession of the electrons.

In order to express this idea of chemical union in symbols I would suggest the use of a colon, or two dots arranged in some other manner, to represent the two electrons which act as the connecting links between the two atoms. Thus we may write Cl_2 as Cl:Cl. If in certain cases we wish to show that one atom in the molecule is on the average negatively charged we may bring the colon nearer to the negative element. Thus we may write Na :I and I :Cl. Different spacings to represent different degrees of polarity can of course be more freely employed at a blackboard than in type.

It will be noted that, since in the hydrogen-helium row we have the rule of two in the place of the rule of eight, the insertion of one electron into the shell of the hydrogen atom is entirely analogous to the completion of the cube in the case of the halogens. Thus we may consider ordinary hydrogen as a hydride of positive hydrogen in the same sense that chlorine may be regarded as a chloride of positive chlorine. But H_2 is far less polar even than Cl_2. The three main types of hydrogen compounds may be represented therefore by H :Cl, H : H, and Na :H.

We may go further and give a complete formula for each compound by using the symbol of the kernel instead of the ordinary atomic symbol and by adjoining to each symbol a number of dots corresponding to the number of electrons in the atomic shell. Thus we may write

$$\text{H:H, H:}\overset{..}{\underset{..}{O}}\text{:H, H:}\overset{..}{\underset{..}{I}}\text{:, :}\overset{..}{\underset{..}{I}}\text{:}\overset{..}{\underset{..}{I}}\text{:,}$$

but we shall see that in many cases such a formula represents only one of the numerous extreme tautomeric forms. For the sake of simplicity we may also use occasionally formulae which show only those electrons concerned in the union of two atoms, as in the preceding paragraph.

It is evident that the type of union which we have so far pictured, although it involves two electrons held in common by two atoms, nevertheless corresponds to the single bond as it is commonly used in graphical formulae. In order to illustrate this point further we may discuss a problem which has proved extremely embarrassing to a number of theories of valence. I refer to the structure of ammonia and of ammonium ion. Ammonium ion may, of course, on account of the extremely polar character of ammonia and hydrogen ion, be regarded as a loose complex due to the electrical attraction of the two polar molecules. However, as we consider the effect of substituting hydrogen by organic groups we pass gradually into a field where we may be perfectly certain that four groups are attached directly to the nitrogen atom, and these groups are held with sufficient firmness so that numerous stereochemical isomers have been obtained. The solution of this problem in terms of the theory here presented is extremely simple and satisfactory, and it will be sufficient to write an equation in terms of the new symbols in order to make the explanation obvious. Thus for

$$
\mathrm{NH_3 + H^+ = NH_4^+} \text{ we write } \mathrm{H\!:\!\overset{..}{\underset{..}{N}}\!:} + \mathrm{H} = \mathrm{H\!:\!\overset{..}{\underset{..}{N}}\!:\!H.}
$$

with H above and H below each nitrogen.

When ammonium ion combines with chloride ion the latter is not attached directly to the nitrogen, but is held simply through electric forces by the ammonium ion.

While the two dots of our formulae correspond to the line which has been used to represent the single bond, we are led through their use to certain formulae of great significance which I presume would not occur to anyone using the ordinary symbols. Thus it has been generally assumed that what is known as a bivalent element must be tied by two bonds to another element or elements, or remain with an "unsaturated valence." On the other hand, we may now write formulae in which an atom of oxygen is tied by only one pair of electrons to another atom and yet have every element in the compound completely saturated. To illustrate this important point we may write the formula of perchlorate, sulfate, orthophosphate and orthosilicate ions, in which each atom has a complete shell of eight electrons. Thus

$$
\begin{array}{c}
\mathrm{:\overset{..}{O}:} \\
\mathrm{:\overset{..}{O}:\overset{..}{X}:\overset{..}{O}:} \\
\mathrm{:\overset{..}{O}:}
\end{array}
$$

represents all of these ions. If **X** is **Cl**, the ion has one negative charge; if **S** it has two negative charges, and so on. The union of sulfur trioxide to oxide ion to form sulfate ion is similar to the addition of ammonia and hydrogen ion to form ammonium ion. The acids or acid ions are produced from the above ion by adding hydrogen ion, or **H**, to the oxygen atoms.

We may next consider the *double bond* in which four electrons are held conjointly by two atoms. Thus Fig. 4*A* may represent the typical structure of the molecule of oxygen. A characteristic feature of the double bond is its tendency to "break." When this happens in a symmetrical way, as it will, except in a highly polar environment, it leaves the two atoms concerned in the *odd* state, each with an unpaired electron in the shell. In so far as a substance with a double bond assumes this other tautomeric form, it will show all the properties of the substances with odd molecules. Thus Fig. 4*B* represents this tautomeric form of the oxygen molecule; the equilibrium between forms *A* and *B* is entirely analogous to the

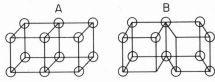

Fig. 4

equilibrium between N_2O_4 and NO_2. At low temperatures almost every known case of combination with oxygen gives first a peroxide. This shows that oxygen exists to an appreciable degree in a form which approximates to the form *B*, in which it can add directly to other atoms precisely as ethylene forms addition compounds. These two forms of oxygen (which, of course, may merge into one another by continuous gradations) can be represented as $:\overset{..}{O}::\overset{..}{O}:$ and $:\overset{..}{O}:\overset{..}{O}:$, and the two forms of ethylene as

$$\begin{array}{cc} H & H \\ H:\overset{..}{C}::\overset{..}{C}:H \end{array}$$

and

$$\begin{array}{cc} H & H \\ H:\overset{..}{C}:\overset{..}{C}:H. \end{array}$$

Further applications of the theory, especially to the color of compounds, are then discussed.

The following selection is from pages 868 and 932–934 in *The Journal of the American Chemical Society 41*, 868–934 (1919).

The Arrangement of Electrons in Atoms and Molecules

IRVING LANGMUIR

The problem of the structure of atoms has been attacked mainly by physicists who have given little consideration to the chemical properties which must ultimately be explained by a theory of atomic structure. The vast store of knowledge of chemical properties and relationships, such as is summarized by the Periodic Table, should serve as a better foundation for a theory of atomic structure than the relatively meager experimental data along purely physical lines.

Kossel and Lewis have had marked success in attacking the problem in this way. The present paper aims to develop and somewhat modify these theories.

The theory is presented and applied in great detail. The important features are then summarized as follows.

The theory presented in this paper is essentially an extension of Lewis' theory of the "cubical atom." It may be most concisely stated in terms of the following postulates:

1. The electrons in atoms are either stationary or rotate, revolve or oscillate about definite positions in the atom. In the most stable atoms, namely those of the inert gases, the electrons have positions symmetrical with respect to a plane, called the equatorial plane, passing through the nucleus at the center of the atom. No electrons lie in the equatorial plane. There is an axis of symmetry (polar axis) perpendicular to this plane through which 4 secondary planes of symmetry pass, forming angles of 45° with each other. These atoms thus have the symmetry of a tetragonal crystal.

2. The electrons in any given atom are distributed through a series of concentric (nearly) spherical shells, all of equal thickness. Thus the mean radii of the shells form an arithmetic series 1, 2, 3, 4, and the effective areas are in the ratios $1:2^2:3^2:4^2$.

3. Each shell is divided into cellular spaces or cells occupying equal areas in their respective shells and distributed over the surface of the shells according to the symmetry required by Postulate 1. The first shell thus contains 2 cells, the second 8, the third 18, and the fourth 32.

4. Each of the cells in the first shell can contain only one electron, but each other shell can contain either one or two. All of the inner

shells must have their full quota of electrons before the outside shell can contain any. No cell in the outside layer can contain two electrons until all the other cells in the layer contain at least one.

5. Two electrons in the same cell do not repel nor attract one another with strong forces. This probably means there is a magnetic attraction (Parson's magnetic theory) which nearly counteracts the electrostatic repulsion.

6. When the number of electrons in the outside layer is small the arrangement of the electrons is determined by the (magnetic?) attraction of the underlying electrons. But when the number of electrons increases, especially when the layer is nearly complete, the electrostatic repulsion of the underlying electrons and of those in the outside shell becomes predominant.

7. The properties of the atoms are determined primarily by the number and arrangement of electrons in the outside shell and by the ease with which the atom is able to revert to more stable forms by giving up or taking up electrons.

8. The stable and symmetrical arrangements of electrons corresponding to the inert gases are characterized by strong internal and weak external fields of force. The smaller the atomic number, the weaker the external field.

9. The most stable arrangement of electrons is that of the pair in the helium atom. A stable pair may also be held by: (*a*) a single hydrogen nucleus; (*b*) two hydrogen nuclei; (*c*) a hydrogen nucleus and the kernel of another atom; (*d*) two atomic kernels (very rare).

10. The next most stable arrangement of electrons is the *octet*, that is, a group of 8 electrons like that in the second shell of the neon atom. Any atom with atomic number less than 20, and which has more than 3 electrons in its outside layer tends to take up enough electrons to complete its octet.

11. Two octets may hold one, two, or sometimes 3 pairs of electrons in common. One octet may share one, two, three, or four pairs of its electrons with one, two, three, or four other octets. One or more pairs of electrons in an octet may be shared by the corresponding number of hydrogen nuclei. No electron can be shared by more than two octets.

The theory explains the periodic properties of all the elements including those of the eighth group and the rare earths. It meets with success in explaining the magnetic properties of the elements, and applies as well to the so-called physical properties such as boiling points, freezing points, electric conductivity, etc., as it does to the "chemical properties." It leads to a simple theory of chemical valence for both polar and non-polar substances. In the case of organic compounds the results are identical with those of the ordinary valence theory, while with oxygen, nitrogen, chlorine, sulfur, and phosphorus compounds, the new theory applies as well as to organic compounds, although the ordinary valence theory fails nearly completely.

This theory explains also the structure of compounds which, according to Werner's theory, are second order compounds with a co-ordination number equal to 4. According to the present theory, such compounds are to be regarded rather as typical primary valence compounds.

The valence theory is based on the following simple equation:

$$e = 8n - 2p,$$

where e is the total number of available electrons in the shells of all the atoms in a molecule; n is the number of octets forming the outside shells, and p is the number of pairs of electrons held in common by the octets. This equation is a complete mathematical statement of the primary valence requirements, not only in organic, but in inorganic chemistry.

The theory leads to very definite conceptions as to the positions of the electrons in the molecules or space lattices of compounds. The structures of molecules of nitrogen, carbon monoxide, hydrogen cyanide, and NO prove to be exceptional in that the kernels of both atoms in the molecule are contained within a single octet. This accounts for the practically identical "physical" properties of nitrogen and carbon monoxide, and for the abnormal inertness of molecular nitrogen.

The results obtained by the use of the postulates are so striking that one may safely reason that the results establish the fundamental correctness of the postulates.

These conclusions, however, are not easily reconciled with Bohr's theory of the atom. Bohr's stationary states have a rather close resemblance to the cellular structure postulated in the present theory. There are also striking points of similarity with J. J. Thomson's theory of the structure of atoms, in which he assumes that the attractive forces are limited to certain tubes of force.

When the basic ideas of polar and nonpolar bonds had been developed as shown above, it became possible to explain other special cases that had seemed anomalous or had not even been foreseen previously. Thus the concept of a hydrogen bond was almost completely new, yet it accounted for many types of association found in chemical compounds. Similarly, the largely empirical explanation given by Werner (H. M. Leicester and H. S. Klickstein, *A Source Book in Chemistry 1400–1900*, Harvard

University Press, Cambridge, Massachusetts, 1952, p. 516.) for the structure of complex inorganic compounds was explained in terms of covalency by Sidgewick, and this extension of the electron theory could also be applied to many different special cases. Thus the electron theory of chemical structure had built up a convincing picture of a static molecule which satisfied many requirements of the chemist.

The following selection is from pages 1430–1432 in *The Journal of the American Chemical Society 42*, 1419–1433 (1920).

Polarity and Ionization from the Standpoint of the Lewis Theory of Valence

WENDELL M. LATIMER AND WORTH H. RODEBUSH

Associated Liquids

The phenomenon of association in liquids has long been recognized as related to dielectric constant and ionizing power as a solvent. According to one view, a so-called polar solvent contains dipoles of considerable moment, that is, positive and negative charges separated by a considerable distance. The high dielectric constant of such a liquid is considered to be due to the orientation of these dipoles in an electric field.   Likewise association is supposed to take place because of the attraction of two dipoles for each other. This explanation is open to serious objections. In the first place it is hard to see why the compounds of very high dielectric constant should be chiefly hydrogen compounds. Also hydrogen chloride should contain dipoles of greater moment than water or hydrogen fluoride, yet it has a much lower dielectric constant both in the vapor and liquid. Nor does hydrogen chloride appear to be associated. It seems then that the explanation is to be sought along other lines.

Let us compare again the compounds ammonia, water and hydrogen chloride. Ammonia adds a hydrogen readily but has little tendency to give one up. Hydrogen chloride, on the other hand, shows just the opposite tendencies. Water occupies an intermediate position and shows tendencies both to add and give up hydrogen, which are nearly balanced. Then, in terms of the Lewis theory, a free pair of electrons on one water molecule might be able to exert sufficient force on a hydrogen held by a pair of electrons on another water molecule to bind the two molecules together. Structurally this may be represented as

$$
\begin{array}{c}
\text{H} \\
\overset{..}{\text{H}}\!:\!\overset{..}{\underset{..}{\text{O}}}\!:\!\text{H}\!:\!\overset{..}{\underset{..}{\text{O}}}\!: \\
\text{H}
\end{array}
$$

Such combination need not be limited to the formation of double or triple molecules. Indeed the liquid may be made up of large aggregates of molecules, continually breaking up and reforming under the influence of thermal agitation.

Such an explanation amounts to saying that the hydrogen nucleus held between 2 octets constitutes a weak "bond."[1] Ammonium hydroxide

$$
\begin{array}{c}
\text{H} \\
\overset{..}{\text{H}}\!:\!\overset{..}{\underset{..}{\text{N}}}\!:\!\text{H}\!:\!\overset{..}{\underset{..}{\text{O}}}\!:\!\text{H} \\
\text{H}
\end{array}
$$

is an example in which the union is fairly strong. This is contrary to the view commonly held that the weak basicity of ammonium hydroxide is due to the fact that it consists largely of a solution of ammonia in water. The idea also departs somewhat from the view taken by Lewis in regard to the polarity of NH_4^+. However, there seems to be no reason for believing that gradations may not exist all the way from the case of ammonium chloride, where the hydrogen is definitely transferred from the chlorine to the ammonia, to the case in the association of water where the hydrogen is still held quite firmly to the original water molecule. Ammonium chloride is probably as nearly completely polar with respect to the separation of charges as sodium chloride, and the crystal, at ordinary temperatures, is held together in a similar manner by forces only slightly less. As we raise the temperature, however, the hydrogen of the bond, being a heavy particle, acquires vibrational energy very rapidly. This breaks up the crystal structure and causes ammonium chloride to dissociate and volatilize without melting. Hydrogen chloride forms a compound of this type with water just as it does with ammonia, but it is even less stable than ammonium chloride for obvious reasons.

It is not assumed that all association is of this type. In acetic acid, for instance, the association doubtless takes place with the formation

---

[1] Mr. Huggins of this laboratory in some work as yet unpublished, has used the idea of a hydrogen kernel held between two atoms as a theory in regard to certain organic compounds.

of definite polymers of 2 molecules. This kind of association however will produce properties radically different from those of a liquid
like water.

If our picture of the association of water is correct, a hydrogen
nucleus may be held between two oxygen octets by forces which,
for quite a distance, obey Hooke's law. Such a hydrogen would be
capable of considerable displacement by an electric field. This is
just the mechanism postulated by the mathematical theory of
dielectric polarization as giving rise to high dielectric constant. It is
quite possible in the case of the hydrogen compounds of the most
electronegative elements, hydrogen fluoride, for example, that the
simultaneous attraction of a highly concentrated octet of electrons,
and the repulsion of the powerful positive nucleus for the hydrogen,
may result in the hydrogen in the single molecule being held elastically. The association of the molecules is, however, very probably
the factor that produces the extremely high dielectric constant.

The following selection is from pages 31–34 of the Presidential Address
to Section B (Chemistry) of the *Report of the Ninety-Fifth Meeting*
(*Ninety-Seventh Year*), *Leeds, 1927* (British Association for the Advancement of Science, London, 1927), pp. 27–42.

Co-ordination Compounds

N. V. SIDGEWICK

The address opens with a review of the Werner theory of co-ordination
compound structure and the Lewis-Kossel-Langmuir electron theory of
structure.

We have therefore got an electronic mechanism which will account
for the two recognized forms of valency, the ionized and the non-
ionized. If these are really the only two forms of linkage which can
exist in a molecule, it must be possible to extend them so as to account
for co-ordination. This is in fact surprisingly simple, and the solution
was foreshadowed by Lewis in his paper of 1916. It is clear that the
link which attaches one of the groups of a co-ordination complex
to the central atom is of the non-polar type. It is an essential point
in Werner's theory that such links are not ionized; this is how they
are distinguished from the links to atoms in the "second sphere."
Thus in the compound $[Pt(NH_3)_4Cl_2]Cl_2$ the two chlorine atoms
outside the bracket enclosing the co-ordination complex are ionized,

while those inside are not. The same conclusion is supported by the fact that the arrangement of the groups in the co-ordination complex round the central atom can give rise to optical activity; for this, as we know from organic chemistry, is only possible with groups which are attached by covalent links, that is, by directed forces. We must therefore look for an explanation of co-ordination in the formation of covalencies, that is, of links formed of pairs of shared electrons. But they must arise in some way different from that which we have hitherto assumed, since their numerical relations are different; their number is not related to the periodic group of their central atom, and also they can be formed with atoms (such as the nitrogen in ammonia or the oxygen in water) which have already completed a stable number of electrons. Now in the normal covalency formation described above it was assumed that one of the two shared electrons of a link came from each of the two atoms concerned. It is obviously possible that both might be derived from one of them; and the recognition of this possibility is all that is required to provide an electronic mechanism for co-ordination. By means of this extension of the idea of covalency formation we can explain all the peculiarities of co-ordination compounds, of which, as we have seen, the most important are the power of further combination shown by apparently saturated molecules such as water and ammonia, the attainment of a valency limit (the co-ordination number) independent of the periodic group to which the atom belongs, and the peculiar change of electro-valency which accompanies the replacement of a univalent radical such as chlorine by a whole molecule such as ammonia. We may consider these in turn. In nitrogen there are five valency electrons; by combination with three hydrogen atoms this number is increased to eight, giving a molecule of ammonia, in which the octet of the nitrogen is complete and the atom is so far saturated. But though complete, the octet is not fully utilized: six of its members are shared with the three hydrogen atoms, but the other two are unshared, and so can form a fourth link if another atom can be found which will share them without sharing some of its own electrons with the nitrogen in return. This may happen in a variety of ways. A hydrogen ion, consisting of a single proton with no attendant electron, is capable of taking up two electrons, and, as we all know, if a hydrogen ion meets an ammonia molecule it combines with it to form an ammonium ion

$$
\begin{array}{c}
\text{H} \\
\text{··} \\
\text{H} : \text{N} : \\
\text{··} \\
\text{H}
\end{array}
+ [\text{H}]^+ =
\left[
\begin{array}{c}
\text{H} \\
\text{··} \\
\text{H} : \text{N} : \text{H} \\
\text{··} \\
\text{H}
\end{array}
\right]^+
$$

The nitrogen has now shared all its eight valency electrons, two with each of the four hydrogen atoms; but since the ammonia molecule is electrically neutral, while the hydrogen ion is positively charged, the resulting NH_4 molecule is also positively charged. Again, boron has three valency electrons; it can share one of them with each of three chlorine atoms (thus completing the octets of the chlorine), and at the same time take a share in one of the electrons belonging to each of the chlorines, This gives boron trichloride BCl_3, in which the boron has increased its valency group from three to six. The boron cannot combine with a fourth chlorine atom, because, although its own octet is not complete, it has no more unshared valency electrons to offer for a covalent link. But if it meets an ammonia molecule it can share the unshared pair of electrons of the nitrogen, and so form a co-ordinate link:

$$
\begin{array}{ccc}
\text{Cl} \quad \text{H} & & \text{Cl} \;\; \text{H} \\
\text{Cl:} \overset{..}{\text{B}} + \; \overset{..}{:\text{N}} : \text{H} = \text{Cl:} \overset{..}{\text{B}} : \overset{..}{\text{N}} : \text{H} \\
\overset{..}{\text{Cl}} \quad \text{H} & & \overset{..}{\text{Cl}} \;\; \overset{..}{\text{H}}
\end{array}
$$

In this way each of the two atoms assumes a covalency (or, if we prefer to call it so, a co-ordination number) of four.

The conditions for the formation of a co-ordinate link thus are that we should have one atom which has a pair of unshared valency electrons to offer, and another which has room for one or more pairs of electrons in its valency group. It is convenient to have a symbol and a nomenclature to express this process, and I have therefore suggested that, while the ordinary covalent link is represented by a line A–B, the co-ordinate link should be written as an arrow A→B pointing away from the atom which contributes the two electrons of the link; also we may call the atom which lends the electrons (A) the donor, and that which receives them (B) the acceptor.

We have now to apply these ideas to the compounds on which Werner based his theory. Any simple cation—that is, an atom stripped of its valency electrons—can act as an acceptor. It can build up a valency group by sharing electrons belonging to other atoms, that is, by forming co-ordinate links. Thus the chromic ion $[Cr]^{+++}$ contains a stable core of twenty-one electrons and has no valency group; the stability of this arrangement is proved by the stability of chromic salts. This ion can then form a series of co-ordinate links with molecules of ammonia, by sharing the "lone pair" of electrons of the nitrogen atom. Since the stable size of the valency group for such an ion is 12, six molecules of ammonia will be taken up, and in this way the hexammine $[Cr(NH_3)_6]Cl_3$

is produced. We have thus accounted for the power which certain complete molecules possess of combining further through co-ordination.

The next point is to explain the peculiar change of electrovalency which accompanies the replacement of an ammonia molecule by, say, a chlorine atom. It is natural that if an ammonia molecule is removed, this should be replaced by another covalently linked atom, because that is required to maintain the valency group of 12. When the ammonia is removed it takes away with it two shared electrons which it originally contributed; the chlorine atom which replaces it supplies one electron to be shared by the chromium, but the chromium is called upon to supply the other electron for the link. Thus the chromium is one electron short of its stable number, and must take up an electron from elsewhere to make up the deficiency. In other words, the replacement of the ammonia by chlorine will reduce the positive charge on the ion by one unit, giving instead of $[Cr(NH_3)_6]^{+++}$ the ion $[Cr(NH_3)_5Cl]^{++}$, or the salt $[Cr(NH_3)_5Cl]Cl_2$. The same change will occur for every replacement of a whole molecule in the complex by a univalent radical. Thus the very peculiar change of electrovalency which Werner established is a necessary result of the electronic mechanism underlying the linkage. The third important characteristic of the co-ordination compounds is the co-ordination number itself. As we have seen, the most remarkable point about these compounds is that the relation observed in ordinary structural chemistry between the valency of an element and its group in the periodic table disappears. Instead of finding that the valency— the number of links which an atom can form—increases from one in the first group to four in the fourth; and then falls (in the simpler compounds at any rate) to one in the seventh, we find that the co-ordination number is independent of the periodic group, and is usually either six or four. But this again follows necessarily from the theory. So long as the valency is expressed by ionization, or by normal covalencies to which each atom contributes one electron, it must be limited either by the number of electrons which the atom has to offer or by the number for which it has room in the valency group; it will therefore be determined by the distance of the atom in question from the nearest inert gas, or, in other words, by the group in the periodic table to which it belongs. In its saturated compounds the atom will usually be left either with an imperfect valency group (like the boron in boron trichloride) or with one which is incompletely shared, like the nitrogen in ammonia. Where co-ordination occurs this limitation is removed; the atom can give or take as many electrons as may be necessary, and in the fully co-ordinated atom it will have a fully shared valency group. Its maximum co-ordination valency, or co-ordination number, is therefore half the number of electrons in its maximum valency group.

In this way the conception of the co-ordinate link as being a covalency, that is, a link of two shared electrons, differing from the ordinary covalency only in this, that the two electrons both come from one of the linked atoms instead of one from each, provides the mechanism required to explain the existence and the properties of the co-ordination compounds of Werner. This conclusion removes the apparent contradiction between organic and inorganic compounds; it refers the structure of molecules of both classes to the same physical principles and exhibits the original co-ordination theory of Werner and the older structural theory as two aspects of the same general process.

The remainder of the address is devoted to generalizations extending the new concept to all of chemistry.

DIPOLE MOMENTS. Methods and ideas developed in other branches of physical chemistry often helped to elucidate structural questions. An excellent example of this was the work of Debye in 1912 in which he showed that certain compounds, because of their molecular structure, exhibited dipole moments. Thus determination of this value could help to show how groups were arranged within organic molecules, and in doubtful cases might settle questions of structure.

The following selection is in *Physikalische Zeitschrift 13*, 97–100 (1912).

Some Results of a Kinetic Theory of Insulators (Preliminary Communication)

P. DEBYE

The view of the structure of a dielectric that is widespread today, as is known, is that electrons are assumed to be in the interior of the molecules that make up the body; they are held to it by a force proportional to their separation from the rest position. Now if an electric field operates on the inner structure of the body, the electrons should be displaced from the rest position by it and so a dielectric polarization of the body would result. The results of this hypothesis are unquestionable for the theory of dispersion and of the Zeeman effect, but as we will show, they do not fit all the known facts. The inadequacy of this hypothesis emerges most clearly and simply as soon as the question of the dependence of the dielectric constant on temperature is raised. The rather scanty observations for the solution of this question that have been made chiefly by Abegg and Seitz, Hasenöhrl, Baedeker, Tangl, and Ratz show that the dielectric constant, ε, increases, very strongly with fall in temperature. Thus, for example, for ethyl alcohol at absolute temperature $T = 293°$, $\varepsilon = 25.8$, while at a temperature 140° lower ($T = 153°$), $\varepsilon = 54.6$, thus more than double. On the other hand, if we seek to construct a kinetic theory of insulators on the basis of the above hypothesis, we obtain the result that the dielectric constant is entirely independent of the temperature.

For an understanding of this contradiction we have two possible answers. First, we can doubt the correctness of the whole calculation in the sense of statistical mechanics and ascribe the discrepancy to a new fiasco of statistical mechanics, which today is no longer surprising. Secondly, however, we can attempt to change the basic hypothesis of the constitution of insulators or to complete it. We have adopted the second way; the results show that it is correct. The assumptions:

The inner structures of insulators contain not only elastically bound electrons, but also permanently existing dipoles with constant electric moment, which puts us in the position of being able to explain the dependence of the dielectric constant on the temperature in a completely satisfactory manner on the basis of classical statistical mechanics.[1] This is valid at least as far as previous observations go. It is true that for still lower temperatures we are justified in doubting these results, by analogy with the deviation from the Curie-Langevin law of magnetic susceptibility established by Perrier.

2. *Results of the Calculation*

We start from the hypothesis given in the introduction, according to which each molecule thus

(a) contains electrons which are bound by elastic forces to their rest positions;

(b) besides these it contains an unchangeable electric moment of size m.

If then we calculate the polarization P that results from the action of a field strength E we find a two-term expression. The first term

---

[1] We have worked out the theory on the assumption that the electric moment shows no dependence on temperature. We will discuss how far this is justified in a subsequent publication.

of the sum of this expression measures the action of the "displacement electrons" and is independent of temperature. It is given by
$(\varepsilon_0 - 1) E$. The second term of the sum has the Curie-Langevin
form $E \cdot a/T$, where a is a constant and T the absolute temperature.
Then for gases:

$$P = E(\varepsilon_0 - 1) + E\frac{a}{T}, \tag{1}$$

so that the dielectric displacement D becomes equal to

$$D = P + E = E\left(\varepsilon_0 + \frac{a}{T}\right) \tag{2}$$

and we obtain for the dielectric constant

$$\varepsilon = \varepsilon_0 + \frac{a}{T} \tag{3}$$

Equation (1) then holds if the change in temperature is produced at
constant volume. If the observation is made at constant pressure, the
variability in volume must be considered in the calculation. For ideal
gases, for example, we will have for the difference $\varepsilon - 1$ an expression
of the form

$$\varepsilon - 1 = \frac{\alpha}{T} + \frac{\beta}{T^2} \tag{3'}$$

Now if we attempt to apply formula (3) to the Abegg-Seitz observations on liquids, we get no satisfactory results. These will be
obtained as soon as we consider not only the "outer" electrical field
strength as a measure of the forces acting within the body, but also,
as usual, the action of the generated molecular field. If we measure
the force developed in the molecular field by $P/3$, then we find as a
first approximation for measuring P at small field strengths the formula

$$P = \left(\varepsilon + \frac{P}{3}\right)\theta, \tag{4}$$

where θ is a temperature function of the form

$$\theta = 3b + \frac{3a}{T}; \tag{5}$$

a and b are constants, which will be discussed further below. Now if we calculate from (4) and (5) the dielectric constant ε using the formula

$$D = E + P = \varepsilon E$$

then it follows that

$$\varepsilon = \frac{1 + 2(\theta/3)}{1 - (\theta/3)} \tag{6}$$

In regard to (5) we can also write

$$\frac{\varepsilon - 1}{\varepsilon + 2} = \frac{\theta}{3} = \frac{a}{T} + b \tag{7}$$

or finally

$$\frac{\varepsilon - 1}{\varepsilon + 2} T = a + bT \tag{7'}$$

In words:

The product of the characteristic expression $(\varepsilon - 1)/(\varepsilon + 2)$ and the absolute temperature T is a linear function of T.[1]

3. Comparison with Experiment

The discussion of formula (3) for gases will be held for the sub-sequent publication; here we will explain only the results of comparison of formula (7') with the Seitz-Abegg observations on the basis of a figure. These observations refer to five alcohols: methyl alcohol, ethyl alcohol, propyl alcohol, isobutyl alcohol, and amyl alcohol, and for ethyl ether. The temperatures at which the observations were made extended from $T = 153$ to $T = 293$. Now if we calculate the magnitude

$$\frac{\varepsilon - 1}{\varepsilon + 2} T$$

and carry the resulting figures to the temperature ordinate, we obtain the picture in the figure. The temperature axis begins at $T = 150$, the vertical axis along which the values of the expression $(\varepsilon - 1)/(\varepsilon + 2) T$ are laid out begins at a value of 100. We see at first glance that the observed points are not far from the indicated

[1] We use the expression in the form given because in what follows we consider only liquids at a relatively low temperature, where we will neglect thermal expansion.
The product of the Clausius-Mosotti expression $(\varepsilon - 1)/(\varepsilon + 2)(1/\rho)$ (ρ is the density) with absolute temperature T is a linear function of the latter.

straight line,[1] that is, formula (7') is established by the observations. The constant a is equal to the height cutting the ordinate at $T = 0$,

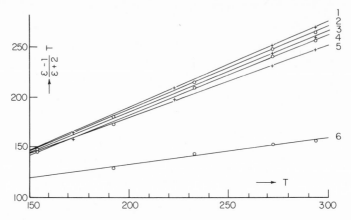

b is equal to the tangent of the angle of slope. A summary of these values is given in Table 1, which can be understood without further explanation.

Table I

		a	b
1	Methyl alcohol	18	0.85
2	Ethyl alcohol	20	0.82
3	Propyl alcohol	21	0.80
4	Isobutyl alcohol	29	0.76
5	Amyl alcohol	32	0.72
6	Ethyl ether	80	0.25

If we extrapolate formula (7) to such a low value of T that $\theta/3 = 1$, that is, so low that T equals a critical temperature T_k, defined by

$$\frac{a}{T_k} + b = 1$$

or

$$T_k = \frac{a}{1 - b},\tag{8}$$

then $\varepsilon = \infty$. Actually, of course, the extrapolation is not justified. However, the critical temperature T_k itself has an important meaning.

---

[1] The numbers 1, 2, etc. in the figure refer to the different substances in the sequence given above. The observed points are marked alternatively by circles and crosses.

If we allow the temperature T to fall below T_k, the complete theory shows that then, without an external field, a polarization can occur within the molecule; that is, we will be able to observe the remaining dielectric polarization. In the cases at present known to me we cannot yet go so far. Thus, before $T = T_k$ the liquid becomes solid and the validity of expressions (7) and (7') ceases, since the molecule can no longer rotate freely. I reserve for the subsequent publication what can be said about such a solid molecule. It should be noted that the critical temperature T_k plays an analogous role to the so-called Curie point in ferromagnetic bodies.

4. Physical Meaning of the Constants a and b. Calculation of the Elementary Electric Moments

The slope of the straight line in the figure against the horizontal axis is restricted by the presence of the "displacement electrons." If these only were present, a would equal 0 and instead of (7') we would have the formula

$$\frac{\varepsilon - 1}{\varepsilon + 2} = b, \tag{9}$$

that is, as was already emphasized in the introduction, ε would thus be independent of the temperature, contrary to the observations. If the charge on the "displacement electrons" is e, and N_1, with a force f_1, is calculated for the displacement unit for return to the rest position, N_2 with force f_2, etc., then b can be expressed also through these magnitudes in the form

$$3b = \sum_P \frac{N_P e^2}{f_P} \tag{10}$$

The magnitude $1 + 3b$ would thus equal the dielectric constant if (a) only displacement electrons were present, and (b) the action of the molecules on each other were ignored.

However, here we are interested chiefly in the constant a. If we assume that all the molecules are supplied with the same fixed electric moment m and call the number of molecules per cm³ N, we obtain the expression for a

$$a = \frac{Nm^2}{9k}; \tag{11}$$

k is here a universal constant by which we must multiply the logarithm of the probability of a system to obtain the entropy. According to

Planck it is $1.346 \cdot 10^{-16}$ erg. The number of molecules–per cm^3 is calculated from the density of the substance, the molecular weight, and the known mass of a hydrogen atom ($1.63 \cdot 10^{-24}$ g). By using the observed value for the density at ordinary temperature, we can now calculate the value of m by the following formula from (11):

$$m = \frac{3}{\sqrt{4\pi}} \sqrt{\frac{ka}{N}}$$

The factor $1/\sqrt{4\pi}$ was added in order to convert to ordinary electrostatic units, since the previous formula referred to rational units for which the unit of electric mass is $\sqrt{4\pi}$ times smaller than the ordinary electrostatic unit. The values for m have the dimensions $g^{1/2} cm^{5/2}$ sec^{-1}; they are given in the following Table 2 for the liquids mentioned earlier, as well as for some others.

Table II

Name	Chemical Formula	m
Methyl alcohol	$CH_3 \cdot OH$	$3.4 \cdot 10^{-19}$
Ethyl alcohol	$C_2H_5 \cdot OH$	$4.3 \cdot 10^{-19}$
Propyl alcohol	$C_3H_7 \cdot OH$	$5.0 \cdot 10^{-19}$
Isobutyl alcohol	$(CH_3)_2 \cdot CH \cdot CH_2 \cdot OH$	$6.5 \cdot 10^{-19}$
Amyl alcohol	$C_5H_{11} \cdot OH$	$7.9 \cdot 10^{-19}$
Water	$H \cdot O \cdot H$	$5.7 \cdot 10^{-19}$
Ethyl ether	$C_2H_5 \cdot O \cdot C_2H_5$	$11.8 \cdot 10^{-19}$
Acetone	$CH_3 \cdot CO \cdot CH_3$	$3.4 \cdot 10^{-19}$
Toluene	$C_6H_5 \cdot CH_3$	$5.1 \cdot 10^{-19}$
Nitrobenzene	$C_6H_5 \cdot NO_2$	$5.7 \cdot 10^{-19}$

These values make no claim to great accuracy, but they show clearly that the type of molecule does not have a marked effect on the magnitude of m. As the chemical formulas show, oxygen occurs in a hydroxyl group, in another case (ethyl ether) serves to bind two alkyl groups, and in acetone is doubly bound to carbon atoms. Moreover, we have also presented two compounds with ring structures, of which toluene contains no oxygen at all, and the two oxygens of nitrobenzene are very different from those mentioned above, being in the NO_2 group. The values of the dielectric constant also vary in the widest limits at ordinary temperature, namely, from 2.33 in toluene to 37.8 in nitrobenzene and 80 in water. To draw a general conclusion on the numerical value of m in my opinion is premature from the preliminary data. In the subsequent communication we will return to this point using extended numerical material.

One thing more should be mentioned here. If we believe that the moment m is the result of two elementary electrical masses, e (of opposite sign) at a distance l, then it follows that with $e = 4.69 \cdot 10^{-10}$ electrostatic units, when we take a mean value for the moment of $m = 5.4 \cdot 10^{-19}$,

$$l = 1.1 \cdot 10^{-9} \text{ cm.}$$

On the other hand, since we must estimate the molecule diameter as a multiple of 10^{-8}, we see that such a dipole can still be provided with considerable latitude in the interior of a molecule.[1]

SPREADING OF FILMS ON LIQUIDS. Another physical investigation also resulted in discovery of a method that could be used to show the shape and structure of rather complex organic molecules. In his general studies on adsorption, Langmuir was led to investigate the manner in which films of insoluble materials spread on water. He was able to show that the structure of the film material determined the orientation of the molecules in the film, and so in many cases this method of spreading could be used to confirm or suggest certain structures. The method later proved very useful in working out complex structures.

The following selection is from pages 1863–1868 in *The Journal of the American Chemical Society 39*, 1848–1906 (1917).

The Constitution and Fundamental Properties of Solids and Liquids. II Liquids

IRVING LANGMUIR

After a review of the work of Rayleigh and Devaux which indicates that an oil film on water forms a monomolecular layer, Langmuir continues as follows.

Cause of the Spreading of Oils on Water

To make further progress in the study of oil films, it is important to know what is the cause of the spreading of the oil upon the water.

---

[1] It should not be said that the electric moment has to be constituted in this way.

The problem is very greatly simplified by the knowledge that the films formed are one molecule thick.

It is natural to assume that the force which causes the spreading is due to an attraction between the group molecules of the oil and those of the water. From the chemical viewpoint developed in Part I of this paper, we should not regard this attraction as emanating from the molecule as a whole, but rather from certain atoms in the molecule. This would follow directly from our conclusion that the range of forces between atoms or molecules is of the order of 0.6×10^{-8} cm. Furthermore, it is evident that any attraction of the water for oil molecules *as a whole* would manifest itself as a solubility of the oil in the water. If, on the other hand, we can assume that a *portion* of the oil molecule is attracted to the water, while the remainder is more attracted to the other oil molecules than to the water, then we have a ready explanation of the spreading on the water.

Let us consider oleic acid as an example. There is no doubt but that the carboxyl group has a marked affinity for water. The solubility of the organic acids in water, as compared with the insolubility of the corresponding hydrocarbons, is a clear indication of this fact. This affinity is due to the strong secondary valence characteristic of oxygen compounds. On the other hand, hydrocarbons have a greater affinity for each other than for water, since they are usually miscible with each other in nearly all proportions, although they are insoluble in water.

Therefore, when oleic acid is placed on water, it is probable that the carboxyl groups *do actually dissolve* in water; that is, they combine with the water chemically (by secondary valence). The long hydrocarbon chains have too much attraction for each other, however, and too little for water, to be drawn into solution merely because of the affinity of the carboxyl for the water.

As a matter of fact, by the spreading of the oil on the surface as a monomolecular layer, the carboxyl group can combine with all the water it requires, without causing the hydrocarbon chains to separate from one another.

The spreading of an oil upon water is thus due to the presence of an "active group" in the molecule; that is, some group which has a marked affinity (secondary valence) for water. This leads directly to the prediction that an oil without active groups, such as pure paraffin oil, should not spread at all. Experiment shows that this is actually the case. Hardy has studied the spreading of many oils upon water and found that pure saturated hydrocarbons do not spread; neither do such substances as benzene, cymene, etc. In attempting to explain this fact, Hardy says, "The great chemical stability of the paraffins makes chemical interaction with water impossible. Some degree of chemical action would seem to be necessary to make one fluid spread as a film between two others (air and water)." He does not, however, go further than this in explaining the mechanism of the spreading. Hardy believes that the oil films are usually many molecules thick.

According to our theory of the spreading of oil films, the group molecules of oleic acid arrange themselves upon the surface, so that each carboxyl group is in contact with and is combined with water, while the hydrocarbon tails are packed in side by side and vertically placed above the carboxyl layer. The upper surface of the oil film thus consists of CH_3 groups. It is therefore evident that there should be no particular tendency for another layer of oil molecules to spread out on top of the first to form a second layer. In fact, since this upper surface consists exclusively of CH_3 (or C_2H_5) groups, while in a globule of oleic acid, carboxyl groups are distributed through the mass, it is natural that the oil should prefer to remain as globules, rather than spread out as a layer two molecules deep. In the mass of liquid the carboxyl groups probably tend to gather into clusters, because of the greater affinity of these groups for each other than for the hydrocarbon chains. This tendency to form minute clusters explains many of the phenomena observed by Devaux in connection with his study of films thicker than monomolecular.

Now Marcelin claims that oil films in equilibrium with globules of oil consist of double layers of molecules—a result inconsistent with the above theory. The best example that Marcelin finds in support of his theory is oleic acid. The molecule of this substance contains, besides the hydrocarbon chain, two distinguishing factors: the carboxyl group and the double bond. The marked difference between the freezing points and other properties of oleic and stearic acids, suggests that the double bond may play an important role in the spreading of oils on water.

In general, from the data available, it seems that the presence of a double bond increases the solubility of a compound in water. Thus ethylene and propylene are several times more soluble in water than ethane and propane. Crotonyl alcohol, C_4H_7OH, is soluble in about 6 parts of water, while butyl alcohol, C_4H_9OH, requires 12. Hexanyl alcohol is given as "very soluble" while hexyl alcohol is "slightly soluble."

This suggests that the double bond as well as the carboxyl groups, may be drawn down onto the surface of the water, if there is only a limited amount of oil on a large surface of water. When a globule of oil is placed on a limited surface, however, the carboxyl groups displace the double bonds. Thus the film is one molecule deep, but in the first case the molecules are partly reclining on the surface, while in the second they are packed tightly side by side and are more or less erect upon the surface.

Fortunately, the experiments with oil films furnish means for testing this theory. Rayleigh, Devaux, and Marcelin determined the thickness of oil films and assumed this to be the same as the diameter of the molecule of oil. From the present theory we are led to believe that molecules of oil on water are oriented and packed in the surface layer so that they cannot, even approximately, be regarded as spherical. We can, however, calculate the area covered by each molecule as easily as we can calculate the thickness of the film. This area is equivalent to the average cross-section of the molecule in a plane parallel to the surface of the water. The thickness of the film is equivalent to the length of the molecule in a direction perpendicular to the surface.

If the square root of this cross-section differs materially from the thickness of the film, we have direct evidence that the molecules are not spherical.

Determinations of the Shapes of Group Molecules

In order to determine the cross-sections and lengths of molecules in oil films, experiments similar to those of Marcelin were undertaken. The oil, or solid fat, was dissolved in freshly distilled benzene (usually 50 mg. in 100 cc.), and, by means of a calibrated dropping pipet, one or two drops of the solutions were placed upon a clean water surface in a photographic tray. The maximum area covered by the film was measured by the method indicated in Figs. 2, 3 and 4 (not included here).

Dividing this area by the number of molecules of oil on the surface, the area of water covered by each molecule is readily obtained. This must also equal the cross-section of the molecules. The results are given in the first column of Table I. The number of molecules of oil on the surface was found by first calculating the number of gram-molecules of substance in the one or two drops of benzene solution added, and then multiplying this by N, the number of molecules per gram molecule, which, according to Millikan, is equal to 6.062×10^{23}.

An examination of these results shows that the cross sections of the molecules vary over quite a wide range—from 21 to 126 $\times 10^{-16}$ sq. cm. The three saturated acids, palmitic, stearic, and

Table I

Preliminary measurements of cross-sections and lengths of molecules

Substance	Formula	I Cross-sect. sq. cm.	II $\sqrt{Cross\text{-}sect.}$ cm.	III Length cm.	IV Length per carbon atom
Palmitic acid	$C_{15}H_{31}COOH$	21×10^{-16}	4.6×10^{-8}	24.0×10^{-8}	1.5×10^{-8}
Stearic acid	$C_{17}H_{35}COOH$	22×10^{-16}	4.7×10^{-8}	25.0×10^{-8}	1.39×10^{-8}
Cerotic acid	$C_{25}H_{51}COOH$	25×10^{-16}	5.0×10^{-8}	31.0×10^{-8}	1.20×10^{-8}
Tristearin	$(C_{18}H_{35}O_2)_3C_3H_5$	66×10^{-16}	8.1×10^{-8}	25.0×10^{-8}	1.32×10^{-8}
Oleic acid	$C_{17}H_{33}COOH$	46×10^{-16}	6.8×10^{-8}	11.2×10^{-8}	0.62×10^{-8}
Triolein	$(C_{18}H_{33}O_2)_3C_3H_5$	126×10^{-16}	11.2×10^{-8}	13.0×10^{-8}	0.69×10^{-8}
Trielaidin	$(C_{18}H_{33}O_2)_3C_3H_5$	120×10^{-16}	11.0×10^{-8}	13.6×10^{-8}	0.72×10^{-8}
Cetyl palmitate	$C_{15}H_{31}COOC_{16}H_{33}$	23×10^{-16}	4.8×10^{-8}	41.0×10^{-8}	2.56×10^{-8}
Myricyl alcohol	$C_{30}H_{61}OH$	27×10^{-16}	5.2×10^{-8}	41.0×10^{-8}	1.37×10^{-8}

cerotic, all occupy nearly the same areas (21–25 × 10⁻¹⁶ sq. cm.), notwithstanding the fact that the number of carbon atoms in the molecule increases from 16 to 26. Each tristearin molecule covers a space of 66 × 10⁻¹⁶, which is exactly three times that of the stearic acid molecule. Furthermore, the molecule of cetyl palmitate takes up an area of 23 × 10⁻¹⁶ sq. cm., which is again about the same as that of stearic acid.

Thus we can see that each

$$-C-O-$$

group occupies an area of about 23 × 10⁻¹⁶ sq. cm., no matter whether it occurs in an acid or an ester. This area is substantially independent of the length of the hydrocarbon chain to which the active group is attached.

These measurements afford striking proof of the theory outlined in the preceding pages, according to which the spreading of an oil on water is caused by the presence of certain active groups in the molecule.

We may also calculate the length of the molecules in a direction perpendicular to the surface. The volume of each molecule is found by dividing the "molecular volume" of the oil (M/ρ) by the Avogadro constant N. By dividing this volume by the cross-section of each molecule, the length of the molecule in a direction perpendicular to the surface can be obtained. The results are given in the third column of Table I.

It is interesting to compare these lengths with the cross-sections. As a rough approximation we may assume that the dimensions of the molecule in directions parallel to the surface can be found by taking the square root of cross-section. This is equivalent to assuming that each molecule in the surface film occupies a volume represented by a square prism with its axis vertical. The length of the square side, which we shall refer to as the average diameter, is given in the second column of Table I, while the height of the prism (or the length of the molecule) is given in the third column.

It is seen at once that the molecules are very much elongated. Thus the length of the palmitic acid molecule is about 5.2 times the average diameter. The results prove that the molecules arrange themselves on the surface with their long dimension vertical as is required by the theory.

The molecule of tristearin has the same length (perpendicular to the surface) as the stearic acid molecule, but three times the cross-section. Thus each of the three active groups has been drawn down on to the surface of the water, while the hydrocarbon chains are packed in side by side and are erect upon the surface.

The case of cetyl palmitate is interesting. Here the length of the molecule is 41×10^{-8} cm., or nearly twice that of the palmitic acid molecule, while the average diameter is only 4.8×10^{-8} cm., or about the same as the palmitic acid molecule. The molecule contains two long hydrocarbon chains connected by a carboxyl group. In palmitic acid the length of such a group is 24×10^{-8} cm. If the length of this group were nearly a constant quantity then we should have to assume that in the cetyl palmitate film the two chains in each molecule are arranged one above the other with the carboxyl in the middle. On this assumption, however, the only part of the molecule in contact with the water would be the CH_3 on the end of one of the hydrocarbon chains, so that there should be no tendency for this substance to form a monomolecular film on water. Solid paraffin for example dissolved in benzene and placed on water does not give a monomolecular film but gives a thick film (10–40 molecules thick), of variable thickness depending on the rate at which the benzene is allowed to evaporate.

The present theory therefore compels us to conclude that the carboxyl group of the cetyl palmitate is on the surface of the water and that both hydrocarbon chains are packed in side by side above the carboxyl group. The area of water covered by the carboxyl is the same as in the palmitic acid, so that the two hydrocarbon chains side by side do not have any greater cross-section than the one in palmitic acid. But each chain is extended to nearly twice the length in the first case than it is in the second.

This result indicates that the hydrocarbon chain does not have any definite shape or arrangement of its atoms in space, but rather that the chain should be regarded as extremely flexible. Thus in the palmitic acid film the arrangement of the atoms in the chain is probably somewhat as follows:

$$\overset{CH_2}{\diagup \diagdown} \overset{CH_2}{\underset{CH_2}{\diagup \diagdown}} \overset{CH_2}{\underset{CH_2}{\diagup \diagdown}} \underset{CH_2}{\diagup}$$

while in the cetyl palmitate the chains are packed more closely so that the arrangement becomes more nearly that represented by the typical formula:

$$\begin{array}{ccccc} H & H & H & H & H \\ | & | & | & | & | \\ -C- & C- & C- & C- & C- \\ | & | & | & | & | \\ H & H & H & H & H \end{array}$$

In a diamond the distance between adjacent carbon atoms is 1.54×10^{-8} cm. and this probably represents the minimum distance within which carbon atoms can approach. In the hydrocarbon molecule we should expect that they would be considerably further apart than this.

Dividing the length of the molecule (Table I) by the number of carbon atoms in the chain we obtain the average *vertical distance* between adjacent carbon atoms in the chain. The results are given in the fourth column of Table I. In all cases except that of cetyl palmitate the distance is less than the distance between atoms in the diamond. This is a clear indication that the atoms cannot be arranged linearly but rather must be arranged along a zig-zag or curved line. The observed cross-section (23×10^{-16} sq. cm.) is ample to allow the carbon atoms to be arranged in some such manner and still be separated from each other by distances greater than 1.54×10^{-8} cm.

The results obtained with the substances containing unsaturated hydrocarbon chains afford striking confirmation of the theory already proposed, according to which the double bond is to be regarded as an active group. Each oleic acid molecule covers a surface of 46×10^{-16} sq. cm. whereas the saturated acids only cover about half as great a surface. The same difference is manifest in triolein and trielaidin when compared with tristearin. The data given in the fourth column shows this effect even more clearly. Whereas with all the saturated molecules the average vertical distance between carbon atoms is greater than 1.2×10^{-8}, it lies between 0.62 and 0.72×10^{-8} for the unsaturated molecules.

We thus have a proof that the film in equilibrium with a globule of oleic acid on water, which Rayleigh and Marcelin supposed to be two molecules thick, is in reality only one molecule thick. Marcelin found that the film in equilibrium with the globule was about twice as thick as that obtained with the maximum extension. Since the latter is clearly one molecule thick, Marcelin concluded that the former must be two molecules thick.

From the data of Table I, however, we see that an oleic acid film, in maximum extension, is only half as thick as that of stearic acid, so that, when doubled in thickness by placing a globule of oleic acid on the surface, the film becomes of the same thickness as that of stearic acid and the cross-sections of the molecules are also the same. There is thus no reason for assuming the existence of a layer two molecules deep.

These preliminary experiments furnish very convincing evidence of the correctness of the theory developed in the present paper.

APPLICATION OF QUANTUM MECHANICS. Having indicated more or less qualitatively how molecules could be held together, chemists next sought to answer two fundamental questions: what was the actual nature of the forces that held the covalent links together, and why did specific reactions take place in one way rather than in another. Although these problems seemed different and were approached in quite different ways, they led to a similar, dynamic picture of the forces acting within a molecule.

In the attempt to answer the question of the mechanisms involved when an organic reaction followed one path when, formally speaking, other paths seemed equally possible, the organic chemists of the first half of the century turned away from a strictly static view of the atom as first developed. They began to consider possible shifts of electrons in molecules and how such shifts might be influenced by electrons or protons in other groups within the same molecule, or in molecules reacting with them. The inductive and electrical effects that occurred were studied especially in England and a unified picture developed that is well summarized in the selection by Ingold given below. This extract illustrates how an approach, originally intended to explain why certain reactions took place as they did, led to the concept of mesomerism which in turn led to a concept essentially similar to the ideas developed by those concerned with the other fundamental question mentioned above.

Their approach led through the methods of the new quantum mechanics that the physicists began to develop to explain many of the facts of spectroscopy. It resulted in a far more quantitative explanation than had been possible by any of the previous efforts in this direction.

The picture of the original Bohr atom was derived from the first form of the quantum theory, but in the twenties theoretical physicists had developed the so-called "new quantum mechanics," and it was soon realized that this approach could be used effectively to explain chemical problems. In 1927 two papers appeared that laid the foundations for major developments in the theory of the chemical bond in the following decades. The first, by Heitler and London, was highly mathematical but its implications were soon explained by Van Vleck in the second following citation in which he also showed chemists the significance for them of the new quantum mechanics.

The Heitler-London theory, the prototype of the valence bond method of explaining the nature of the bond in the hydrogen molecule, involved the use of a wave function of such nature that the two electrons of the bond tended to remain on different atoms. At about the same time, Condon, in the third paper given below, used a quantum mechanical approach in which the wave function involved introduction of an electron pair in an electron orbital extending around two or more atomic nuclei. This was the prototype of the molecular orbital method, described in L. Pauling, *The Nature of the Chemical Bond* (Cornell University Press, Ithaca, N.Y., ed. 3, 1960), pp. 23–24.

The quantum mechanical approach was developed by Hückel and

was considerably extended by Pauling in his application of the concept of resonance. The fourth selection below illustrates how this idea was used to explain the structure and nature of aromatic compounds.

The following selection is from pages 1120–1126 in *Journal of the Chemical Society 1933*, 1120–1127.

Significance of Tautomerism and of the Reactions of Aromatic Compounds in the Electronic Theory of Organic Reactions

C. K. INGOLD

The simplest molecular model which can serve as the basis for an electrical conception of reactions is that which visualizes a distribution of atomic nuclei and electrons as point charges subject to elastic forces. In the development of the theory, the wave-mechanical ideas of a continuous statistical distribution of electron density, of quantized states, and of degeneracy, are introduced, but this does not affect the circumstance that the specification of the model requires two kinds of electrical quantities concerned respectively with the positions and mobilities of the charges. The principal magnitudes describing gross intrinsic polarizations and polarizabilities of molecules, the dipole moment, μ, and the deformation coefficient, α, differ in dimensions by an amount corresponding to the dimensions of an electric force, and thus the total moment developed in the presence of a force is the sum of two terms, $\mu + \alpha F$, for a given direction. Recent work on molecular dipole moments has confirmed Thomson's suggestion that these may roughly be calculated as the vector sum of group contributions. Such a calculation neglects intramolecular interaction, which is an essential matter in the theory of reactions; but it is often convenient to ascribe to groups an intrinsic moment, and treat the modifications caused by interaction as a superimposed effect. Similarly, the approximately additive character of refractivities shows that polarizability may also be regarded as a group characteristic, subject to modification by interaction. Thus groups may also be considered to possess a duplex electrical specification, provided the appropriate magnitudes are not treated strictly as constants. Reagents are regarded as acting by virtue of a constitutional affinity either for electrons or for nuclei,[1] and the organic molecule, in the activation necessary for reaction, is therefore required to develop at the seat of attack either a high or a low electron density, as the case may be. Evidently the extent to which a given group can contribute to an activation is a duplex quantity, in which suitable measures of the polarization, and the polarizability, of the group, and of the electrical demands of the reaction, play parts functionally analogous to those of μ, α and F respectively in the above binomial. On several recent occasions, discussions have arisen because two reactions, each considered to test "polarity," do not place groups in an identical sequence; but it is evident that polarization and polarizability are independent polar properties, and that the relative importance of the two contributing effects, dependent respectively on these groups characteristics, must vary with the nature of the reaction.

Independently of such physical foundations, the electronic theory of valency limits the presumable forms of electron displacement by the principle requiring the preservation of stable electron groups. Displacements ($\rightarrow$ in, e.g., $Cl \rightarrow CH_2 \rightarrow CO_2H$) throughout which the electrons concerned remain bound by their original atomic nuclei were postulated by Lewis (*Valence*, 1923, p. 139); the mechanism was considered to illustrate a state of polarization, and in subsequent organic chemical applications the designation *inductive* effect (Ingold, *Ann. Reports*, 1926, *23*, 140) has been employed as a convenient distinctive term. Displacements

$$(\frown \text{ in, } e.g., \text{ } R_2\overset{\frown}{N}\text{—}C\overset{\frown}{=}\overset{\frown}{C}\text{—}C\overset{\frown}{=}\overset{\frown}{O})$$

in which there is a substitution of one duplet for another in the same atomic octet were first assumed by Lowry; the process was regarded as exemplifying an activation or polarizability effect, and this understanding is contained in the distinguishing term *electromeric*,[2] as introduced by Ingold and Ingold in relation to the mechanism.[3]

---

[1] As Brönsted and Lowry have observed in reference to the special case of affinity for a proton (basicity), the state of electrification of a reagent is trivial in relation to so fundamentally constitutive a classification as that indicated in the text. For this reason the terms *electrophilic* (electron-seeking) and *nucleophilic* (nucleus-seeking) are suggested in place of the adjectives anionoid and cationoid introduced by Lapworth. Ammonia behaves as it does, not because it *is like* an anion, but because it *is* a base (more generally it is nucleophilic), and analogous reactivity is suppressed in the chloride ion, not, of course, because this is not a typical anion, but because it is not a base. Many cations are nucleus-seeking, *e.g.*, the ferrous ion, and many anions electron-seeking, *e.g.*, the permanganate ion.

[2] The term *electromerism* (= electron-tautomerism) which was introduced by Fry clearly contains the idea of mobility.

[3] A fuller outline should refer to the analogues of these mechanisms in pre-electronic theories of reaction, especially the theories of Flürschein and Lapworth.

The synthesis of the two processes must be credited to Lucas and his collaborators, who showed how the inductive effect may be supposed to direct and facilitate the electromeric (as, *e.g.*, in $CH_3 \rightarrow CH{=}CH_2$). The generalization of these ideas, and the proof that, suitably developed, they yield a satisfactory interpretation of the numerous results concerning so extensive a group of reactions as those of aromatic substitution, were given by Robinson and Ingold and their collaborators, and elaborated further with reference to aromatic substitution by the subsequent investigations of both authors.[1]

In the further development of the theory, outlined later, the two mechanisms are not regarded as being *sharply* differentiated, the one as a permanent polarization, and the other as a polarizability effect occurring in reaction, but it is recognized that the difference in time-dependence between the two processes lies in this direction. Slightly modifying an earlier suggestion, the terms *general inductive* (symbol *I*) and *tautomeric* (symbol *T*) may be used to distinguish the two mechanisms (denoted $\rightarrow$ and $\frown$ respectively), without reference to whether they represent a permanent molecular state or an activation phenomenon. Much evidence in favor of the view that the tautomeric effect is more time-variable than the general inductive effect may be adduced from the special refractivity contributions of simple and conjugated unsaturated systems,[2] and, in the field of organic reactions, a single example may be given to illustrate the consequences of this conception.

In aromatic substitution by electrophilic reagents, the normal correlation of *op*-orientation with nuclear activation and of *m*-orientation with deactivation is subject to certain exceptions, in which *op*-orientation and deactivation occur together, although the conjunction of *m*-orientation with nuclear activation is unknown. The orienting groups concerned in the known kind of anomaly all possess structures such that they exhibit opposing polar influences, and indeed they belong to the category of substituents which exert the effect symbolized $-I + T$[3] (*e.g.*, Cl in $\overset{\frown}{Cl{-}Ar}$), although they

---

[1] The second paper was communicated before the first appeared. For a summary of further investigations by the writer and his co-workers in the field of aromatic substitution, see *Rec. trav. chim.*, 1929, *48*, 797.

[2] Such contributions are sometimes included in so-called atomic constants, as may be illustrated by a comparison of the "constant" $[\beta L]_D$ for nitrogen in NH_2.Alphyl (2.45), NH_2.Aryl (3.21), and NH_2.C:C.C:O (4.88).

[3] Electron probability (density) being the physical variable concerned in a polar effect, it has been usual to write arrow signs in the direction of its positive increase, and to distinguish a positive increase as a $+$ effect, so that a $+$ effect is one which is activating towards electrophilic reagents. The suggestion (Baldwin and Robinson, *J.*, 1932, 1445) of interchanging the customary prefix signs should be followed only in conjunction with a corresponding reversal of the arrows.

constitute only a small section of that category. The interpretation offered concerning these facts starts from the difference in time-dependence already mentioned. Evidently a polarization effect permanently conferred on the *op*-positions will be permanently relayed to the *m*-positions, whilst a corresponding polarizability effect will be absorbed by the exciting reagent, and therefore will not be relayed. It follows that the greater *op*-time-variability of the tautomeric than of the general inductive effect must be reflected in a greater *op*-selectivity of the former effect in its distribution over the aromatic nucleus. It is this difference of selectivity which makes provision for a class of orienting substituents showing the anomaly of *op*-orientation in conjunction with depressed nuclear reactivity. The anomaly will arise when, after the general inductive deactivation ($-I$ effect) of the whole nucleus, *m*-positions included, the tautomeric restoration of activity ($+T$ effect) selectively to the *op*-positions is strong enough to raise their reactivity above that of the still deactivated *m*-positions, but yet is not sufficiently strong to bring *op*-reactivity up to the standard of unsubstituted benzene. The matter is diagrammatically illustrated in Fig. 1. Groups of the $(-I + T)$

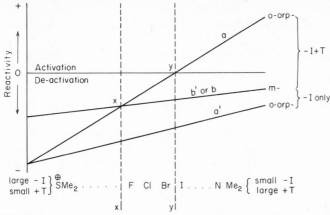

Fig. 1

category are arranged horizontally in order of diminishing $-I$- and increasing $+T$-component, whilst reactivity is measured vertically by a logarithmic function of the velocity of substitution at each nuclear position in terms of the velocity of substitution at a single position in benzene. If the general inductive effect operated alone, the points representing the activity of the various nuclear positions should yield curves such as a' and b', which, if extended, should meet on or near the horizontal axis. The superposition of the tautomeric effect, and its great *op*-selectivity, are expressed by the large angular displacement of curve a' to position a, and the small, or zero, displacement of curve b' to position b. Curve a must now cut curve b before it cuts the axis, and thus the diagram becomes divided into three regions by the points of intersection, x and y. To the left of x is a normal region: curve b is above curve a (*m*-orientation) but below the axis (deactivation). The region to the right of y is also normal, since curve a is above curve b (*op*-orientation) and the uppermost curve is above the axis (activation). The abnormal region is comprised between x and y, and the anomaly there represented is of the type observed.

As already indicated, the recognition of the general inductive mechanism as a state of polarization (inductive effect), and of the tautomeric mode of electron displacement as a polarizability (electromeric effect), is contained in the earlier development of the theory. The conception of a permanent polarization associated with the mechanism of the tautomeric effect was first advanced by E. H. Ingold and the writer; and a physical test for such a polarization was proposed, which depended on finding a group ($\cdot$ NMe$_2$ was suggested) such that, when it is linked to an unsaturated system, *e.g.*, phenyl, the polarization effect of the kind sought opposes and is strong enough to outweigh the inductive effect; it then had to be shown by dipole moment measurements that the direction of the electric moment associated with the aliphatic union of the group (Alphyl $\overset{\oplus\ominus}{\longrightarrow}$ NR$_2$) is reversed in the corresponding aromatic combination (Aryl $\overset{\ominus\oplus}{\longrightarrow}$ NR$_2$). The first test of this kind was completed (for the group $\cdot$ NH$_2$) by Höjendahl with definitely positive results, subsequently confirmed by other workers. Extensive further confirmation emerges from a generalized form of the same test conceived and applied by Sutton, who has shown that, independently of the relative directions and intensities of component polarizations, the vector difference between the dipole moments associated with the types Alphyl $\cdot$ R and Aryl $\cdot$ R is in the direction of the tautomeric effect in the latter combination for a wide range of substituents, R. As Sutton's conclusions have been criticized on the grounds of his use of *tert*-butyl and phenyl as arbitrary aliphatic and aromatic types, the view may be expressed that this necessarily arbitrary element in the theoretical treatment cannot affect the *comparison* of the groups, R, nor therefore the main significance ascribed to the results. The permanent polarization associated with the tautomeric effect was originally distinguished by the name "electronic strain," but this term has not proved convenient and, on account of considerations indicated later, the designation *mesomeric* effect is now substituted. A single example of the chemical significance of the effect may be given.

The normal relation between the direction of a group dipole and the effect of that group on the strengths of acids and bases is subject to a small number of exceptions in the aromatic series. The anomalies considered relate to substituents which permanently attract electrons, as is shown by the direction of their dipole contributions, but nevertheless depress the association of a suitably located carboxyl group. These substituents all belong to the class which exerts the effect symbolized by $-I + T$, although they constitute only a small section of that category. Thus, the methoxyl group, despite its electron-attracting dipole, decreases the strength of benzoic acid when introduced into the p-position. Since the effect illustrated has reference to an equilibrium, it must depend on the statistical condition of the system, and this includes factors relating to polarization, polarizability, and entropy. It is highly improbable that the entropy effect can be responsible for more than a small proportion of the difference in free energy of dissociation between benzoic and p-anisic acids; and the polarizability effect works in the wrong direction, since the additional polarizability due to the methoxyl group in p-anisic acid must evidently increase the energy of dissociation. One is therefore thrown back on the polarization effect of the methoxyl group, despite the difficulty concerning its direction, and the interpretation offered is that the opposing inductive and mesomeric components differ in their distribution, and, in particular, in their selectivity concerning the p-carboxyl group. Evidently the inductive effect will influence mainly the electrons of the aromatic nucleus, whilst the mesomeric effect will pass through the nucleus to the other extremity of the conjugated system, *viz.*, the carboxyl oxygen atom. A rough representation of the situation may be obtained by replacing the component effects by dipoles of different pole-strength, q, and pole-separation, d, as indicated in Fig. 2. The

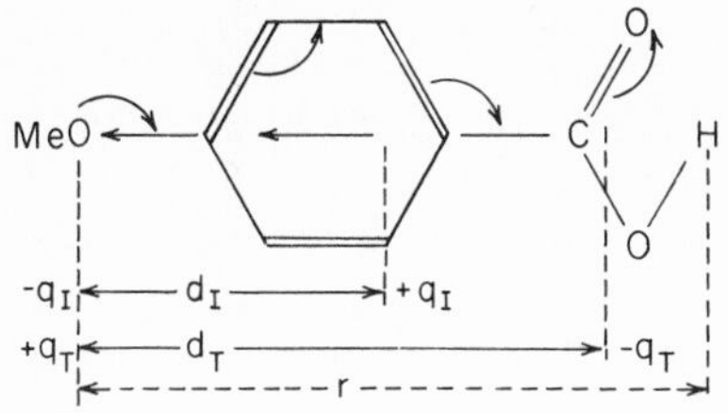

Fig. 2

total polarization due to the methoxyl group will be the sum of two terms, $-q_I d_I$ and $+q_T d_T$, and will correspond to electron attraction if the former term predominates, *i.e.*, if the excess of q_I over q_T

is sufficiently large. On the other hand, the effect of the methoxyl group on the free energy of dissociation will contain terms proportional to $-q_T (r - d_T)$ and $+q_I (r - d_I)$, together with smaller terms in $1/r$ and polarizability and entropy corrections; it is clear that the first term might dominate the expression provided that the excess of q_I over q_T is not *too* large, and in that event the whole effect would be to weaken the acid notwithstanding the direction of the dipole. Generally, the anomaly illustrated will arise when the mesomeric polarization, although weaker than the inductive, is not too weak to allow its greater selectivity to bring about a dominating influence over the dissociating group; and thus a series of substituents of the $(-I+T)$ category, arranged as previously illustrated, will contain two critical points, one, y, where the dipole contribution changes direction, and the other, x, where the effect on the dissociating group changes sign, the central region thus marked off being the region of anomaly:

$$
\left.\begin{array}{c} \text{large} -\text{I} \\[2em] \text{small} +\text{T} \end{array}\right\} \text{SMe}_2 \quad \text{Hals} \begin{array}{c} x \\ \vdots \\ x \end{array} \text{OMe} \begin{array}{c} y \\ \vdots \\ y \end{array} \text{NMe}_2 \left\{\begin{array}{c} \text{small} -\text{I} \\[2em] \text{large} +\text{T} \end{array}\right.
$$

It cannot be doubted that a counterpart of two coexisting polarizations obtains also for the polarizability effects, and that an inductive polarizability or *inductomeric* effect completes the scheme annexed:[1]

	General inductive $(\rightarrow)$	*Tautomeric* $(\frown)$
Polarization	Inductive	Mesomeric (M)
Polarizability	Inductomeric	Electromeric (E)

The refractometric evidence of this need not be elaborated, but an example may be given in the field of reactions by reference to the problem of the polarity of alkyl. Alkyl groups are regarded as exerting a $+I$ effect (*e.g.*, $CH_3\rightarrow$), relatively, as always, to hydrogen, notwithstanding that, according to the most acceptable definition of group dipole moments which are also related to hydrogen [for a group X, $\mu(X) = \mu(RX) - \mu(RH)$, where R is Alphyl], the moment of the methyl group, and therefore of all alkyl groups, is zero.

---

[1] The general inductive effect is regarded as being propagated partly outside the molecule (compare Lewis). This is the *direct* effect introduced in relation to specific phenomena of reactivity and orientation by Ingold and Vass, and extended by Bennett and Mosses.

Evidently alkyl polarity is often induced by the groups the reactions of which are employed to demonstrate it (*e.g.*, Cl or CO_2H). This may be proved by comparisons of dipole moments, *e.g.* (10^{-8} e.s.u.)

$$CH_3\text{—H} \qquad CH_3\text{—}\overset{\displaystyle CH_3}{\underset{\displaystyle CH_3}{CH}} \qquad CH_3{\rightarrow}Cl \qquad CH_3{\rightarrow}\overset{\displaystyle CH_3}{\underset{\displaystyle CH_3}{C}}{\rightarrow}Cl$$

$$(\mu=0) \qquad (\mu=0) \qquad\qquad (\mu=1.88) \qquad (\mu=2.15)$$

and a simple chemical example is provided by the strengths of formic, acetic, and propionic acids. On the other hand, a general inductive effect of the same kind persists *even in hydrocarbons* when the practical issue is reactivity towards an electrophilic reagent, as illustrated by the orientation Rules (Markownikoff) for the nitration of paraffins. Clearly, the polarizability of carbon is the important factor here, and thus, despite a zero moment, a condition such as may obtain during reaction. The possibility of an inductomeric ($-I$) effect of alkyl groups in the presence of nucleophilic reagents may be foreseen.

The energy necessary for a polarizability effect is assumed to be derived from without the molecule, but that associated with the polarization must be contained within, and the existence of two modes of polarization, in particular the occasional coexistence of opposing polarizations originating in the same atom or group, raises the question of the nature of the intra-atomic forces responsible for conditions so obviously incapable of interpretation on any purely electrostatic basis. The driving power of the inductive effect is evidently octet stability (including the influence thereon of nuclear charge and of inner electrons), and thus may be regarded as essentially quantum mechanical, if the success of the quantum theory in the interpretation of the duplet be taken as an earnest of its ability eventually to deal with the octet. The driving force behind the mesomeric effect cannot be the same (for the two effects may clash), and its nature therefore requires elucidation. This question may be approached by considering together the structures of an anion, a neutral molecule, and a cation, each constitutionally capable of the tautomeric effect. Each entity must have at least two normal modes of representation, as illustrated in the first and third of the columns of formulae in the subjoined scheme; and the circumstance that some of the systems are charged as a whole whilst others are neutral as a whole, and that transitions may involve a displacement, a neutralization, or even a separation, of local atomic charges, is trivial in comparison with the essential similarity of the three relationships exhibited. From the present point of view, the important feature of the analogy is that

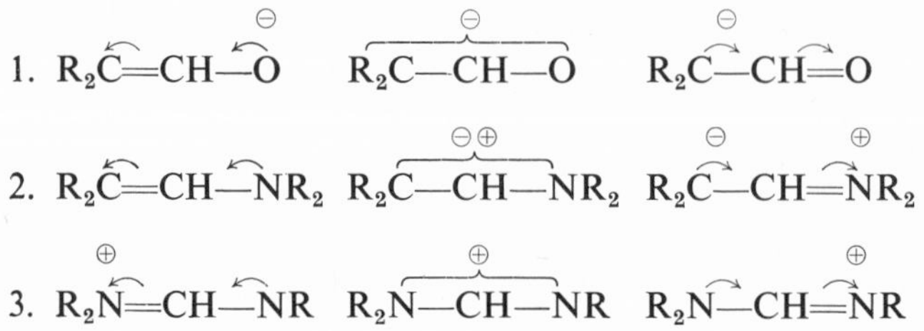

1. $R_2C{=}CH{-}\overset{\ominus}{O}$ $\quad R_2C{-}CH{-}\overset{\ominus}{O}$ $\quad R_2\overset{\ominus}{C}{-}CH{=}O$

2. $R_2C{=}CH{-}\overset{\ominus\oplus}{NR_2}$ $R_2C{-}CH{-}\overset{\ominus\oplus}{NR_2}$ $R_2\overset{\ominus}{C}{-}CH{=}\overset{\oplus}{NR_2}$

3. $R_2\overset{\oplus}{N}{=}CH{-}NR$ $R_2\overset{\oplus}{N}{-}CH{-}NR$ $R_2\overset{\oplus}{N}{-}CH{=}\overset{\oplus}{NR}$

all three systems show in greater or less degree the qualitative features of a wave-mechanical degeneracy. First, each pair of formulae represents the same entity in different electronic states (hereafter called the unperturbed states); secondly, in one of the cases these states have the same energy, and in the others they may be assumed to have sufficiently nearly the same energy to preserve the essential features of the analogy; thirdly, it may be considered to be the principal significance of the phenomenon of tautomerism that these states are coupled with respect to energy in the sense of the perturbation theory. Mutual perturbations will therefore supervene with the production of states which, by analogy with calculable examples of degeneracy, are expected to have lower energy than the unperturbed states, and therefore to correspond to the most stable condition of the system. Where there is an exact equivalence of unperturbed energies, the degenerate state must be symmetrically related to the unperturbed states, whilst in other cases the relationships, although not identical, must be similar (hence, the term *mesomeric* = between the parts); accordingly the degenerate or mesomeric states may be represented as shown in the centre column of the above scheme of formulae, in which the symbol ⌣ denotes the distributed proper functions of the omitted electrons. Thus the independent source of energy without which the existence of the mesomeric effect would be impossible is identified as the energy of degeneracy.

The article concludes by illustrating the theory with a number of examples of organic compounds.

The following selection is from pages 467–468, 476–480, and 497–504 in *Chemical Reviews 5*, 467–507 (1928).

The New Quantum Mechanics

J. H. VAN VLECK

I. Introduction

The quantum theory has been revolutionized within the past three years by the development of a new quantum mechanics which is a far more comprehensive and satisfying theory than the original form developed by Bohr, Sommerfeld and others in 1913 and subsequent years. This remarkable new mechanics cannot be regarded as the product of any one man, but instead must be considered the result of the reaction of mind on mind among European talent in theoretical physics. This new quantum dynamics has, in fact, been developed in a great diversity of mathematical forms, which present a rather confusing array to the student beginning the subject. However, it must be emphasized that these various formulations, though different in mathematical structure, are in harmony with each other, and yield substantially equivalent results when applied to physical or chemical problems. The three main mathematical forms are the following: (1) the matrix theory of Born, Heisenberg, and Jordan, (2) Schroedinger's wave mechanics, (3) the so-called "transformation theory," based on kinematical indeterminism, developed by Dirac and Jordan, and interpreted by Heisenberg. Of these three formulations, the third is the most comprehensive, and includes the other two as special cases. In this paper I shall not endeavor to give the mathematical foundations of the quantum mechanics, as that would be too long a task. Instead I shall begin by explaining some of the philosophy and logic underlying the new theory and shall later survey some of its accomplishments. The philosophy may be summarized in the statement that at atomic distances our concepts of space and time must be revamped. In fact Heisenberg's epoch-making development of the matrix theory was spurred by Born's repeated emphasis to his colleagues at Göttingen that the reason the old quantum theory was then (1925) failing was that we were all too anxious to use the same concepts of space and time within the atom as in ordinary measurable large-scale events. Einstein and the relativists made us rescrutinize the space-time correlation at cosmic distances, and now the quantum theories bid us do this at the other extreme of size. Now, after all, the concepts of distance and time have a meaning only when we tell how they can be measured. This is very nicely emphasized in Bridgman's recent book, *The Logic of Modern Physics*. At ordinary distances we determine lengths by means of measuring rods and time intervals by clocks. However, one cannot use a meter stick to measure the diameter of an atom, or an alarm clock to record when an electron is at the perihelion of its orbit. Consequently we must not be surprised if within the atom the correlation of space and time is something which cannot be visualized, and that models cannot be constructed with the same kind of mechanics as Henry Ford uses in designing an automobile. After all, within the atom there may be no geometry in the ordinary sense.

Matrix mechanics and the uncertainty principle are then discussed. The paper continues:

Twentieth century developments, especially relativity and quantum mechanics, have forced the physicist to rescrutinize the real meaning of the variables entering in his equations and in so doing he has discovered that many customary concepts (*e.g.*, absolute time, in cosmogony and instantaneous position of the electron in atomistics) which are as superfluous as the twelfth camel in the preceding story, and which have sprung up because one is too prone to visualize either cosmic or atomic space and time in terms of the same picture as for ordinary measurable distances. I wonder whether the chemist has not also suffered from the same kind of prejudices and likewise introduced concepts which prove to be hallucinations when put to close scrutiny. The chemist has often thought that he has found strong evidence on the instantaneous positions of electrons, and first and last there has been considerable controversy as to whether the facts of organic chemistry can be explained as well by assuming that the electrons are moving, as the physicist would like, as by supposing that they are standing still. However, is it really necessary to suppose that the structural bonds of the organic chemist represent instantaneous positions of the electrons, or would it not do just as well to suppose that they represent average positions, for the mathematics indicates that it is the average rather than instantaneous positions of the electrons which determine whether the nuclei are in equilibrium? Or going a step further from a picture, would it not perhaps do to suppose that these structural diagrams are simply a way of indicating diagrammatically some of the symmetry properties of the solutions of Schroedinger's wave equation, to be discussed later? Recent work of London and Heitler seems to indicate that the systematization of chemical compounds is closely related to the group theory of mathematicians. However, one must not necessarily infer from this that the group characteristics are the geometrical characteristics. There is, of course, much evidence for tetrahedral models of the carbon atom, but does this necessarily mean that the instantaneous positions of the electrons project out in four directions; could not this evidence mean that this symmetry is only true of average positions of the electrons, or even that there is some dynamical function, important for the mechanics of chemical combination, but without any immediate geometrical significance, which is symmetrical mathematically in the variables representing the coördinates of the four electrons?

According to the theoretical physicist, one has no right to speak of the *instantaneous* position of the electron in its path within the atom, for if one knew where the electron were located each successive instant of time, one would know both the position and velocity of the electron, which we have seen is contrary to the Heisenberg indeterminism principle. It can, however, be shown that it is legitimate to introduce the concept of the *average* position of the electron; such averages are, in fact, given by the diagonal elements of properly chosen Heisenberg matrices. It is these average positions, and not the instantaneous ones which are revealed by experiments on the scattering of X-rays of the type which Professor Jauncey has so interestingly discussed in another paper of this symposium. Clearly the time of scattering of an X-ray quantum cannot be measured with any accuracy compared to the average time required for the electron to move from one side of the atom to the other. Chemists have often asked me this question, "Where are the electrons located in, say, the bond between two hydrogen atoms to form a hydrogen molecule? Does each electron remain with its own nucleus, or are the two electrons shared 50–50 by both nuclei?" According to the quantum mechanics, the latter alternative comes the closer to the true state of affairs, for in the hydrogen molecule the average electronic charge distribution is symmetrical with respect to the two nuclei, and the two electrons are continually exchanging places, so that it is impossible to say which electron belongs with which nucleus. When the hydrogen atoms are too far apart to form a molecule, say at a distance 3×10^{-7} cm. comparable with the distances of approach between molecules in the kinetic theory of gases, the exchange of places is very infrequent, only about once in 10^{30} years on the average, whereas when the atoms are so closely knit together as to form a molecule, the exchange transpires on the average about 10^{10} times per second! The statistical or average charge distribution in the hydrogen molecule can be calculated directly from the quantum postulates, and is shown in Figure 2, taken from a paper by London. The contour lines in these figures represent the statistical charge density. Thus this density is large where the lines are close together and small where they are far apart. The densest region is, of course, in general near the two nuclei. The mathematical analysis shows that there are two solutions of the Schroedinger wave equation corresponding to the interaction between two hydrogen atoms. In one of them,

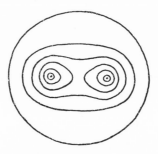

Fig. 2. Attraction.

shown in Figure 3, the forces exerted on the nuclei are entirely of a repulsive nature. The meaning of this is that two hydrogen atoms may be brought into contact without necessarily forming a molecule. In the other solution, Figure 2, there is attraction as well as repulsion, and this is what makes possible the formation of a stable molecule. It is seen from Figure 2 that in this other solution the negative electronic charge tends to pile up between the two nuclei, and it is the attraction of this negative charge which tends to bring the nuclei together, and offsets the purely repulsive forces which exist between two positive charges by themselves. In the solution shown in Figure 2, the nuclei are in positions of equilibrium, whereas in Figure 3 they will fly apart.

The concept of a statistical or average charge density, such as is shown in Figures 2 and 3, can perhaps be rendered more graphic

Fig. 3. Repulsion.

by the following comparison. Supposing one were to photograph a swarm of fireflies at night by means of an exceedingly sensitive camera. If one were to take an instantaneous photograph or "snapshot," each firefly would appear as a bright point on the photographic plate. If we took snap-shots at frequent intervals we could then trace the motion of each of the flies. Suppose, however, that instead we were to take a time exposure extending over a long period. Then the luminous points would be blurred out into a cloud of light upon the plate. The cloud would be brightest where the fireflies are most apt to congregate. Now the information which it is possible to obtain about the motion of the electron within the atom in quantum mechanics is analogous to that given by the time exposure in the firefly illustration. The statistical charge density corresponds to the density of the luminous cloud. Efforts have sometimes been made to interpret the electron in quantum mechanics as itself a sort of nebulous body spread over the entire atom, but that is no more correct than to say that a firefly is a bright cloud extending over a large distance. In either case it is only the time average of position that has the cloud or fluid-like appearance. The essence of the Heisenberg indeterminism principle is that a "snap-shot" of the electronic motion is inherently impossible, for position cannot be instantaneously specified if the energy has a definite value corresponding to a stationary state of the atom. It appears almost paradoxical that although one can never say *when* an electron is in a given position within the atom, one can nevertheless talk of the fraction of the time that it is in this position, for clearly the places of large average charge density are those where the electron spends a large fraction of its time.

Schroedinger's wave version and its physical applications are then discussed.

IV. What the Quantum Mechanics Promises to Do for the Chemist

Before passing to the chemical application we must first describe one aspect of the quantum mechanics which seems to be of particular importance for chemistry. This is the so-called *Pauli exclusion principle*, which states that *no two electrons can have simultaneously all four quantum numbers the same*. The reason that there are four quantum numbers per electron is that the electron seems to be a spinning body having a fourth or internal degree of freedom in addition to the three translational degrees of freedom. Just what we take as the four quantum numbers depends somewhat on the type of quantization, which itself varies with the relative magnitude of the various atomic forces. The simplest thing is to suppose that the magnetic field is so powerful that it completely overpowers the interelectronic forces, so that the orbital and spin angular momentum vectors of each electron are quantized separately relative to the axis of the field. Actually no ordinary magnetic field is powerful enough to do this, but our supposition nevertheless involves no loss of generality because the exclusion principle is a purely formal rule for eliminating certain combinations of quantum numbers, and in any field strength the states will be excluded which pass gradually ("adiabatically") over into states not allowed in extremely strong fields. In a strong field the four quantum numbers of each electron are the principal quantum number, n, the azimuthal quantum number, k, and the two "magnetic" or "equatorial" quantum numbers, m_k and m_s, quantizing the components of orbital and spin angular momentum in the direction of the applied field. The range of values for the quantum numbers k, m_k, m_s are

$$k = 0, \ldots, n - 1$$
$$m_k = -k, -(k - 1), \ldots, 0, \ldots, k - 1, k \qquad (7)$$
$$m_s = -\tfrac{1}{2}, +\tfrac{1}{2}$$

It is to be noted that the azimuthal quantum number is usually numbered one unit lower in the new than in the old quantum theory, as formerly we had $k = 1, 2, \ldots, n$. We now have $k = 0, 1, 2, 3$ for optical s, p, d, f terms respectively instead of 1, 2, 3, 4. (This is purely a formal difference in notation and to emphasize the distinction the notation l instead of k is sometimes used in the new theory.) The range of values for m_k is $-k$ to $+k$ because m_k being a component of k, cannot exceed k in absolute magnitude. The quantum number m_s has only the two values $-\tfrac{1}{2}$ and $+\tfrac{1}{2}$, because according to the hypothesis of Uhlenbeck and Goudsmit, the internal spin of the electron is associated with a half quantum of angular momentum. Now for given k, equation (7) shows that m_k has $2k + 1$ possible values, while m_s has just two possibilities. There are thus $2(2k + 1)$ different pairs of values for m_k and m_s. Hence one way of stating the exclusion principle is that *in any atom there are at most $2(2k + 1)$ electrons having the same values of n and k.*

Pauli advanced his exclusion principle on more or less empirical grounds before advent of the new mechanics, but the latter has placed this principle on a better and more general basis, as it amounts to using only solutions of Schroedinger's wave equation which are of a certain peculiar type of symmetry (viz., the so-called antisymmetric solutions which change sign when electrons are interchanged). We will not try to enter into the details of the mathematical description of what this type of symmetry is. The only point that need be emphasized is that *because of Pauli's principle we must not only limit ourselves to "civilized" solutions of Schroedinger's equation, but also in particular only those which are of the "antisymmetric variety."*

Pauli's principle should appeal particularly to chemists because it yields immediately the well-known interpretation of the Mendeléeff periodic table proposed by Smith and Stoner. These two men showed independently that by making certain apparently rather arbitrary assumptions about the assignment of quantum numbers to electrons of the various groups, one could account very nicely for the structure of the periodic table of the elements—why, for instance, there are 2 elements in the first period, 8 in each of the two next, 18 in the fourth and fifth, but 32 in the sixth. Also within the period many of the chemical properties of the elements, the existence of sub-periods, rare earths, etc., come out nicely.

Now Pauli's principle gives automatically the Smith-Stoner assignment of quantum numbers. We will illustrate this, for simplicity, only for the first two periods, i.e., for the K and L shells. In the K shell the principle quantum number n has the value 1, and hence by (7) the azimuthal number k can only have the value zero. On the other hand in the L shell the principle quantum number n equals 2, and by (7) there are the two possibilities $k = 0$ and $k = 1$. The various possibilities for the four electronic quantum numbers are then by (7) those indicated in table 3. The essence of Pauli's principle

Table III

	K shell ($n = 1$)		L shell ($n = 2$)							
n . . .	1	1	2	2	2	2	2	2	2	2
k . . .	0	0	0	0	1	1	1	1	1	1
m_k . . .	0	0	0	0	-1	-1	0	0	1	1
m_s . . .	$-\frac{1}{2}$	$+\frac{1}{2}$	$-\frac{1}{2}$	$+\frac{1}{2}$	$-\frac{1}{2}$	$+\frac{1}{2}$	$-\frac{1}{2}$	$+\frac{1}{2}$	$-\frac{1}{2}$	$+\frac{1}{2}$

is that no two columns can have four identical entries. As each column corresponds to a different electron, there are indeed two electrons in the K-shell and eight in the L.

The quantum mechanics should go further than furnish a model of the periodic table. It should tell us what atoms can combine and what do not. There is no essential difference between the mathematical procedure in the quantum mechanics of calculating a heat of dissociation and of calculating a spectroscopic frequency or critical potential. This fact does not seem quite as universally recognized as it should be. In either case what is required is a knowledge of the magnitude of the various allowed energy levels. The only distinction is that chemical problems involve more than one nucleus, and this considerably increases the labor of calculation. For the latter reason it may well be a long time before the quantum mechanics achieves as many quantitative results for the chemist as for the physicist, but from a standpoint of pure logic there seems to be no apparent reason why the quantum postulates as they now stand should not be adequate to explain the phenomena of chemical reactions. A dynamics which works for the physicist must also work for the chemist and vice versa. It seems scarcely conceivable that a theory which has been so successful in explaining atomic energy levels should fail in the closely related realm of molecular energies. *The mathematical problem of a chemical reaction seems to be this: to investigate whether there are stable solutions of the Schroedinger equation corresponding to the interactions between two (or more) atoms, using only the wave functions which have the type of symmetry compatible with Pauli's exclusion principle.*

A beginning in this program of investigating chemical reactions by means of quantum mechanics and Pauli's exclusion principle has been made within the past few months in important papers by London and by Heitler. Although this work is very new, it is already yielding one of the best and most promising theories of valency. The general trend of the work seems to be that because of the critical examination of symmetry properties required by the Pauli exclusion principle, the theory of the classification of valences in complicated organic compounds, etc., must be closely related to the group theory of the mathematicians. Some of the specific results which have already been obtained in the papers of London and Heitler are the following:

1. Two hydrogen atoms can combine to form a hydrogen molecule.

2. Two helium atoms cannot combine, unless excited, without violating Pauli's exclusion principle. This, of course, agrees with the monatomic property of helium gas. Spectroscopists, to be sure, have observed the spectra due to helium molecules, but such molecules are transient, unstable creatures in which the electrons are in excited rather than normal states.

3. Inert gases cannot exhibit valences.

4. Halides may have the valences 1, 3, 5, 7 except that the valence of fluorine may only have the value 1.

5. S, Se, Te may have valences 0, 2, 4, 6 but oxygen only the values 0, 2.

6. P, As, Sb, Bi may have 1, 3, 5 but N only 1, 3.

7. C, Si, Ge, etc., may have 0, 2, 4.

Chemists will immediately recognize that these predicted possible valences are in the main in excellent accord with experiment. Oxygen, for insteance, is found to be pronouncedly only divalent, whereas S, Se, etc., have sometimes higher valences. Thus only OCl_2 is observed, whereas on the other hand one finds compounds such as SCl_4, SF_6, $SeCl_4$, SeF_6, etc. Similarly it is well known that Cl and I can exhibit higher valences than the unit valence characteristic of F. Some of the valences listed above are not realized experimentally. A notable example is that the valence of nitrogen is never unity, even though according to item 6 the values 1 and 3 are both possible. However, this state of affairs is not a serious difficulty, for I have attempted to list the valences which are possible from a standpoint of elementary symmetry considerations rather than those which actually exist. I have been careful to say, in every case "may have" according to the theory, rather than "should have." The different valences correspond to different apportionments of various values of the quantum numbers k, m_k among the electrons, and the relative prevalence of the different valences depends upon the relative prevalence of the states corresponding to different values of the quantum numbers k, m_k but given n. Some of these states may have such high energies that they are occupied only very infrequently, and so the corresponding valences may not exist. In other words, the preceding inventory indicates only how valency is restricted by the Pauli exclusion principle, and energy considerations may give further limitations. Definite predictions in this respect should be possible if there were available complete spectroscopic evidence on the atomic stationary states corresponding to all assignments of quantum numbers. London's work, in fact, seems to show that there is a very intimate connection between valences and the spectroscopists' classification of spectral terms. Thus he finds that valences 1, 3, 5 in the nitrogen group are associated respectively with doublet, quartet, and sextet structures in the spectroscopists' "multiplets." The spectroscopists find experimentally that the normal state of the nitrogen atom is a quartet rather than a doublet spectral term, and this is in agreement with the fact that the normal valence of N is 3. Complete absence of univalence in nitrogen must mean that the lowest doublet terms have considerably greater energy than the lowest quartet terms. Similarly the spectroscopists' observation that the normal spectral term of the O atom is of the triplet rather than singlet type means that normally oxygen is divalent rather than non-valent. This, of course, accords with the fact that oxygen gas is diatomic rather than monatomic. Apparently the spectroscopists classifications into multiplets is going to be useful in correlating the relative prevalence of different possible valences.

It must also be mentioned that sometimes valences are observed which are not allowed according to the above scheme. Thus, nitrogen is sometimes observed to be quintavalent. Such exceptions London explains on the ground that his theory is only one of what he calls "homopolar valences," in which the molecule dissociates into neutral atoms rather than into ions. The valence 5 for nitrogen he claims belongs to the "polar" category in which the molecule breaks up into ions, in which case the symmetry arguments may lead to quite different results. It must be mentioned that London's use of the terms "homopolar" and "polar" may prove a bit confusing, as it has nothing whatsoever to do with the presence of an electric moment, but rather refers to the mode of dissociation. As mentioned in Dr. Darrow's paper in this symposium, recent experimental work shows that molecules are much more apt than has been previously supposed to dissociate into neutral atoms rather than ions. Thus optical dissociation of HBr furnishes H and Br rather than H^+ and Br^-. Hence London would presumably classify the formation of HBr as a homopolar bond despite the electrical polarity of the HBr molecule. He is forced to admit that there is no hard and fast distinction between the two terms homopolar and polar as he uses them, since some molecules may dissociate in either of two ways. According to London a valence is of his polar type only if the electron affinity of one atom is greater than the ionization potential of the other.

A point which is to be particularly emphasized is that according to London the reason certain valences or bonds do not occur (e.g., componds involving inert gases) is not that such bonds lead to molecules which are energetically unstable, but that the bonds, when stable, correspond to solutions of the Schroedinger wave equation which are of a type of symmetry contrary to Pauli's exclusion principle. Thus considerations of symmetry (group theory) are often quite as vital as those of energetics. The failure of a chemist to find a compound does not necessarily mean that the corresponding molecule is energetically unstable, but may mean rather that it would demand electronic groupings contrary to the exclusion principle. As an example, consider the question of whether two normal helium atoms can combine to form a helium molecule. Here the mathematical analysis of Heitler and London shows that there are energetically stable solutions of the wave equation corresponding to the interaction of two helium atoms, as well as also energetically unstable ones. In the stable solutions the statistical charge distribution is roughly of the general type shown in Figure 2, whereas in the unstable ones it is more of the type illustrated in Figure 3. Hence helium gas might be diatomic, were it not for the fact that the stable solutions are all contrary to Pauli's exclusion principle, leaving only some of the unstable solutions corresponding to repulsion of the atoms rather than chemical affinity. On the other hand in the case of the hydrogen molecule the stable solution satisfies Pauli's principle.

The paper concludes with a calculation of the heat of dissociation of H_2 by quantum mechanical methods.

The following selection is in *Proceedings of the National Academy of Sciences of the United States of America 13*, 466–470 (1927).

Wave Mechanics and the Normal State of the Hydrogen Molecule

EDWARD UHLER CONDON

The problem of the motion of a particle attracted by two fixed centers of force according to the Coulomb force law can be treated by classical mechanics and has been used in quantum theory by Pauli and Niessen for a theory of the hydrogen molecule ion. In the quantum mechanics, where the energy levels are determined as the "eigenwerte" of Schrödinger's equation, the variables are separable and the boundary value problem is easily set up. But thus far a satisfactory treatment of the differential equations involved is lacking. Burrau has recently carried out a numerical integration of the problem for the lowest energy level of an electron moving under the influence of two fixed centers of Coulomb attraction as a function of the distance apart of these centers. In this paper, Burrau's data are used to give a semi-quantitative discussion of the neutral hydrogen molecule. His values are:

Nuclear separation	1.0	1.3	1.6	1.8	2.0
Electronic energy	2.896	2.648	2.436	2.309	2.204
		2.2	2.4	2.95	
		2.109	2.025	1.836	

The unit of separation is the Bohr 1_1 orbit radius of hydrogen atom, that of energy is the ionization potential of atomic hydrogen.

In all this work the tacit assumption is made that, because of the large masses of the nuclei the problem can be solved regarding the nuclei as fixed at a distance which is one of the parameters of the problem. When the energy of the electronic motion as a function of the distance is known, the energy of the Coulomb repulsion of the fixed nuclei is added and so the variation of the total energy of the non-rotating, non-vibrating molecule with nuclear distance is found. The minimum of this curve is taken as the "equilibrium" separation of the nuclei and the value of the minimum is taken as the energy of the molecule in that electronic state. (More correctly, the small amount $\frac{1}{2}h\nu$; is to be added to the minimum value.) If the nuclei are no longer regarded as fixed this curve is regarded as giving the "law of force" governing the rotational and vibrational motions of the molecule. That this is the correct procedure in the classical mechanics was shown by Born and Heisenberg: that it remains correct in the quantum mechanics has not yet been definitely proved. There is no reason to believe, however, that it is not correct, and it will be used here without further justification.

When the nuclei of a hydrogen molecule ion are far apart one is dealing virtually with free hydrogen atom and a proton. The electronic energy is then mainly that of the Coulomb interaction between the proton and the electronic charge of the atom. If the atom were not Stark-affected by the proton, this would be just equal to the nuclear repulsion and the total energy would be simply R for all values of the nuclear separation (all values are negative), where R is the Rydberg constant. But the proton induces a polarization of the H-atom and, therefore, the energy of proton-electron interaction is greater than that of proton-proton. On the other hand, when the nuclear separation is zero and the electron moves under the influence of a double central charge, the energy is that of the lowest state of ionized helium. Burrau's numerical integrations supply values of the electronic energy for intermediate electronic separations. When the nuclear repulsive energy (curve b, Fig. 1) is added to Burrau's values there results curve a, Figure 2, which is Burrau's curve for H_2^+. The equilibrium separation is 2 units (i.e., 2 times the radius of the Bohr 1_1 hydrogen orbit) and the minimum energy is $1.204R = 16.28$ volts. The heat of dissociation is $0.204R = 2.76$ volts. Burrau checks the value with experiment by an indirect comparison with the ionization potential of H_2 as discussed later in this paper.

Turning now to the neutral molecule one expects, on the Pauli principle of assigning quantum numbers, that the two electrons will be in equivalent orbits. The starting point, therefore, for the approximate treatment of the problem is a model in which the two electrons have no mutual influence and each moves as it would if alone in the ground state of H_2^+ as given by Burrau. The electronic energy of this model at each distance is evidently just twice that for H_2^+. This curve of doubled H_2^+ values is given here as *a* of Figure 1. Combined with the Coulomb proton-proton energy this yields curve *b*, Figure 2, for the energy curve of the neutral H_2 molecule with uncoupled electrons. This gives an equilibrium separation of 1.075 units, i.e., a moment of inertia of 2.7×10^{-41} gr. cm^2. The heat of dissociation is $1.800R = 24.36$ volts.

Naturally, such a model gives only a very rough approximation to the truth. But it is to be observed that the above model does set a definite lower limit on the moment of inertia of the molecule. For the electronic interaction, whatever its amount, will be positive and will decrease monotonously with increasing nuclear separation, since it is the repulsive potential of interacting-like charge. It acts to increase the ordinates of curve *b*, figure 1, by decreasing amounts and,

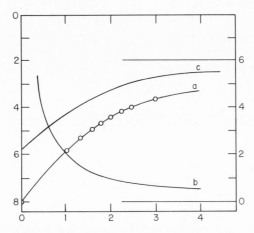

Fig. 1. Electronic and nuclear energy in H_2. *a*, Values for non-interacting electrons. *b*, Coulomb energy of nuclear repulsion. *c*, Approximate electronic energy curve for interacting electrons. Units: ordinates, 1 = Rydberg constant, abscissas, 1 = radius of first Bohr orbit in hydrogen atom.

therefore, shifts the minimum of the resultant curve to larger abscissas. This seems to be an important conclusion inasmuch as *the lower limit here definitely given by quantum mechanics is greater than nine of the thirteen values obtained on various theories from specific heat data* as presented in the recent thorough review of the subject by Van Vleck and Hutchisson.

Turning now to the electronic interaction, the analysis of Hund provides the important result that the electronic term of the lowest state of a molecule changes continuously from its value for a neutral atom of equal number of electrons to its value for the dissociated atoms, according to the new quantum mechanics. Herein lies an important difference between the old and the new quantum theory which is essential to the argument of this paper. That unexcited molecules dissociate into two unexcited atoms as a result of vibrations of infinite amplitude has been shown empirically by Birge and Sponer.

The first approximation to the electron interaction in unexcited helium has been computed by Unsöld, by means of the wave mechanics, who finds $5.5R$ for the whole atom, i.e., $1.5R = 20.3$ volts for the ionization potential. Empirically the value is $5.818R$ for the total energy. At large distances the model goes over into two neutral hydrogen atoms. The electronic energy will, therefore, be asymptotically equal to the Coulomb interaction of an electron and a proton, for it is made up of the repulsion of the two electrons and the attraction of each proton for the electron of the other atom. Moreover, the situation is now that of the interaction of two neutral units so that polarization deformation of each atom by the other will be much smaller than in the case of H_2^+. Inasmuch as Burrau's work shows that at a distance of 2.95 units the electronic part of the H_2^+ energy differs from the pure Coulomb by about $0.1R$, it is safe to assume for the H_2 molecule a closer approach to Coulomb value for abscissas greater than 3 units. For intermediate points, a natural assumption is to reduce the doubled Burrau value in the ratio $5.818:8.00$ in order to secure agreement with helium. If this is done it is found that the resulting curve joins on to the Coulomb curve smoothly. Curve c of Figure 1 has been drawn from the theoretical values so reduced up to the value for 2.4 and joined on to a Coulomb curve for abscicca values of 3 and greater.

The result of combining c and b of Figure 1 is to give c of Figure 2 as the energy curve for the hydrogen molecule. The minimum of this curve corresponds to a moment of inertia of 4.26×10^{-41} gr. cm^2., and to a heat of dissociation of 4.4 volts. The latter value agrees to within 0.1 volt with the band spectrum value of Witmer and of Dieke and Hopfield. These figures should be compared with a moment of inertia of 4.91×10^{-41} gr. cm^2. and $1.422R$ heat of dissociation found by Hutchisson from a cross orbit model of H_2 on classical quantum theory.

Another interesting consequence follows from the relation of the H_2 energy curve to that of H_2^+. According to a principle put forward by Franck, changes involving the electrons in a molecule will affect the nuclei mainly indirectly through the change in molecular binding. According to this view, the most probable event in an electron collision experiment by means of which an electron is removed from H_2, is the removal of an electron while the nuclei are at a distance of 1.350 units. This requires an amount of energy given by the difference between $2.325R$ and the ordinate of the H_2^+ curve at 1.350, namely $1.125R$. This is the theoretical apparent ionization potential and amounts to $1.2R$ or 16.2 volts in good agreement with the mean experimental value of 16.1 given by Franck and Jordan. On the other hand, the true energy of the process $H_2 \rightarrow H_2^+ + e^-$, where

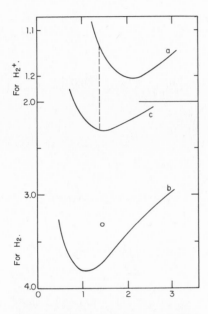

Fig. 2. Resultant energy curves in H_2^+ and H_2. a, Burrau's curve for H_2^+. b, Curve for H_2 for non-interacting electrons. c, Approximate curve for H_2 with interacting electrons. The small circle in the crook of curve b represents the equilibrium position and energy on Hutchisson's classical crossed-orbit model of H_2. Units: same as Fig. 1 (note different scales of ordinates for H_2 and H_2^+).

H_2^+ is in the lowest state, is the difference between the ordinates of the minimum of the H_2 and H_2^+ curves, i.e., $1.12R = 15.2$ volts, comparing favorably with the value of Witmer and of Dieke and Hopfield from the ultra-violet band spectrum of H_2.

The theoretical value of the frequency of vibration, depending on the curvature of the curve at its minimum, is naturally more uncertain. Calculation shows that the curve gives a frequency of vibration of 5300 cm^{-1}, about 20% higher than the value of 4360 cm^{-1} from experiment. As for the moment of inertia, while it is larger than most of the values from specific heat theories, it is in accord with the larger values which have been found by Richardson and Tanaka from analyses of the hydrogen bands.

In conclusion it seems proper to emphasize that Burrau's calculation of H_2^+ and the extension here to H_2 constitute the first quantum-theoretic quantitative discussion of the binding of atoms into molecules by electrons—the valence forces of chemistry. The quantitative success of the new quantum mechanics in the face of the classical theory's failure must serve to lend strong support to the new methods.

The following selection is from pages 362–365 in *The Journal of Chemical Physics 1*, 362–374 (1933).

The Nature of the Chemical Bond. V The Quantum Mechanical Calculation of the Resonance Energy of Benzene and Naphthalene and the Hydrocarbon Free Radicals

LINUS PAULING AND G. W. WHELAND

A number of structural formulae have been proposed for benzene, but none of them is free from very serious objections. The oldest

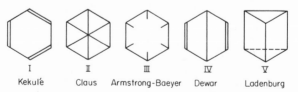

| I | II | III | IV | V |
| Kekulé | Claus | Armstrong-Baeyer | Dewar | Ladenburg |

and best known structure is that proposed by Kekulé (I). The objections to it are twofold. First, it suggests that ortho-disubstituted derivatives should exist in two isomeric forms—a phenomenon which has never been observed. Kekulé avoided this difficulty, however, by assuming that the double bonds were in a state of constant oscillations such that any two adjacent carbon atoms were connected part of the time by a single bond and part of the time by a double bond. For example:

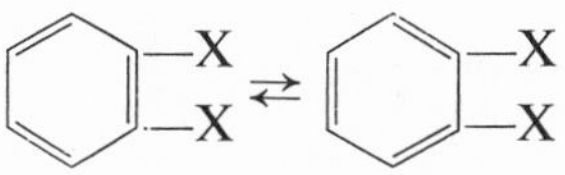

Second, the Kekulé structure suggests that benzene should be a highly unsaturated and comparatively unstable compound, in complete contradiction to the observed facts. Since this point has been discussed in considerable detail in various places, we shall not go into it here. The two centric structures (II and III) were proposed to avoid both of the above difficulties. They are indeed successful in eliminating the necessity for the oscillation hypothesis, but they can hardly account for the stability of the molecule. In the Claus structure the diagonal bonds would be very weak, as a result of the large distance between the atoms in the para positions, and the structure would probably represent a molecule less stable even than the Kekulé structure. In the Armstrong-Baeyer structure the meaning of the six lines pointing toward the center is not at all clear. If these "central bonds" are left undefined, the structure is essentially meaningless; if they are considered to represent free valences, the molecule should be highly unsaturated.

The Dewar structure (IV) has never been seriously considered since it suffers from the same defects, in an accentuated form, as the Kekulé structure. Its advantage over the other structures is largely that it explains the intimate relationship that usually obtains between the para positions in the benzene ring.

The Ladenburg prism structure (V) can be definitely ruled out, since we know that the benzene ring lies in a plane, or very nearly in a plane. The chemical evidence is also unfavorable in this case.

This by no means exhausts the list of structures proposed for benzene. The remainder however, such as the structure of Thiele based upon his theory of partial valence and that of Collie based upon a dynamic model, are usually complicated and cannot be represented in any simple valence scheme.

In the case of the aromatic hydrocarbons with condensed ring systems that state of affairs is quite similar. Thus the following structures have been proposed for naphthalene:

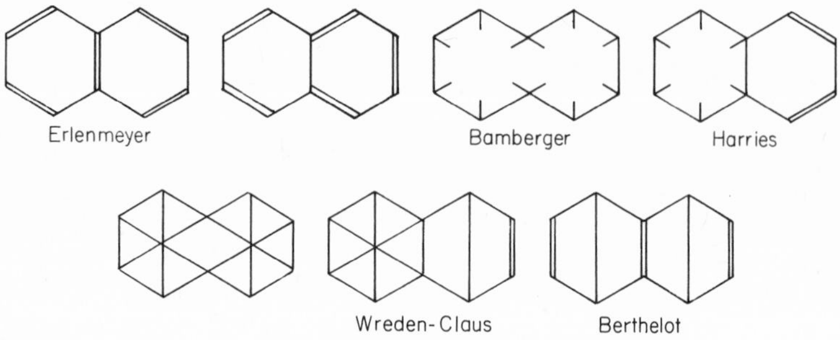

Erlenmeyer   Bamberger   Harries

Wreden-Claus   Berthelot

for anthracene:

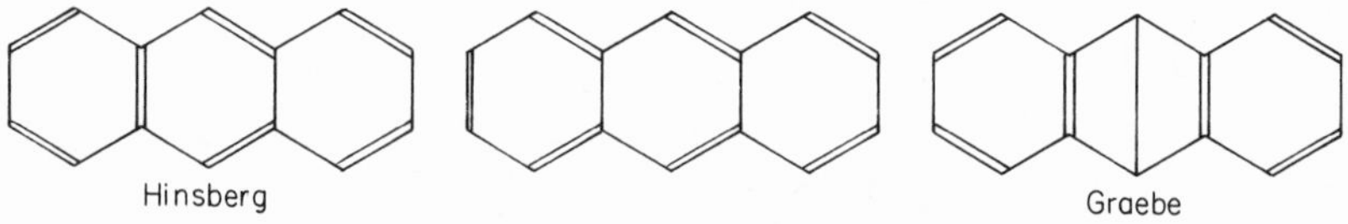

Hinsberg   Graebe

and so on for the other aromatic hydrocarbons. As in the case of benzene, however, the proposed structures are all unsatisfactory, on account both of the non-occurrence of predicted types of isomerism and of the unexpected stability of the molecules.

Apparently here we have a case where the classical ideas of structural organic chemistry are inadequate to account for the observed properties of a considerable group of compounds. With the development of the quantum mechanics and its application to problems of valence and molecular structure, it became evident to workers in this field that the resonance of benzene between the two equivalent Kekulé structures was an essential feature of the structure of this molecule, accounting for the hexagonal symmetry of the ring and for its remarkable stability; and it seemed probable that the quantum mechanical treatment of aromatic molecules would lead to a completely satisfactory explanation of their existence and characteristic properties. E. Hückel has made a valuable start in this direction in a series of papers on the quantum mechanics of benzene. His method of attack, however, is very cumbersome. In this paper we present a treatment of the problem which is rather closely similar to that of

Hückel's and which leads to the same result in the case of benzene, but in which the calculations are simplified to such an extent that the method can be extended to the naphthalene molecule without undue labor. Furthermore, with the aid of additional simplifications and approximations we have been able to treat the problem of free radicals and to obtain results in surprisingly good qualitative agreement with experiment. We shall leave the discussion of these latter calculations to the second part of the paper.

We shall set up the problem in essentially the same way as Hückel. We assume that each of the six carbon atoms possesses two K electrons, and four L electrons, one for each of four orbital functions formed by linear combination of the $2s$ and the three $2p$ orbits. Three of these L orbits, each a combination of the $2s$ orbit and the two $2p$ orbits in the plane of the ring, form single bonds to the attached hydrogen atom and the two adjacent carbon atoms. The fourth orbit for each atom remains a pure p-orbit, projecting at right angles to the ring. We neglect the energy of the electrons forming the system of single bonds in the plane and of their interaction with the electrons occupying the pure p-orbits (these energy quantities occurring in the same way for all the structures considered, and hence leading to only a change in the arbitrarily-chosen zero of energy), and consider only the interaction energy of the latter electrons, which may interact with one another in different ways. That is, we treat benzene simply as a six-electron system with spin degeneracy only, and naphthalene as a ten-electron system with spin degeneracy only.

Considerable justification for this choice of orbital functions and of bond distribution is provided by the fact that each of the single exchange integrals between a pure p-orbit and an orbit in the plane of the ring is positive (arising from the e^2/r_{ij} term in the Hamiltonian only), and the chosen distribution of bonds causes these integrals to occur with the negative sign in the expression for the energy of the molecule, while the bonding energy integrals, which are negative, occur with the positive sign.

In carrying out the calculations we make certain further simplifying assumptions. We neglect all exchange integrals of unity, and all exchange integrals of the energy H except single exchange integrals involving two adjacent atoms. The single exchange integrals involving adjacent atoms, $(abcdef|H|bacdef)$, $(abcdef|H|acbdef)$, etc., are represented by the symbol α. These integrals are seen to be equal in benzene; in naphthalene and other aromatic molecules, in which they are not all required to be equal by the symmetry of the molecule, the reasonable assumption is made that no serious error is introduced by giving them all the same value. The Coulomb integral $(abcdef/H/abcdef)$ is represented by the symbol Q.

$$\begin{vmatrix} (Q-W)+3\alpha/2 & \tfrac{1}{2}(Q-W)+3\alpha/2 & \tfrac{1}{2}(Q-W)+3\alpha/2 & \tfrac{1}{2}(Q-W)+3\alpha/2 & \tfrac{1}{2}(Q-W)+3\alpha/2 \\ \tfrac{1}{2}(Q-W)+3\alpha/2 & (Q-W)+3\alpha/2 & \tfrac{1}{2}(Q-W)+3\alpha/2 & \tfrac{1}{2}(Q-W)+3\alpha/2 & \tfrac{1}{2}(Q-W)+3\alpha/2 \\ \tfrac{1}{2}(Q-W)+3\alpha/2 & \tfrac{1}{2}(Q-W)+3\alpha/2 & (Q-W) & \tfrac{1}{2}(Q-W)+3\alpha/2 & \tfrac{1}{2}(Q-W)+3\alpha/2 \\ \tfrac{1}{2}(Q-W)+3\alpha/2 & \tfrac{1}{2}(Q-W)+3\alpha/2 & \tfrac{1}{2}(Q-W)+3\alpha/2 & (Q-W) & \tfrac{1}{2}(Q-W)+3\alpha/2 \\ \tfrac{1}{2}(Q-W)+3\alpha/2 & \tfrac{1}{2}(Q-W)+3\alpha/2 & \tfrac{1}{2}(Q-W)+3\alpha/2 & \tfrac{1}{2}(Q-W)+3\alpha/2 & (Q-W) \end{vmatrix} = 0.$$

This quintic equation is easily reduced to three linear factors and one quadratic factor, the roots being -2α, -2α, 0, $(-(13)^{\frac{1}{2}}-1)\alpha$, and $((13)^{\frac{1}{2}}-1)\alpha$. Since α is negative, the last of these roots, $(13)^{\frac{1}{2}}-1)\alpha = 2.6055\alpha$, represents the normal state of the molecule. The eigenfunction corresponding to this is (before normalizing) $\psi = \psi_\lambda$.

Benzene

The benzene molecule can now be treated very simply by the Slater method, with the help of the rules formulated by one of us for finding the matrix elements occurring in the secular equation. The bonds between the six eigenfunctions can be drawn so as to give the independent canonical structures shown in Fig. 1. Any other structures that can be drawn can be represented by eigenfunctions which are linear combinations of the five above. It will be seen that structures A and B are simply the two Kekulé structures, and C, D, and E

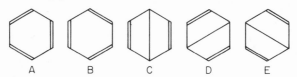

A   B   C   D   E

Fig. 1. The five canonical structures contributing to the normal state of the benzene molecule.

are three different forms of the Dewar structure. The Claus centric structure does not belong to the canonical set, but it can be represented as a linear combination of canonical structures; and the same is true of the Ladenburg structure if it be considered spread out in a plane, as:

(The Claus structure $= A + B - C - D - E$; the Ladenburg structure $= A + B - D - E$.)

As can be easily verified, the secular equation is $+\psi_B + 0.4341$ $(\psi_C + \psi_D + \psi_E)$. If we had neglected the resonance phenomenon and calculated the energy for one of the structures A or B, we would have obtained the value $W' = Q + 1.5\alpha$. Hence the extra energy of the molecule resulting from resonance among the five independent structures is 1.1055α. It is interesting to see how much of this extra energy is due to resonance between the two Kekulé structures and how much is contributed by the excited structures C, D and E. A single calculation shows that 0.9α or approximately 80 per cent of the resonance energy comes from the Kekulé structures alone and only about 20 per cent from the three excited structures.

In the following paper of this series a value of about 1.7 v.e. has been found from thermochemical data for the resonance energy of benzene. Equating the negative of this quantity to 1.1055α, we calculate the value of α to be about -1.5 v.e. This value may not be very reliable, however, since it is based on the assumption that values of bond energies obtained from aliphatic compounds can be applied directly to aromatic compounds.

The results of the calculation for benzene are summarized in Table I. They are identical with those obtained by Hückel.

Table I

	Total energy	Resonance energy	$a:b$
Single Kekulé structure	$Q + 1.5\alpha$	0	
Resonance between two Kekulé structures	$Q + 2.4\alpha$	0.9α	$1:0$
Resonance among all five structures	$Q + 2.6055\alpha$	1.1055α	$1:0.4341$

The ratio $a:b$ is the ratio of the coefficient of structures A and B to that of the singly-excited structures C, D, and E.

The conclusions we draw regarding the structure of the normal benzene molecule are the following. The principal contributions to the structure are made by the two Kekulé structures, resonance between them stabilizing the molecule to the extent of 0.9α or about 1.35 v.e. over a ring with three double bonds. In addition, however, the excited structures contribute appreciably to the energy (0.2055α) and to the eigenfunction.[1] In a sense it may be said that all structures

---

[1] The Claus centric structure, an old-quantum-theory analogue of which was suggested several years ago by one of us, is found to make a less important contribution to the normal state of benzene than do the Kekulé structures.

based on a plane hexagonal arrangement of the atoms—Kekulé, Dewar, Claus, etc.—play a part, with the Kekulé structures most important. It is the resonance among these structures which imparts to the molecule its peculiar aromatic properties.

These ideas are then applied to naphthalene and free radicals in the remainder of the paper.

PHYSICAL CHEMISTRY

While the studies on chemical bonding and structure were supplying chemists with a basis for understanding the nature of the molecules with which they were concerned, other physical chemists were making discoveries—apparently as isolated or unrelated pieces of information —that were ultimately fitted together to give a clearer picture of the nature of matter.

COLLOIDS. The concept of colloids had been introduced in the mid-nineteenth century by Graham; see H. M. Leicester and H. S. Klickstein *A Source Book in Chemistry 1400–1900* (McGraw-Hill, New York, 1952) p. 340. However, the properties of colloidal substances were so confusing and the methods of dealing with them so unsatisfactory that little progress was made in colloid chemistry during the rest of the century. The ultramicroscope of Zsigmondy (p. 19) opened a prospect of clarifying the properties of colloids, but it was not until Wolfgang Ostwald in 1907 developed a systematic definition of the various types of colloidal systems that rapid progress could be made. The later work of colloid chemists is based on Ostwald's paper that is extracted here.

The following selection is from pages 296–297, 331, 333–334, and 338 in *Kolloid-Zeitschrift 1*, 291–300, 331–341 (1907).

On the Systematics of Colloids

WOLFGANG OSTWALD

2. Moreover, disperse heterogeneous systems show differences in form and structure that depend on the phases that are in contact through the development of large surfaces. We will first consider two-phase systems; two cases occur here. As a rule, one phase is in the form of separate particles that are mostly actually spherical or can at least be considered so for theoretical discussion; these may be dispersed movable or non-movable in the other phase. Examples of such systems are suspensions, emulsions, and foams which most

often have a two-phased disperse structure. The other phase, which has the same absolute surface, though not specifically the same (see below), is mostly continuous and is separate from the suspended particles, droplets, or bubbles. Since in what follows we will very frequently have to consider the two phases separately, we should give them special names, and so we will call the finely divided, separated phase the disperse phase,[1] in contrast to the continuous phase, which we will call the dispersion medium.

If we are discussing a heterogeneous system with more than two phases, the relationships are naturally more complicated and varied. The most usual cases are systems with two or more completely dispersed or discontinuous phases and one continuous one, for example, a colloidal solution that is mixed with pulverized animal charcoal or barium sulfate, etc. The number of theoretical possibilities of such systems with more than two phases is naturally very large; some of the more interesting and well-known cases of three-phase systems will be mentioned below. Giving special names for the individual possibilities seems to be superfluous at present, but in what follows we will call all disperse heterogeneous systems in which at least one continuous phase, or dispersion medium is present a disperse system of the first type.

In addition we will briefly mention still another type in which both phases are in the dispersed and separated condition. The only ones of this type known are those in which the phases are solid. Examples of such systems are mixtures of dry powders, for example, dry sand or soil, if gases are not here considered as dispersion media.

3. A characteristic property of disperse heterogeneous systems is the strong curvature or great specific surface with which the spacially connected phases touch each other. In fact, the main difference between the properties of disperse heterogeneous systems and the more general type lies entirely in the relationship of the two phases due to their contact, and the very slight and indistinct effect of the specific surface in the second case grows so fast when the surface increases that the first type shows its characteristic properties. The speed with which the surface increases when a constant volume is divided will be illustrated by the following mathematical considerations.

If we assume that the volume to be divided is in the form of a cube 1 cm.^{3} in size, its surface is 6 cm.^{2} If we divide the edges into 10 parts we obtain 1000 smaller cubes of 0.1 cm.^{3} size with individual surfaces of 0.6 cm.^{2} and a total surface of 600 cm.^{2} If we continue

[1] Most authors (*e.g.*, Hardy) have also used the expression 'inner phase" for this phase.

this decimal dividing, we obtain, for example, 1 trillion cubes with side length 0.1μ and 600,000,000 cm.^{2} = 60,000 m.^{2} total surface.

Now with the aid of the ultramicroscope of Siedentopf and Zsigmondy we are able to differentiate small particles with a diameter of 0.006 to 0.25μ optically. If we take the approximate limiting value of visibility as a diameter of about 0.01μ and consider this value as the side length of a cube, we obtain by the corresponding division of a cubic centimeter 1 quadrillion cubes of 0.01μ side length and 6,000,000 m.^{2} or 6 square kilometers total surface.

If we assume, as is probably actually more correct, that the small particles actually have the form of spheres, we obtain by a similar division to the limit of visibility, corresponding to the minimum surface of the spheres a minimum value for the total surface of such particles. From the relation of the surface of a sphere and a cube of equal volume (1 cm.^{3}) a surface of over 4.8 square kilometers. The true surface value for a cubic centimeter by division to the limit of visibility thus lies between 4.8 and 6 square kilometers, but apparently closer to the first than the second value.

Since these total surfaces were taken from an initial volume of 1 cm.^{3}, they are also valid as a measure of the specific surface shown by the ratio of a surface to a volume.

In fact, we must hold the view that in structures with this type of immense surface, forces and factors that depend on the surface or preferably show their effects there (surface energy and also, for example, electrical energy, etc.) play a role that with the usual ratio— that is, with small surface area—is not evident, considering the "concentration" of the surface to the volume (specific surface), since they are too small to be important.

4. Heterogeneous systems can be classified by the number of phases which compose them as well as by the form (condition of aggregation) of these phases. With respect to the number of phases the two-phase systems are especially important; some systems of more than two phases are also of interest and will be considered later. If we first devote our attention to the two-phase disperse heterogeneous systems we have the following 8–9 possibilities that correspond to the type of form of the phases that compose them (S = solid phase, L = liquid phase, G = gas or vapor phase).

1	S + S	4	L + S	7	G + S
2	S + L	5	L + L	8	G + L
3	S + G	6	L + G	[9	G + G]

Ostwald then discusses each of these systems briefly. He comes to a consideration of the systems most important for colloids.

5. Now we come to the class of disperse heterogeneous systems that are of special concern for the systematics of colloidal solutions, namely the class in which the dispersion medium is a liquid. Depending on the disperse phase we have suspensions, emulsions, and foams. I might mention here that sometimes the literature does not distinguish between suspensions and emulsions in the sense given here, and the word suspension is very often used for systems in which the disperse phase is recognizably a liquid. Naturally there are all stages of transition between solid and liquid bodies so that it is an arbitrary distinction as to whether a resin at a certain temperature is called a solid or a liquid. However, we shall attempt to show that practically speaking there is a whole series of differences between disperse heterogeneous systems with solid and with liquid phases and these also result from constant alterations in the internal forces[2] of the dispersed bodies that change other properties of the whole system irregularly or by jumps. There are also other inconsistencies in the literature, since many authors use the word foam for systems that are obviously composed of two liquid phases (for example, the "oil soap foam" of Bütschli). Consequently, in what follows we will call systems with the composition $L + S$ suspensions, $L + L$ emulsions, and $L + G$ foams.

First of all, systems with liquid dispersion media and a gaseous disperse phase are called foams; there have been very interesting studies on their properties in the well-known work of Lord Rayleigh, von Kober, and Zawidski. Very valuable results have come from the work of von Kober and his students on the stability of foams from saponins. I myself have often had the opportunity to observe tap water which was artificially aerated at low temperature followed by warming to room temperature and gave a milk-white color and a completely non-transparent appearance because of separation of an unusually large amount of many small droplets in the reagent tube. The stability of these unusually dispersed foams in which the liquid phase of the dispersion medium outweighed the gas phase as compared with the opposite behavior of the ordinary foams was very great. In a 100 cc. measuring cylinder after about 2 minutes (average of several concordant experiments) the gradually increasing turbidity had risen above the lowest 30 cc. It is not impossible that the presence of some aluminum silicate as a "protective colloid" was responsible for this stability. I may mention that in unpublished studies that I have made with these foams additions of substances

---

[2] Large internal forces (and the properties which depend on them, for example, surface tension) seem, in fact, to be the single characteristic of solid bodies, especially since the discovery of liquid crystals.

such as acids, inorganic salts, alcohol, ether, etc. increase the speed of clearing, while small concentrations of alkalis retard it. Similar results have also been found for saponin foams. Thus, the solution of gases in liquids must now be added to the field of molecular dispersions.

For disperse homogeneous systems with the composition L + L and L + G there are so many known examples that enumeration seems superfluous. This is especially true for systems that can be differentiated optically and particularly microscopically, systems that occasionally are called "true" suspensions and emulsions. We are especially interested in systems with such a disparity that they can no longer be differentiated microscopically, but at best can show ultramicroscopic heterogeneity; in other words, they are in the colloidal stage of division as suspensions and emulsions. From these considerations it follows that according to this system of systematics we must expect from the types of the phases two types of colloidal solutions which must be called suspension colloids and emulsion colloids. The first name has already been used in the literature as a term for the "stable hydrosols" of Perrin, the colloids of class 2 of Bechhold, and the "non-viscous, non-gelatinizing, but readily coagulable mixtures, or colloidal suspensions" of Noyes, etc. It is pertinent to ask whether the second class of colloidal solutions that are distinguished from the first type by their differences should thus characterize the "hydrophilic colloids" of Perrin, the "viscous, gelatinizing colloidal mixtures, not coagulated by salts or colloidal solutions" of Noyes and could correctly be called emulsion colloids, that is, could be counted among the disperse heterogeneous systems with the composition L + L. This question is equivalent to the differences of suspensions and emulsions as determined from the physical and physicochemical properties especially in systems of such dispersity that it is no longer possible to differentiate the disperse phase into solid and liquid microscopically. We will compare some properties of "true" or coarse suspensions and emulsions with each other and see whether by increasing the dispersity of the systems the previously existing differences between both systems are changed in any way so that the characteristics of the two groups of colloidal solutions which will be thus named in the newer literature are shown.

Ostwald compares all the properties of such systems as are known to him in considerable detail and finally concludes:

I believe that this comparison gives greater assurance, first, that the type of the disperse phase has, in fact, a meaningful effect on the properties of the disperse system with a liquid dispersion medium, and, second, the proof that the differences that have served to characterize the two great classes of colloidal solutions as shown in ordinary suspensions and emulsions gives us the right to call these two classes suspensions and emulsions, or, in other words, the different types of their disperse phases are responsible for their different behavior.

THERMODYNAMICS. Although other branches of physical chemistry were assuming new importance, thermodynamics remained a live and significant field. Much of the early thermochemical work of Berthelot and J. Thomsen as well as the thermodynamic theories of affinity of van't Hoff and others was not yet interpreted in a satisfactory manner. The hypothesis proposed by Walther Nernst in 1906 that at absolute zero the entropy of pure crystalline compounds is zero resolved many of the difficulties. The next selection shows his development of this "Nernst heat theorem" or "third law of thermodynamics," which resulted in great expansion of thermodynamics by such leading workers as G. N. Lewis and T. de Donder.

The following selection is from pages 1–7 and 39 in *Nachrichten von der königlichen Gesellschaft der Wissenschaften zu Göttingen, Mathmatisch-physikalische Klasse, 1906, 1–39.*

On the Calculation of Chemical Equilibrium from Thermal Measurements

W. NERNST

The famous Berthelot believed that he had found a very simple solution for the relationship between chemical energy and heat development in chemical processes, since he equated both quantities with each other.

Very closely connected with this is the so-called Thomsen rule which had already been established. According to this, the electrical work furnished by a galvanic element should be equal to the heat developed in the process which yields the current.

However, two ways have been found for the determination of the chemical energy, that is, the maximum work that can be obtained from a chemical process: by deriving both quantities in the one case from chemical equilibrium, and in the other from the electromotive force of a reversible galvanic element, and this shows us that the maximum work does not agree at all with the heat effect as determined thermodynamically.

Even before Berthelot, however, Helmholtz stated especially clearly[1] that the electromotive force is given by the heat developed (so-called Thomsen Rule), and then later (1882) he formulated rigorously the relationship between both quantities as given by the mechanical heat theory.

According to this, the following relationship holds for the maximum work A and the alteration of the total energy U

$$A - U = T\frac{dA}{dT} \tag{1}$$

in which T is the absolute temperature. Only if A were independent of the temperature would

$$A = U \tag{2}$$

hold at all temperatures, and at the same time U would also have to be independent of temperature. The last requirement would be that the specific heat of a substance that took part in the reaction would involve certain relations that as a rule are not found to exist.

At the same time, it can also be seen that the calculation of A from U is not possible, but perhaps if

$$A = f(T)$$

were a solution of equation (1), then

$$A = f(T) + BT$$

in which B is some constant, would likewise be a solution of differential equation (1).

Thus we find that in treating chemical processes from the standpoint of both heat quantities, this problem remains unsolved, since in the equations concerned we cannot determine more closely the integration constant; without making new assumptions, using only the mechanical theory we cannot obtain a relationship between A and U. However, a closer consideration of the matter should lead in a simple way to a new hypothesis, and, as I may be able to show in detail, the materials that have already been gathered may permit us to establish some hypothesis. However, before we proceed to this, let us recall briefly the most important formulas of chemical thermodynamics.

[1] Law of Conservation of Energy, 1847.

In what follows, we will first confine ourselves to gaseous systems. As I believe has been shown, it is the chemical equilibria in a homogeneous phase which are especially characteristic for the occurrence of chemical processes.

The question of whether, for example, solid substances coexist with the homogeneous phase is merely a matter of their vapor tension or solubility and is only loosely connected with the true chemical process. The further question of how the equilibrium in two coexisting homogeneous phases (liquid or gaseous) is regulated is answered by the value of the partition coefficients of the molecular types that react.

Thus if in what follows we seek to solve the problem of whether chemical equilibrium can be calculated from caloric data only, we can, at least at first, limit ourselves to *equilibrium values in the homogeneous phase*, and we can in fact choose the gaseous phase as the one.

Thus if we calculate the course of a chemical reaction (for example, $2H_2 + O_2 = 2H_2O$) from

$$\nu_1 A_1 + \nu_2 A_2 + \ldots = \nu_1' A_1' + \ldots$$

then we have the following relationship for the equilibrium concentration c

$$K = \frac{c_1^{\nu_1} c_2^{\nu_2} \cdots}{c_1'^{\nu_1'}} \tag{3}$$

in which K is the constant from the law of chemical mass action. Now in what follows for greater clarity the reaction formula is always written in such a way that *the reaction takes place from left to right with development of heat*. If Q is the amount of heat thus developed, the two heat quantities are given in the expression used by van't Hoff

$$Q = RT^2 \frac{d \ln K}{dT} \quad RT^2 \frac{d \ln K}{dT} \tag{4}$$

(equation for the reaction isochore).

Now, experience teaches that the heat effect of a chemical process is not altered very strongly with temperature: we therefore give

$$Q = Q_0 + T \Sigma \nu \alpha + T^2 \Sigma \nu \beta + \ldots \tag{5}$$

in which Q_0 is the heat developed at absolute zero. The values of $\alpha, \beta, \ldots$ are the characteristic coefficients of the individual substances reacting, and from the first heat quantity

$$\frac{dQ}{dT} = \Sigma \nu Cv = \Sigma \nu \alpha + 2T \Sigma \nu \beta + \ldots \tag{6}$$

in which Cv is the molecular heat at constant volume.

The question of whether the specific heat from absolute zero on up can be expressed by a progressive series according to whole powers of T or whether it would be better later to insert a different sort of temperature function for this appears to me to remain open. For the time being we do not have enough observational material, so that we cannot do otherwise than to choose first the two simplest expressions, (5) and (6). However, after all, the specific heat usually is only a correction value in equation (5).

Equations (4) and (5) give by integration the equation

$$\ln K = -\frac{Q_0}{RT} + \frac{\Sigma \nu \alpha}{R} \ln T + \frac{\Sigma \nu \beta}{R} T + \ldots + J \qquad (7)$$

where J is the integration constant already mentioned above and at first entirely undetermined.

Finally, still in the case of an equilibrium between a vapor and a solid or liquid phase (vaporization or sublimation), we should remember that here we have the analogous series with the corresponding formulas

$$\lambda - RT = \lambda_0 + T(\alpha - \alpha_0) + T^2(\beta - \beta_0) + \ldots \qquad (5a)$$

$$C_\nu - C_0 = \alpha - \alpha_0 + 2T(\beta - \beta_0) + \ldots \qquad (6a)$$

$$\ln \xi = -\frac{\lambda_0}{RT} + \frac{\alpha - \alpha_0}{RT} \ln T + \frac{\beta - \beta_0}{R} T + \ldots + i \qquad (7a)$$

In the above formulas, ξ is thus the equilibrium concentration, $\lambda - RT$ is the heat of condensation corrected for outside work, and λ_0 is the heat of condensation at absolute zero; i is an individual integration constant for each substance. C_ν is again the molecular heat of the gas, c_0 that of the liquid or solid substance at temperature T.

Determination of the Integration Constant for Gaseous Systems

Although, as already mentioned above, the values of A and U in general do not equal each other, yet it is still very remarkable that as a rule the difference of the two values remains within moderate limits, at least at temperatures that are not too high. Of course gases and dilute liquids must be omitted in this comparison because here as is known, Q but not A is independent of the concentration. For a long time I have been surprised by the fact that in galvanic combinations in which only solid bodies and very concentrated solutions take part, in the equations of the chemical processes that yield the current the difference between A and U is astonishingly small; moreover, this is reminiscent of the behavior of so-called ideal concentrated solutions. This suggests the hypothesis that in such a case, close to absolute zero, a *complete* agreement of both values will be found and we will have as the limiting law

$$\lim \frac{dA}{dT} = \lim \frac{dQ}{dT} \text{ for } T = 0 \tag{8}$$

Thus, in considering a reaction between pure solid or liquid substances taking place in the pure state, we may use as an example for illustration the formation of solid or liquid (supercooled) water from pure solid or liquid oxygen and hydrogen. We will as usual consider the water formation to be carried out isothermally and reversibly, since we distill hydrogen and oxygen into a space in which chemical equilibrium prevails, and at the same time distill out the water which forms, isothermally and reversibly. If, as above, we denote by ξ the saturation concentration of the individual reacting components, and by K the equilibrium constant at the temperature concerned, we will obtain in the usual way, derived from a homogeneous gaseous system in the equilibrium space

$$A = RT \left(\Sigma v \ln \xi - \ln \mathrm{K} \right) \tag{9}$$

while on the other hand, if as above, Q is the heat effect in a homogeneous gaseous system and λ has the usual meaning, $\lambda - RT$ is the heat of vaporization corrected for the performance of work

$$U = Q - \Sigma v (\lambda - RT)$$

or, according to (5) and (5a),

$$U = Q - \Sigma v (\lambda_0 - \alpha_0 T - \beta_0 T^2) \tag{10}$$

If then we place in equation (9) the values of equation (7) and (7a) and differentiate,

$$-\frac{dA}{dT} = \Sigma v \alpha_0 + \Sigma v \alpha_0 \ln T + R(J - \Sigma v i) + 2T \Sigma v \beta_0 \tag{11}$$

while on the other hand, by differentiation of equation (10) we get

$$\frac{dU}{dT} = \Sigma v \alpha_0 + 2T \Sigma v \beta_0 \tag{12}$$

Now, comparing (11) and (12) on the one hand with (1) and (8) on the other, we obtain what seems to me a result both noteworthy and in many respects surprising. Here, then, A and U at a definite and equal limiting value, absolute zero, converge and the member $\Sigma \nu \alpha_0 \ln T$ is neither infinitely large nor indefinite, that is,

$$\Sigma \nu \alpha_0 = 0 \tag{13}$$

and equally also

$$\ln T \cdot \Sigma \nu \alpha_0 = 0;$$

the Kopp rule that the molecular heats are additive would thus hold strongly at absolute zero, indeed both for liquid (amorphous) and solid bodies.

It thus happens as a further consequence of (12) and (13) that at absolute zero dU/dT converge about zero, and since from (8) the corresponding equation for dA/dT must hold, it follows that

$$J = \Sigma \nu i \tag{14}$$

so that the problem which was posed is solved. Thus the integration constant J, at first completely undetermined, is derived from the sum of the integration constants i, *which are specific for every individual substance and which can be determined by measurements carried out on each individual substance.*

Finally we obtain the two equations

$$\frac{dA}{dT} = -2T\Sigma \nu \beta_0, \frac{dU}{dT} = +2T\Sigma \nu \beta_0$$

which not only show the convergence of dA/dT and dU/dT at a zero value for $T = 0$, but at the same time also indicate a symmetrical behavior of A and U close to absolute zero.

In these considerations in (5) and (5a) members higher than T^2 are omitted, but it can be seen at once that this does not change the argument at all. In what follows we will omit members higher than 8 for lack of sufficient observations.

In the rest of the article, Nernst calculates vapor pressure curves, chemical equilibria in homogeneous gaseous systems, heterogeneous systems, stability of chemical compounds, sublimation equilibrium, and physical mixtures. He concludes the paper as follows:

If we summarize the results of our considerations briefly, we can say that the final goal of thermochemistry, namely the exact calculation of chemical equilibria from the heat effects, seems possible if as an aid we take the new hypothesis, according to which the curves of free and total energy of chemical reactions between pure solid or liquid bodies meet at absolute zero.

For the time being there is lack of enough information for an exact test of the formulas derived with the help of this hypothesis.

Data for the specific heats at low temperature are not available, and so in this work we have derived approximate formulas that can be tested in practice under varied conditions. The connection between heat and chemical affinity appears to be essentially clear and is obviously important.

Practical applications of the principles of thermodynamics led to many important developments in the following years. Two of these are illustrated in the following selections. The recognition of the effect of the presence of large charged ions in cases of osmotic membranes led Donnan to his theory of membrane equilibria, which proved to be of the greatest significance in understanding many biological problems. Giauque applied thermodynamic theory in developing his method of producing temperatures very close to absolute zero. This work had important theoretical and practical results.

The following selection is from pages 1572–1577 in *Journal of the Chemical Society 99*, 1544–1577 (1911).

The Osmotic Pressure and Conductivity of Aqueous Solutions of Congo-Red, and Reversible Membrane Equilibria

FREDERICK GEORGE DONNAN, AND ALBERT BUCKLEY HARRIS

Before discussing another possible explanation of the effects produced by sodium chloride and sodium hydroxide on the osmotic pressure, an account will be given of experiments which have revealed a new and hitherto quite unsuspected phenomenon. It will be shown that when Congo-red is present on one side of a parchment diaphragm, sodium chloride (that is, total Cl'-ion) does not distribute itself in equal concentrations on both sides, although the membrane of parchment paper is perfectly permeable to both Na · and Cl'.

In the first experiment, 5 grams of Merck's Congo-red dissolved in 200 c.c. of distilled water, free from carbon dioxide, were placed inside a parchment dialysing tube suspended in a large beaker containing a litre of pure distilled water. By means of three changes of water the greater portion of the admixed salts was removed, the dialysis being continued for twenty-four hours. Then the outer water was replaced by a litre of N/10-sodium chloride solution.

After thirteen days the chlorine content of the inside and outside liquids was determined. This was done by withdrawing 50 c.c. of each by means of a pipette, evaporating to dryness, heating the residues over a Bunsen flame for about a quarter of an hour (by which procedure the Congo-red from the inner liquid was charred, the residue from the outer liquid being subjected to the same process so as to have similar conditions), extracting with hot water, and estimating as silver chloride by precipitation in the usual way. The results were as follows:

Outer liquid: 5.106 grams of sodium chloride per litre.
Inner liquid: 4.478 grams of sodium chloride per litre.

The concentration of the Congo-red in the inner solution was determined, and found to be 1.074 per cent. At the same time the conductances of a given cell (at 25°) filled with each of the two solutions were determined, with the following results:

Liquid used	Conductance of cell (in mhos)
Inner	12.99×10^{-2}
Outer	12.50×10^{-2}

The foregoing experiment shows that after thirteen days' dialysis the concentration of the sodium chloride in the outer solution is undoubtedly greater than that in the inner solution containing the Congo-red. In order to obviate the natural objection that in the above experiment the sodium chloride might have been still diffusing into the inner solution, two further experiments were made, in which the concentration of the sodium chloride was initially higher in the inner solution (containing the Congo-red). In the first experiment, a mixture of approximately 2.8 grams of pure Congo-red and 7.2 grams of sodium chloride dissolved in 200 c.c. of conductivity water was placed inside the dialyser and a litre of pure water outside. After six days' dialysis the inner liquid contained 5.136 grams of sodium chloride per litre, and the outer liquid 5.728 grams. The concentration of Congo-red in the inner liquid was 0.917 gram per 100 c.c.

In the next experiment the inner solution consisted initially of about 2.1 grams of pure Congo-red and 3.9 grams of sodium chloride, dissolved in 200 c.c. of pure water, the outer liquid being, as before, a litre of pure water. After five days' dialysis the inner liquid contained 2.53 grams of sodium chloride per litre, and the outer liquid 3.03 grams. The concentration of Congo-red in the inner liquid was 0.875 gram per 100 c.c.

These results show that we are dealing with a reversible equilibrium, and that the equilibrium state corresponds with a greater concentration of sodium chloride on the opposite side of the membrane to the Congo-red. Now this unequal distribution will clearly set up, in the osmotic pressure experiments, a counter osmotic pressure, which will make the observed osmotic pressure lower than that corresponding with the Congo-red.

The following calculation will serve to indicate the amount of this counter pressure. Consider the first of the three experiments given above. The osmotic pressure (at $0°$) of the outer solution of sodium chloride will be $22.4 \times 760 \times 5.106/58.5 \times i_1$ mm. Hg, where $i_1 =$ van't Hoff's factor for a solution of this concentration. The osmotic pressure due to the sodium chloride concentration in the inner solution will be similarly $22.4 \times 760 \times 4.478/58.5 \times i_2$. Putting $i_1 = i_2 = 1.85$, we get for the counter osmotic pressure at $17°$ (in mm. Hg.)

$$22.4 \times 760 \times \frac{290}{273} \times \frac{0.628}{58.5} \times 1.85,$$

or 359 mm. Now the osmotic pressure at $17°$ of the Congo-red solution present in the experiment (containing 1.074 per cent, of Congo-red) would, according to the data given previously, amount to about 290 mm. Hence the approximately N/12-solution of sodium chloride of the experiment would more than suffice to annul the osmotic pressure of the 1.074 per cent Congo-red solution.

These considerations show that the unequal concentrations of an electrolyte (such as sodium chloride) with a common ion, which exist at equilibrium on either side of the membrane in presence of Congo-red on one side only, are sufficient to explain the apparent lowering effect of these electrolytes on the osmotic pressure of a solution of Congo-red. The results obtained by Bayliss with Congo-red and by Biltz and Vegesack with benzopurpurine are now intelligible, without any special assumptions as to the effect of the electrolytes on the aggregation of the molecules of the electrolytic colloid. It is, of course, possible that some such aggregation may occur, but the results of the present paper show that the unequal distribution discovered in the present work is a sufficient explanation.

The unequal distribution can be easily shown to be thermodynamically necessary.[1] Suppose we have on one side of a membrane a solution of the salt NaX, the membrane being supposed permeable to Na ·, but impermeable to X' and to undissociated NaX. Let now

---

[1] In a paper which is ready for publication, the thermodynamical theory of such "membrane equilibria" will be more fully considered.

a solution of sodium chloride be put on the other side of the membrane, the latter being supposed permeable to Cl′ and sodium chloride. The initial state can be represented as follows:

Na ·	Na ·
X′	Cl′
(1)	(2)

Na·- and Cl′-ions will now begin to diffuse from (2) to (1). Equilibrium will be attained when the work gained by the isothermal reversible transport of δn gram-mol. Cl′-ion from (2) to (1) is equal to the work required for the isothermal reversible transport of δn gram-mol. Na·-ion from (2) to (1), that is:

$$\delta n \,.\, RT \log \frac{[\text{Na·}]_1}{[\text{Na·}]_2} = \delta n \,.\, RT \log \frac{[\text{Cl′}]_2}{[\text{Cl′}]_1},$$

where the square brackets indicate molar concentrations at equilibrium.

$$\text{Hence:} \quad \frac{[\text{Na·}]_1}{[\text{Na·}]_2} = \frac{[\text{Cl′}]_2}{[\text{Cl′}]_1}.$$

Now since at equilibrium we have in (1) both NaX and sodium chloride, in general $[\text{Na·}]_1 > [\text{Cl′}]_1$. Also from the above $[\text{Cl′}]_2{}^2 = [\text{Na·}]_1 \times [\text{Cl′}]_1$. Hence $[\text{Cl′}]_2 > [\text{Cl′}]_1$. For highly dissociated solutions we shall therefore find the total "chlorine" concentration in (2) greater than in (1). This has actually been shown to be the case in the experiments described in this paper.

The following selection is from pages 1175–1176, 1179–1180, and 1184–1185 in *The Journal of the American Chemical Society 57*, 1175–1185 (1935).

The Production of Temperatures below One Degree Absolute by Adiabatic Demagnetization of Gadolinium Sulfate

W. F. GIAUQUE AND D. P. MACDOUGALL

This paper contains a description of the experimental methods and apparatus used in the initial demonstration of the feasibility of producing temperatures considerably below one degree absolute by adiabatic demagnetization of suitable paramagnetic substances. Two preliminary reports have been published elsewhere. More recently adiabatic demagnetization has been used to produce temperatures below one degree absolute by de Haas, Wiersma and Kramers and by Kurti and Simon. The experiments described in this paper cover only the work of the first half of the year 1933 and many later results will appear shortly.

The idea of utilizing the thermal effects associated with magnetization for producing these low temperatures was first proposed by Giauque. Debye has independently arrived at similar conclusions. Briefly, the method depends on the fact that any substance whose magnetic susceptibility, χ, varies with temperature exhibits a thermal effect on magnetization. The entropy change is given by the thermodynamic relation,

$$\left(\frac{\partial S}{\partial \mathbf{H}}\right)_T = \mathbf{H}\left(\frac{6\chi}{\partial T}\right)_{1^+} \tag{1}$$

where S represents entropy and H the magnetic field strength.

In the normal case Curie's law

$$\chi T = \text{constant} = C \tag{2}$$

is obeyed approximately and heat is evolved during isothermal magnetization. However, quantum statistical situations are readily imaginable where the application of a field would produce cooling. In fact magnetic susceptibilities which decrease with decreasing temperature are experimentally known in several substances. While such cases are of interest and perhaps of experimental importance, it is the former type which has been utilized in the work described here.

From Equations 1 and 2

$$\Delta S = -\frac{C}{2T^2}(\mathbf{H}_2{}^2 - \mathbf{H}_1{}^2) \tag{3}$$

One may observe that ΔS is 10^5 times larger near one degree absolute than at ordinary temperatures. It may be shown that the constant C is roughly proportional to the square of the atomic magnetic moment for larger values of this quantity. It should be emphasized that Equation 3 is very approximate since even in the ideal case the susceptibility is dependent on field strength. However, the above is useful in gaining a sense of proportion about the factors involved in the process.

$Gd_2(SO_4)_3 \cdot 8H_2O$ was used for the first measurements because this substance has been subjected to many careful and extensive magnetic investigations by Kamerlingh Onnes and his co-workers. They have shown that this substance obeys Curie's law from ordinary temperatures to $1.3°K$. within the limits of experimental measurement. In particular, the measurements of Woltjer and Kamerlingh Onnes were of great interest since they investigated the approach to saturation at liquid helium temperatures. These measurements and their thermodynamic and quantum interpretation have been discussed by Giauque, who also calculated the theoretical entropy of magnetization. Giauque and Clark determined the heat capacity of $Gd_2(SO_4)_3 \cdot 8H_2O$ down to $14°K$. From these measurements it may be shown that what may be called the ordinary heat capacity is negligible below one degree absolute.

From the data mentioned above it is evident that we have to deal with a system in which the effects are, to a high degree of approximation, due to the gadolinium atoms alone and their interactions on each other. That these interactions will occur sufficiently to destroy the ideal characteristics of the system above $0°K$. is a necessary consequence of the third law of thermodynamics. Simon and Kurti have measured the heat capacity of $Gd_2(SO_4)_3 \cdot 8H_2O$ at the temperatures of liquid helium and the results indicate that the gadolinium atoms have sufficient interaction to produce a marked effect even above one degree absolute.

The apparatus is then described and illustrated with Figs. 1 and 2, which are not included here.

Experimental Procedure and Results. The first experiment was carried out with coil I on the apparatus described above and in Fig. 2. The 61 g. of $Gd_2(SO_4)_3 \cdot 8H_2O$ was enclosed with about 10^{-4} mole of helium gas in a sealed glass tube. Liquid hydrogen was placed in container D, Fig. 1, and finally the liquid helium was transferred until the apparatus was immersed. The liquid helium was transferred very easily through a vacuum-jacketed tube about four meters long. About half of the exterior of this tube was at or near room temperature. The liquid helium was produced in a liquefier of about seven liters per hour capacity. This liquefier will be described in a later paper.

The sample cooled very slowly as it approached the temperature of the helium bath and it soon became evident that the thermal contact through the conical bottom was not working satisfactorily. Helium gas which had been pumped from the space surrounding the sample before the addition of the liquid helium was readmitted. This greatly facilitated the cooling but there was evidence that the pressed crystalline gadolinium sulfate octahydrate had adsorbed most of the helium within the sample tube. A later experiment with a tube leading into the same sample showed that this had been the case and that cooling occurred very rapidly when a small amount of helium gas was present. Somewhat to our surprise, little difficulty was found in obtaining a vacuum better than 10^{-5} mm. in the insulating space at the temperatures of liquid helium and for this reason no further attempts were made to obtain thermal contact by means of the conical bottoms.

In the first exploratory experiment on March 19, 1933, the full field of about 8000 gauss was used in all cooling experiments. The liquid helium was boiling under a somewhat reduced pressure, the magnitude of which was not accurately known for most of the measurements. Cooling experiments were carried out at intervals between 3:00 A.M. and 9:50 A.M. In each case the field was applied, the heat developed was allowed to escape by means of a small pressure of helium gas in the insulating vacuum space, a vacuum was pumped and the current turned off. The first four trials were rather impatiently made at about ten-minute intervals and neither good equilibrium nor a good vacuum could be obtained in this total time. The temperatures produced were 0.72, 0.68, 0.67 and 0.65°K. The bath temperature, a short time after the above measurements, was read on a helium vapor pressure thermometer and found to be 3.2°K. (previously given as 3.4°K.). As mentioned above, the helium within the sample tube appeared to have been adsorbed so that equilibrium conditions were very unsatisfactory. On lengthening the time for equilibrium with the bath and for evacuation, temperatures obtained at about half-hour intervals were 0.612, 0.575, 0.554, 0.548, 0.540 and 0.530°K. At least part of the progressive lowering which occurred in successive measurements was due to a gradually lowering bath temperature. The bath temperature at the time of the first observations was probably about 4°K.

It was evident that much lower temperatures could be produced by lowering the starting temperature and that better thermal equilibrium was desirable.

The apparatus was altered by sealing a 3-mm. glass line to the sample tube. This not only permitted control of the gas pressure in the sample tube but allowed the vapor pressure of liquid helium to be accurately compared with the magnetic temperature scale. A better vacuum pump was connected to the liquid helium bath but otherwise the apparatus was left as in the first experiment. On April 8 the apparatus was again cooled and this time the sample approached the helium bath temperature with great rapidity.

Starting at a temperature of 1.8°K. (previously given as about 2°K.)

and about 8000 gauss a temperature of 0.422°K. was obtained on reducing the field to zero. During this experiment a considerable amount of helium gas was in the sample tube and the connecting vacuum line. The condensation of this helium prevented a lower temperature, but of still greater interest was the fact that most of the helium did not condense. When the helium was pumped out, the same field and starting temperature produced a final temperature of 0.346°K. It became evident that in the experiment producing 0.422°K. the outer portion of the sample had condensed helium and as a result had not cooled very much while the interior, blocked off, and lacking a mechanism for rapid equilibrium cooled considerably. The temperature represented an average. That this explanation was correct was also shown by the fact that, when helium gas was admitted to the insulating space, it required sixteen minutes to warm the sample to the bath temperature 1.81°K. In later work, with small crystals, the time of warming in a similar experiment would be about a minute. The above explanation was also substantiated by other cooling experiments with various amounts of helium gas present and as a result experiments with the pressed crystalline material were discontinued after April 9. It appears that the very high pressure used in making the cylindrical sample had fractured the material into countless small pieces, thus increasing adsorption surface and also making thermal conduction very difficult. No such evidence of these conditions has been observed in later work with small crystals of several substances.

Further refinements and details of experimental technique are described, and the paper is summarized as follows.

Summary

This paper contains a description of methods and apparatus for producing temperatures in the range below 1° absolute by adiabatic demagnetization of suitable paramagnetic substances.

A description of the first exploratory and very successful experiments demonstrating the feasibility of this method has been presented. The working substance was $Gd_2(SO_4)_3 \cdot 8H_2O$.

An inductance coil surrounding the sample but thermally insulated from it by an evacuated space has been used to measure the differential magnetic susceptibility.

The variation of magnetic susceptibility with field strength gave no indication of ferromagnetism in $Gd_2(SO_4)_3 \cdot 8H_2O$.

The reversible character of the magnetization is shown by the fact that results obtained with alternating fields of 60 and 1000 cycles per second were in agreement.

A calorimetric experiment, in which a 60-cycle field with a maximum of 52 gauss was applied, showed that of the maximum energy, $\chi H_{max}^2/2$, temporarily withdrawn from the field by the substance at each alternation, less than 0.01 % was lost by magnetic hysteresis or eddy currents.

The lowest temperature produced in the above work was 0.242°K. A starting temperature of 1.29°K. and a field of about 8000 gauss gave this result. The lower temperature is based on the assumption of Curie's law.

Measurements by means of an inductance bridge have permitted a precision of about 0.0003° in temperature measurements at the lower temperatures.

Exact equations have been given to permit the determination of thermodynamic temperatures corresponding to magnetic susceptibilities. Complete experimental application of this method has been left for a later paper. Here the equations have been used to extend the Curie scale to the determination of temperature from differential susceptibility measurements in the presence of a magnetic field.

Tables have been presented showing the change of temperature, differential susceptibility, energy and heat content accompanying adiabatic magnetization from a number of temperatures below 1°K.

The interaction of gadolinium atoms gives rise to energy levels whose separation is comparable to kT at temperatures below 1°K. This effect which tends to make the magnetic system approach zero entropy in accordance with the requirements of the third law of thermodynamics leads to a considerable heat capacity below 1°K. This heat capacity has been determined to 0.3°K. by means of a series of adiabatic demagnetizations from known starting temperatures and magnetic fields. The entropy corresponding to the initial conditions being known, the variation of entropy over the low temperature range is thus determined. $dS/d \ln T = C$ approaches a maximum of 1.60 cal./deg. per one-half mole of $Gd_2(SO_4)_3 \cdot 8H_2O$ at 0.3°K.

It has been made evident that, when obviously practicable improved experimental conditions become available, the temperature range at present open for various investigations can be greatly extended. The term greatly seems very applicable since temperature range is most significant and should be thought of in logarithmic increments. On this proper basis there is still infinite room for extension.

ELECTROLYTES. The Arrhenius dissociation theory was enthusiastically received by most chemists at the end of the nineteenth century because it explained so much of the behavior of acids, bases, and salts in solution. However, it was still unsatisfactory in some respects, chiefly its inability to account for the behavior of strong electrolytes. Niels Bjerrum in 1918 with his osmotic coefficient and G. N. Lewis a little later with his concept of activity coefficients overcame this difficulty to some extent, and Debye and Hückel in 1923 gave a generally satisfactory theory to account for the behavior of strong electrolytes. As modified by Onsager shortly afterward, this theory served as the basis for further developments in this field. The original paper of Debye and Hückel was highly mathematical, but in a footnote Debye told how the theory has been evolved. The footnote is given here, followed by the somewhat less mathematical exposition of the theory that Debye presented to the Faraday Society in 1927.

The following selection is from pages 321–324 in *Zeitschrift für Elektrochemie 24*, 321–328 (1918).

The Dissociation of Strong Electrolytes

NIELS BJERRUM

The theory that has had the greatest significance for the development of chemistry during recent decades is surely the theory of free ions introduced by Arrhenius. For the first time by using it we have obtained a true understanding of the nature of acids, bases, and salts, and have learned the true difference between strong and weak acids as well as between normal and complex salts.

If the degree of dissociation, α, of a weak electrolyte is calculated from the electrolytic conductivity by the equation

$$\alpha = \frac{\mu}{\mu_\infty}$$

the degree of dissociation determined in this way varies with the concentration exactly as it should according to the mass action law of Guldberg and Waage; this behavior has in its time led to many victories for the ionic theory. However, if the degree of dissociation of a strong electrolyte is calculated in the same way, a number of anomalies appear that have created considerable difficulty for the theory: the degree of dissociation calculated from conductivity usually does not agree with the degree of dissociation calculated from osmotic pressure as determined by the equation

$$\alpha = i - 1$$

in which i is the so-called van't Hoff coefficient, and none of the observed values agrees with the mass action law. In what follows we will attempt to show how this and other difficulties of the Arrhenius theory result from the fact that in strong electrolytes it has erroneously been considered that $\mu:\mu_\infty$ and $i - 1$ are degrees of dissociation. The fact that $\mu:\mu_\infty$ and $i - 1$ in strong electrolytes always decrease more than 1 with increasing concentration should not be explained as a consequence of an increasing dissociation, but can be explained in another way, and a reconsideration of the foregoing material has led me to the view that the strong electrolytes, considered practically, must be completely dissociated. This new view can therefore appropriately *be called the hypothesis of complete dissociation of strong electrolytes.*

Foundations of the Hypothesis

A number of studies on salts of chromium led me in 1906 to the result that strong electrolytes in both dilute and concentrated solutions showed the color of ions only when they had not formed complex compounds in the solution; Hantzsch came to the same results at this time from other studies. On the basis of this fact, that the color of an electrolyte is independent of its concentration, in 1909 I proposed the hypothesis that strong electrolytes in solution conjecturally are split into ions (insofar as no complex compounds have been formed). This hypothesis meant that the influence of concentration on molecular conductivity and on the van't Hoff coefficient i had to be explained differently than before and even then it seemed that these effects probably would have to be explained as a result of the electrical forces between the ions. This was supported by the results, previously difficult to understand, that it is chiefly the electrical properties (number of ions, magnitude of their electrical charge, and dielectric constant of the solvent) that are decisive for the effects. It was further emphasized that the anomalies of the strong electrolytes drop away if $\mu:\mu_\infty$ and $i - 1$ are no longer considered as measures of the degree of dissociation. However, it is naturally clear that the justification for the assumption of a hypothesis of complete dissociation of strong electrolytes depends on whether it is possible to explain in a plausible way the magnitudes of $\mu:\mu_\infty$ and $i - 1$ as a consequence of the electrical charge of the ions.

For some time I have occupied myself once more with this hypothesis and I have succeeded in calculating approximately how much the electrical force between the ions must reduce the osmotic pressure; and it was found, that the effect had somewhat the magnitude that it should. After I had progressed this far, I discovered that meanwhile Milner in the years 1912 and 1913 had performed a similar calculation and since his calculation showed a considerably higher degree of accuracy than mine, I have based what follows on his results.

The decrease in osmotic pressure brought about by the electrical charges of the ions, which can appropriately be called the Milner effect, is shown in Fig. 90 by the solid curve; the curve gives the decrease for one of the two monovalent ions of the electrolyte used. For comparison the crosses give the decrease found experimentally by the freezing point determination for potassium chloride. As can

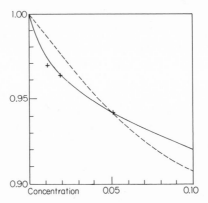

Fig. 90. Fall in osmotic pressure
—— according to Milner
– – – according to the mass action
law
+   + according to freezing point
measurements.

be seen, the Milner effect has the correct order of magnitude, especially for the concentrations, which are neither so small that the experimental determinations are not certain, nor so large that Milner's calculation, the accuracy of which falls with increasing concentrations, is too unreliable. The broken curve shows how the osmotic pressure should behave if explained by the assumption of undissociated molecules formed according to the law of Guldberg and Waage. This curve fits much worse than the Milner curve, although in calculating it a corresponding selected dissociation constant was used while no such choice was used in the Milner curve.

The Milner effect is a direct consequence of the fact that the ions attract and repel each other according to Coulomb's law, and if we explain the behavior of the osmotic pressure by the assumption of incomplete dissociation, then we must necessarily first explain how we can disregard the Milner effect.

If we assume that strong electrolytes are completely ionized, we must also be able to explain the alteration of the conductivity with concentration as a consequence of the electrical charge of the ions. Hertz in 1912 studied the influence of conductivity of ions by the electrical forces that are active between them and he found that this effect, which can appropriately be called the Hertz effect, must act in such a way that the conductivity of the ions decreases with increasing concentration. He has also derived the formula for this effect and shown that for an explanation of the experimentally observed behavior of the conductivity, e.g., for sodium chloride, it can be used; but since his formula contains quantities that are known only slightly (e.g., the free path of the ions in solution), and since the values that must be used for these quantities are not the most plausible ones, it is necessary to have further investigation before it can be safely considered that the Hertz effect can fully explain the alteration of the conductivity of strong electrolytes with concentration.

After we have seen that freezing point determinations and conductivity determinations, based on the Milner effect and the Hertz effect, are not suitable for measuring the degree of dissociation of strong electrolytes, we must still consider how the third method that has been used for this behaves, the one that depends on the catalytic activity of ions. Since it is particularly the hydrogen ions that act catalytically, there has been an especial attempt to determine the degree of dissociation of acids in this way. Most investigators who have thus studied strong acids have found that the catalytic activity of the acids is proportional to the gross concentration of the acids without regard to the fact that the molecular conductivity of the acids varies within wide limits. As an example of this, I give some measurements of Goldschmidt and Thuesen on the esterifying action of hydrogen chloride on organic acids dissolved in methyl alcohol (Table 1).

Snethlage has brought out emphatically the remarkable facts in this respect and has shown that this means that strong electrolytes either are not dissociated at all, or are completely dissociated. But while Snethlage prefers the first assumption on grounds to which I can give no weight, my view is that strong electrolytes are completely ionized, since it seems to me to be impossible to give up the Arrhenius idea of free ions. If we wish to preserve $i - 1$ and $\mu : \mu_\infty$ as measures of the degree of dissociation of strong acids, then to explain the catalytic measurements we must assume that it is not only the hydrogen ions, but also the undissociated acid molecules, that catalyze ester formation, an auxiliary hypothesis that can be entirely set aside by the use of the ionic theory.

Briefly, we can now give the following ideas on the basis of what can be said of the degree of dissociation of strong electrolytes:

The osmotic measurements and the catalytic measurements indicate complete dissociation, and the conductivity measurements do not contradict a complete dissociation.

Anyone who wishes to maintain the $i - 1$ and $\mu:\mu_\infty$ as measures of the degree of dissociation of a strong electrolyte must first establish clearly how the Milner effect and the Hertz effect can occur, and then must adduce the auxiliary hypothesis of the catalytic action of undissociated acid molecules in order to explain the catalytic measurements, and after these difficulties have been overcome, it is still necessary to find by suitable auxiliary hypotheses usable explanations for the many "anomalies of strong electrolytes."

Table I

Esterifying action of hydrogen chloride in methyl alcohol

| c | k/c for | | | $\mu:\mu_\infty$ for hydrochloric acid |
	isobutyric acid	benzoic acid	acetic acid	
0.1	—	0.308	—	0.601
0.05	31.0	0.311	97.1	0.672
0.025	31.7	—	100.2	0.734
0.01	—	—	92.7	0.806

c = molar concentration of hydrogen chloride
k = rate constant in esterification

Program for Work on This Hypothesis

If we assume that strong electrolytes are fully dissociated, we can no longer understand the degree of dissociation as $\mu:\mu_\infty$. The value $\mu:\mu_\infty$ is then only a coefficient that gives the ratio of the conductivity of the ions in the solution under consideration to their conductivity in an infinitely dilute solution; this quantity can appropriately be called the conductivity coefficient and designate it as f_μ. The van't Hoff coefficient, i, which gives the osmotic action of the electrolyte (e.g., its influence on the freezing point) can no longer equal $1 + x$, where x is the degree of dissociation; we must calculate with an osmotic coefficient, $f_0 = p : p_0$, where p is the osmotic pressure of the solution and p_0 the osmotic pressure we should have if the ions behave like charged molecules. (For binary electrolytes, $f_0 = i/2$.) Finally, we must introduce an activity coefficient, f_a, which gives the relation between the active mass and the concentration of the ions, since we must not assume that this relation is equal to the degree of dissociation defined by the conductivity coefficient. (In certain cases it may be practical to calculate with $-\log f_a$ instead of the activity coefficient f_a, and this value can appropriately be called the exponential variation or potential variation)

$$f_a = \frac{\mu}{\mu_\infty}; \; f_0 = \frac{p}{p_0} \left(= \frac{2}{i} \right) f_a = \frac{\text{active mass}}{\text{concentration}}$$

The hypothesis now sets us the task of determining the values of these coefficients by experimental investigations and theoretical discussions and finding the governing laws for them; thus among other things determining whether relations exist between the different coefficients. As far as I can now judge the materials, all these coefficients depend chiefly on the ionic concentration of the solution, the valence of the ions, and the dielectric constant of the solvent, and only to a slight extent on the other properties of the ions, e.g., weight and spacial content. These relationships signify that it is easy to obtain an idea of the values of these coefficients in an electrolyte solution. A formula like

$$-\log f_a = 26 \cdot \frac{n^2}{K} \sqrt[3]{C_{\text{ion}}}$$

where n is the valence of the ions, K the dielectric constant of the solvent, and C_{ion} the ionic concentration of the solution, in many cases gives an approximation of the value of the activity coefficient.

For the value of the conductivity coefficient we know there is a great mass of experimental material, and the laws governing its value are well known through the studies of Walden and Noyes. This coefficient has been used up to now in a large number of calculations in which the activity coefficient should actually have been used, e.g., in calculations of the equilibrium constant of homogeneous and heterogeneous chemical equilibria and in calculations of electromotive force; up to now it has been assumed that these coefficients are identical; however, this is far from being the case, and perhaps a considerable number of the anomalies for which we must assume a hypothesis of the effect of neutral salts on chemical equilibria will disappear if we calculate with the correct value of the activity coefficient instead of with the conductivity coefficient.

Methods for determining the activity coefficient experimentally are described in the remainder of the paper.

The following selection is from pages 1112–1114 in *The Journal of the American Chemical Society 43*, 1112–1154 (1921).

The Activity Coefficient of Strong Electrolytes

GILBERT N. LEWIS AND MERLE RANDALL

It has long been recognized that the formulas which first sprang from Arrhenius' theory of electrolytic dissociation, and which very satisfactorily accounted for the behavior of weak electrolytes, were by no means adequate to account for the behavior of strong electrolytes. This was particularly the case with the Ostwald dilution law,

$$\frac{\left(\frac{\Lambda}{\Lambda^0}\right)^2 \cdot m}{1 - \frac{\Lambda}{\Lambda^0}} = K_\Lambda \tag{1}$$

where Λ and Λ^0 are the equivalent conductivities at the molality[1] m, and at zero molality, and K_Λ must be a constant if two assumptions are correct: (1) that the molality of each ion is independent of the concentration, and (2) that for each substance concerned the molality is proportional to the "active mass" or, as we should now say, to the activity.

To those who have not examined this question closely it may be surprising to learn how far K_Λ is from being a constant. For potassium chloride, at three concentrations, $m = 0.001$, 0.01 and 0.1, K_Λ is 0.046, 0.148 and 0.528, respectively.

It will be seen that K_Λ increases nearly 12-fold when the molality changes 100-fold, and while these figures might be changed materially on account of possible errors in Λ^0, such uncertainties are in no

---

[1] The term molality is used to express the number of mols of solute per 1000 g. of water.

way adequate to account for the enormous departure from the Ostwald dilution law. It must, therefore, be concluded for such strong electrolytes, either that Λ (because of some variation in the mobility of the ions) does not measure the ion concentration, or that the substances concerned are very far from obeying the ideal laws of the dilute solution.

These very peculiar characteristics of strong electrolytes in aqueous solutions, together with the presumption that the constituents of an electrolytic solution, even at low concentrations, would depart radically from the ideal solution, led Lewis to propose a general study, by purely thermodynamic methods, of the activities of such constituents. In 1912 he collected the meager data which were then available for such thermodynamic treatment, and showed that in all cases the activity of the ions is very appreciably less than the ion concentration as calculated from Λ/Λ^0. He employed in these calculations measurements of electromotive force, of the solubility of salts in the presence of other salts, and of freezing points; showing how freezing-point data could be exactly employed in these thermodynamic calculations.

Since the publication of that paper an extensive literature on the subject has developed, and the data obtained not only confirm Lewis' conclusions, but furnish the abundant material for the calculation of ionic activities which we are to employ.

Notation and Conventions

It is our custom to denote the activity of a solute by a_2. If this solute is a substance like sodium chloride we may denote by a_+ and a_-, respectively, the activities of cation and anion, while a_2 is called the activity of undissociated NaCl, or more simply, of NaCl. In the case of a binary electrolyte like this, the exact thermodynamic equation of chemical equilibrium takes the form

$$\frac{a_+ a_-}{a_2} = K, \tag{2}$$

where at any given temperature K is an exact constant.

We are using the term activity in the newer sense of "relative activity." Thus, at infinite dilution, we make the activity of each ion of sodium chloride equal to its molality, which, assuming complete dissociation, is the molality of NaCl. Now in the complete absence of any reliable information as to the *concentration* of the undissociated salt, we shall find it extremely convenient to choose our standard state of that substance, so that K in equation (2) becomes unity.[1] We thus define the activity of NaCl as the product of the activities of its two ions,

$$a_+ a_- = a_2 \qquad (3)$$

At finite concentrations the two ions may not have the same activity, and it is often expedient to consider the geometrical mean of the two ion activities, which we may denote by $a_\pm$ and define by the equation

$$a_\pm = (a_+ a_-)^{\frac{1}{2}} = a_2^{\frac{1}{2}} \qquad (4)$$

The mean activity of the ions $a_\pm$, divided by the molality of the electrolyte, gives a quantity which has been called the thermodynamic degree of dissociation, since it may be used to replace the degree of dissociation as used in the older approximate formulas. This quantity has also been called the activity coefficient[2] and, in order to avoid any implication as to the molecular species which may be present, this is the term we shall ordinarily employ henceforth. It will be denoted by γ.

So far we have been considering the case of a binary electrolyte like KCl or $CuSO_4$. When we treat the more complicated types, such as K_2SO_4, $K_4Fe(CN)_6$ and $La_2(SO_4)_3$ our equations become a little more complicated. If an electrolyte dissociates into $\nu = \nu_+ + \nu_-$ ions according to the equation $X = \nu_+ X_+ + \nu_- X_-$, we write for equilibrium

$$a_+^{\nu_+} a_-^{\nu_-} = a_2; \ a_+ = (a_2)^{\frac{1}{\nu}} \qquad (5)$$

If now we wish to define the activity coefficient, γ, so that in dilute solutions it may be regarded as a thermodynamic degree of dissociation, and become equal to unity at infinite dilution, we must no longer write it equal to $a_\pm/m$. In a solution of barium chloride in which the molality m is very small, $a_+ = m$, $a_- = 2m$, and $a_\pm = [(m)(2m)^2]^{\frac{1}{3}} = 2^{\frac{2}{3}}m$. By defining the activity coefficient by the equation $\gamma = a_\pm/(2^{\frac{2}{3}}m)$ it becomes equal to unity at infinite dilution. In the case of lanthanum sulfate, $La_2(SO_4)_3$, which gives 2 positive

---

[1] Likewise it is thermodynamically convenient, in the case of strong electrolytes, to take the activity of any assumed intermediate ion, such as $BaCl^+$, as equal to the product of the activities of Ba^{++} and Cl^-.

[2] The term activity coefficient has been used in two senses, sometimes to mean the ion activity divided by the assumed ion molality, and sometimes to express the ion activity divided by the gross molality of the electrolyte. The latter usage, to which we shall find it desirable to adhere in the thermodynamic work, is more expressly designated by Brönsted as the *stoichiometrical* activity coefficient.

and 3 negative ions, the corresponding factor is $(2^2 3^3)^{\frac{1}{2}}$. In general we shall define the activity coefficient by the equation

$$\gamma = \frac{a_\pm}{m(\nu_+{}^{\nu+}\nu_-{}^{\nu-})^{\frac{1}{\nu}}} \tag{6}$$

We might have made this derivation clearer if we had introduced the individual activity coefficients of the several ions. If in a solution of a chloride the stoichiometrical molality of the chloride present is designated by m_-, and if the activity of the chloride is a_-, the activity coefficient of chloride ion is defined as $\gamma_- = a_-/m_-$. Furthermore, if we define the mean molality of the ions, as we have their mean activity, and write it as $m_\pm$, it is readily seen that

$$m_\pm = m(\nu_+{}^{\nu+}\nu_-{}^{\nu-})^{\frac{1}{\nu}} \tag{7}$$

and in place of equation 6 we may write for the mean activity coefficient (which we might for consistancy have called $\nu_\pm$)

$$\nu = a_\pm/m_\pm = (\nu_+{}^{\nu+}\nu_-{}^{\nu-})^{\frac{1}{\nu}} \tag{8}$$

The rest of the paper is devoted to the practical determination of the activity coefficients of various electrolytes.

The paper in which Debye and Hückel presented their theory was entitled "The Theory of Electrolytes. I. Freezing Point Lowering and Related Phenomena." It appeared in *Physikalische Zeitschrift 24*, 185–206 (1923). The footnote at the beginning of the article reads as follows.

"I became interested in these considerations at a lecture by E. Bauer at the Physical Society on the work of Ghosh. The general view-point which emerged from this for calculation of freezing point lowering and conductivity led me, among other things, to the limiting law with the square root of the concentration. In the winter of 1921 I was able to report on this at a colloquium. With the active help of my assistant, Dr. E. Hückel, I reached a detailed consideration of the results and their significance in the winter of 1922."

The following selection is from pages 334–339 in *Transactions of the Faraday Society 23*, 334–340 (1927).

Report on Conductivity of Strong Electrolytes in Dilute Solutions

P. DEBYE

1. It is a well-established fact, that the change of the *activity coefficient* of ions with concentration in highly dissociated solutions

can be represented by a square root law. The experimental evidence supports the view that for the change in *conductivity* of strong electrolytes with concentration Kohlrausch's square root law holds. The interionic attraction theory of activity gives an explanation of the square root law, based on the fact that the thickness of the ionic atmosphere of mean charge surrounding each ion has to be proportional to the square root of the concentration, if the principal forces between ions are the ordinary Coulomb forces. In this way, remembering that Coulomb's law puts the forces inversely proportional to the square of the distance, a close correspondence is brought forward between the exponent 2 in this law and the exponent $\frac{1}{2}$ of the concentration in the activity law. The occurrence of the same exponent in Kohlrausch's law makes it at once probable that its explanation has to be found along the same lines. This report contains an account of the reasoning by which Coulomb's law and the square root law in conductivity have been connected.

2. In the following pages it will be necessary to refer constantly to what we will call the ionic atmosphere and the space distribution of its charge density. We may therefore begin by defining this density. Suppose a straight line of length r connected with the ion in such a way, that during the migration of the particle the direction in space of this line as well as its length is always kept the same. At the end of this line we imagine an element of volume. Now considering the ion with its element for a certain time, we find that sometimes an excess of positive and sometimes an excess of negative electric charges is contained within the element. Taking the time integral of this charge and dividing this integral by the whole time of observation, we obtain the mean charge of the element of volume. What we call the density of the ionic atmosphere is this mean charge divided by the volume of our element. It is obvious that so far as Coulomb forces alone are considered, the density in the ionic atmosphere will be of opposite sign to the charge of the central ion and will increase with decreasing distance from the centre.

3. Between the electrostatic potential at the surface of the ion in an infinitely dilute solution (considering the ion for the sake of clearness of the underlying picture as a sphere with a surface charge) and this potential for a finite concentration will exist a difference due to the existence of the oppositely charged ionic atmosphere. The whole charge of this atmosphere must necessarily be equal and opposite to the charge of the central ion. So the difference between the two potentials, *i.e.*, the potential due to the atmosphere, will depend chiefly on the distance over which this total charge is spread out. Under certain limiting conditions, which we have not to discuss

here, it is possible to show that the significant factor in representing the decrease in density with the distance is the exponential $\varepsilon^{-\kappa r}$ wherein κ has the dimension of a reciprocal length and is given by the formula

$$\kappa^2 = \frac{4\pi}{DkT} \Sigma n_i e_i{}^2$$

(D = dielectric constant of the solvent, $k = 1.37 \times 10^{-16}$ = Boltzmann's constant, T = absolute temperature, n_i = number of ions of kind i in 1 c.c., e_i = charge of one ion of kind i.)

For a uni-univalent electrolyte of concentration γ calculated in mols. per litre and in the solvent water, we find

$$K = 3.27 \cdot 10^7 \sqrt{\gamma} \frac{1}{K} = \frac{3.06 \cdot 10^{-8}}{\sqrt{\gamma}} \text{ cm.}$$

We will call the length $1/K$ the radius of the ionic atmosphere. As the potential due to a charge E at a distance r in a medium of dielectric constant D is equal to E/Dr, we should expect that the potential of the central ion due to the charged atmosphere of thickness $1/K$ is proportional to

$$-\frac{EK}{D}$$

It can be shown that this potential is not only *proportional* to the given expression, but that it is *exactly equal* to it, if now by E we denote the charge of the central ion. The activity of an ion is very closely connected with its potential, and as K is proportional to the square root of the concentration, the given expression involves an explanation for the square-root law in activity.

4. Now coming to the discussion of the interionic attraction theory of conductivity, we may begin with the statement that in a most general way the conductivity λ of any electrolyte solution can always be expressed by the formula

$$\lambda = \sum \frac{n_i e_i}{\rho_i}$$

(λ = conductivity, n_i = number of ions in 1 c.c. of kind i, e_i = charge of one ion of kind i, ρ_i = friction coefficient of an ion of kind i). The notation ρ_i is introduced in such a way that ρ_i, multiplied by the mean velocity of the ion in the direction of the external force gives the frictional force in the medium, which has to be overcome during the steady motion.

Obviously we have possibilities, in trying to explain how the conductivity will change with the concentration. We can first consider the number of ions n_i as variable, which is the way of the classical theory supposing a thermodynamic equilibrium between the undissociated molecule and the dissociated ions. But secondly it is also possible to focus attention on possible changes with concentration of the friction coefficients ρ_i or their reciprocals, the mobilities. Now the theory of the square root law in activity has to be built up on the assumption of total dissociation, and we must therefore make the same assumption in the case of strong electrolytes. But this assumption involves that n_i is exactly proportional to the total concentration. To explain the deviations of the proportionality between the conductivity and the concentration, therefore, only the second possibility is left.

5. Let us consider the ionic atmosphere again. In the equilibrium case this atmosphere has central symmetry. Applying an external field, so as to create a current and a mean movement of each ion in one direction, we may expect that the central symmetry will be destroyed. In fact, if for instance the central ion moves to the right, then during its motion it will constantly have to build up a charge density constituting its atmosphere to the right, whereas to the left the charge density will have to die out. Of course if the creation of the ionic atmosphere could be done instantaneously no effect of the motion would be perceptible. But if a finite time of relaxation, as we will call it, exists, during the motion of the central ion the atmosphere will in the right-hand part never reach its equilibrium density, whereas in the left-hand part the density will constantly be larger than its equilibrium value. If now we remember the fact that the charge density in the atmosphere always has a sign opposite to the charge of the ion, we see at once that, owing to the dissymmetry of its atmosphere, the central ion will be acted upon by a force tending to *decrease* its velocity. As the amount of dissymmetry increases with increasing velocity, this force will also increase, so that it will have the same effect as an increase of the friction constant would have.

This reasoning having shown that a change of mobility with concentration may indeed be expected, provided a time of relaxation characteristic of the ionic atmosphere exists, we will now consider the process of an ion building its atmosphere.

6. The question we have to consider is essentially that of finding an expression for the space distribution of ions not in the equilibrium case but taking into account its variation in time. Therefore we cannot appeal to the Maxwell-Boltzmann function. However in the general equations describing the Brownian movement we possess a

more general mathematical tool, which can lead us to an answer. In this way the details of the following statement can be worked out.

Suppose a charge E (of small dimensions) has been long enough at some point of the liquid, so that its ionic atmosphere has reached its equilibrium value. Now let us annihilate this central charge at the instant $t = 0$. We will ask how the charge density of the atmosphere spreads out to zero density. The mathematical expression for the charge density or the potential as a function of the distance from the centre r and the time t turns out not to be very simple. The principal point however is, that there exists an essential time constant τ governing the decrease. We will call this constant the time of relaxation; in the case of an electrolyte with two univalent ions of equal mobility (like KCl) τ is given by the expression

$$\tau = \frac{\rho}{\kappa^2 kT}.$$

For a KCl solution of concentration γ mols. per litre, this gives

$$\tau = \frac{0.55}{\gamma} \cdot 10^{-10} \text{ sec.}$$

The following table shows the values of the potential ψ at a distance $r = 1/K$ (the radius of the ionic atmosphere) divided by the potential ψ_0 at the instant $t = 0$ for different times t and for a millimolar KCl solution.

t	0	0.068	0.136	0.204	0.272	0.408	$\begin{cases} 0.544 \\ 10^{-7} \text{ sec} \end{cases}$
$\dfrac{\psi}{\psi_0}$	1	1.14	1.02	0.826	0.666	0.445	0.307

Even for this millimolar solution the time of relaxation is only of the order of magnitude 10^{-7} seconds. If in such a solution we apply an external field of 1 volt/cm., an ion will obtain a velocity of $6.7 \cdot 10^{-4}$ cm./sec. so that it will take $1.4 \cdot 10^{-3}$ seconds to travel over a distance equal to the radius of the ionic atmosphere. At first glance, it is obvious that there will be only a very slight dissymmetry in the charge density distribution of the ionic atmosphere and it seems improbable that the apparent change in mobility due to this dissymmetry should be appreciable. However, this attitude changes if we evaluate the magnitude of the force in the vicinity of an ion. If the dissymmetry were large enough to be compared with a concentration of the charge of one single ion ($4.77 \cdot 10^{10}$) at a distance equal to the radius of the ionic atmosphere from the central ion ($97 \cdot 10^{-8}$

cm.), this particle would be in a field of 1900 volts/cm. So we understand how even a slight dissymmetry will be sufficient to create an appreciable additional force owing to the relatively enormous value of the elementary electronic charge.

7. The same general equations, which gave us the information for the foregoing discussion, enable us also to calculate the stationary dissymmetry around an ion, which we move with a given constant velocity v in the direction of the external field. We find a dissymmetry of the kind expected, which in a diagram of lines of force could be described as a slight bending of these lines away from the direction in which the ion proceeds. The additional field intensity is in the direction opposite to the mean velocity of the central ion and is given by the expression

$$F_1 = \frac{1 Ek\rho}{6 DkT} V,$$

if E is the charge of the central ion and ρ is a mean friction coefficient of the solution, calculated according to the formula

$$\rho = \frac{\Sigma n_i e_i^2 \rho_i}{\Sigma n_i e_i^2}.$$

For a KCl solution in which the ions have equal mobilities we can easily compare the additional force, *i.e.*, the product of the ionic charge and the additional field intensity, with the friction at force $R_0 = \rho v$ in infinitely dilute solution. This quotient is given by the expression,

$$\frac{E F_1}{R_0} = - \frac{E^2 K}{6 DkT},$$

which has the absolute value $0.384\sqrt{\gamma}$ for a KCl solution in water of concentration γ mols. per litre, showing that the effect is of practical importance.

In our note on the subject we took the sum of the external field intensity F_0 and this calculated additional field intensity F_1 as the total field intensity acting on the central ion. Here it is that a criticism of Onsager enters. His argument is that an ion which is moved with constant velocity in a solution is not strictly the same as a real ion, which besides its mean motion in one direction also possesses a Brownian movement. This irregular motion can indeed be expected to have an effect on the dissymmetry of the ionic atmosphere. Onsager calculates, for instance, that for a uni-univalent electrolyte our expression has to be multiplied by the numerical factor $2 - \sqrt{2} = 0.586$. For details I refer to Onsager's own report.

8. Thus far we have focused our attention on the electric forces

acting on an ion. But in the steady state of motion these forces have to be in equilibrium with the force due to the impacts of the surrounding molecules introduced as a fractional force. In an infinitely dilute solution we can formally put this frictional force on a certain ion, say of charge E and friction constant P, equal to

$$R_0 = Pv,$$

because this is the only expression which will lead to Ohm's law. But it is consistent with Ohm's law that in a solution of finite concentration the apparent frictional constant may be different from its limiting value P. To find the amount of this supposed difference it seems necessary to start with a definite picture and so we treated the case of a charged sphere of radius C moving with a constant velocity under the influence of a constant external electrical field of intensity F_0 in a solvent containing ions. Now around this particle there will again exist an ionic atmosphere, supplying elements of volume of the liquid with a charge density. In Stokes' formula, giving for the frictional force the expression

$$R_0 = 6\pi\eta Cv$$
$$(\eta = \text{internal friction constant of the liquid}),$$

it is supposed that on the elements of volume of the liquid no external force acts at all. But in our case such forces exist, since the external electric field will act on the charges constituting the atmosphere. That is why a new calculation had to be carried out. This calculation is however a familiar one, as it is essentially similar to the calculation carried out by Helmholtz in his theory of electrophoresis. It is even sound to say that no essential difference exists between the well-known Helmholtz double layer and our ionic atmosphere and that the principal part of the interionic attraction theory really is a theory of that part of a Helmholtz double layer which extends in the solution surrounding each ion.

The charges in the liquid and the charge of the sphere always have opposite sign. The additional motion due to the existence of these charges will therefore have velocities oppositely directed to the velocity of the particle and we have to expect an increase in the apparent frictional force. That results also from the calculation, from which it follows that, in addition to the Stokes' force $R_0 = 6\pi\eta Cv$ an additional force,

$$R_1 = EF_0 CK,$$

will act in a direction opposite to the direction of motion. We found for a uni-univalent solution in water

$$K = 3.27 \cdot 10^7 \sqrt{\gamma}$$

The additional force will in this case be represented by the expression

$$R_1 = EF_0 \, 0.327 \cdot 10^8 C \, \sqrt{\gamma},$$

showing that for particles of the size of ions (*i.e.*, values of C of the order 10^{-8} cm.) this additional force will also be of practical importance.

9. The only thing left now is to combine all results and to calculate the migration velocity of the central ion from the condition that the whole electric force $E(F_0 + F_1)$ has to be equal to the whole frictional force $R_0 + R_1$, giving the equation,

$$EF_0 - \frac{E_0}{6D} \frac{\rho K}{kT} v = P_v + ECKF_0,$$

if we use the value of F_1 given in our first paper. Hence it follows that the migration velocity of an ion with charge E and the frictional constant P should be represented by the formula,

$$V = \frac{EF_0}{P} \frac{1 - C_\kappa}{1 + \dfrac{\rho}{P} \dfrac{E_\kappa^2}{6DkT}} = \frac{EF_0}{P} \left[1 - C_\kappa - \frac{\rho}{P} \frac{E_\kappa^2}{6DkT} \right].$$

The principal feature of this formula is the fact that the correction of the migratory velocity in infinite dilution is proportional to K (the reciprocal of the radius of the ionic layer) and therefore proportional to the square root of the concentration. So it seems proved that the interionic attraction theory is adequate to explain Kohlrausch's law.

The paper concludes with remarks on later criticisms of certain points in the theory.

ACIDS, BASES, AND SALTS. The new interest in the structure of the particles with which the chemist dealt and the newer concepts of the nature of ions led to revisions in the simple older theories of acids, bases, and salts. Thus, when Bjerrum considered the nature of amino acids from the newer viewpoint and recognized that as amphoteric molecules they had certain peculiar properties in solution, he was led to the concept of the zwitter ion—an idea that has proved very useful to the biochemist, since not only the amino acids, but also the proteins are zwitter ions. Much of the extreme reactivity of these vital substances has been found to be due to their amphoteric nature. The next selection shows the development of this idea.

The following selection is from pages 147–151 and 172–173 in *Zeitschrift für Physikalische Chemie 104*, 147–173 (1923).

The Constitution of Ampholytes, Especially the Amino Acids, and their Dissociation Constants

NIELS BJERRUM

1. Bredig [1894] was the first to call attention to the fact that an amphoteric electrolyte, such as betaine, is an inner salt, and thus can carry in the same molecule a positive and a negative charge which neutralize each other. Some years later Küster [1897–1898] proposed a theory for the color change of methyl orange according to which this substance can occur in such an electrically charged, but still electrically neutral form. According to Küster yellow methyl orange is thus

$$(CH_3)_2N \cdot C_6H_4 \cdot N_2 \cdot C_6H_4 \cdot SO_3^-$$

and the red form which occurs in acid is

$$^+H(CH_3)_2N \cdot C_6H_4 \cdot N_2 \cdot C_6H_4 \cdot SO_3^-$$

Küster calls such "ions" that bear equally positive and negative charges, like the red methyl orange, and thus cannot contribute to any conductivity, "zwitter ions." It is usually accepted that such types of ionization occur only in slight amounts, and up to now the dissociation constants of the amino acids are still calculated on the assumption that these forms of ionization play no part. Thus Walker [1907] writes, "The further complication from the assumption of a zwitter ion

$$^+NH_3 \cdot R \cdot COO^-$$

need not be considered, since in the present state of our knowledge of amphoteric electrolytes this assumption is not necessary for an explanation of the observed phenomena." Michaelis expresses this still more strongly in the new edition of his well-known book on hydrogen ion concentration (p. 62). He writes of the zwitter ions of the amino acids, "Their amount is doubtless always vanishingly small," and later, "We have up to now no means for recognizing the existence of zwitter ions. Because of their always very slight concentration they are not in a condition to displace measurably the equilibrium between the other known dissociation forms of the amino acids."

As I will seek to show in what follows, however, the matter is exactly the opposite. *In all the physiologically important amino acids, it is just the non-ionized (that is, not behaving as a cation or anion*) *part of the dissolved substance that almost exclusively occurs as a zwitter ion in the form charged equally positively and negatively.* Only the dissociation constants calculated on the basis of this assumption have a truly plausible value. Fortunately, it is equally valid for the calculation of the equilibrium between cations, anions, and the electrically neutral molecule whether we start from the old or the new viewpoint. The important results obtained by Bredig, Walker, Michaelis, and others in this field remain correct, and merely take on a clearer form.

2. Küster came to his conclusions, still convincing today, on the state of methyl orange in red, acid solution from the following considerations. All sulfonic acids are strong acids. The sulfo group of the methyl orange must therefore always be strongly dissociated; the ion formation in the sulfo group can therefore have nothing to do with the color change. We must here assume that methyl orange behaves as an indicator because it contains an amino group. The color change occurs if this group is changed by a hydrogen ion into an electrically charged ammonium group. In agreement with this is the fact that methyl orange as an indicator shows a very great similarity with the mother substance, dimethyl aminoazobenzene, which does not contain the sulfonyl group. The colors of both indicators are similar, and the color change occurs in the same hydrogen ion region (region of change according to Sörensen), for methyl orange $P_H = 3.1$–4.4, for dimethyl aminoazobenzene $P_H = 2.9$–4.0). According to Küster the red form of methyl orange is thus not

$$(CH_3)_2N \cdot C_6H_4 \cdot N_2 \cdot C_6H_4SO_3H,$$

but

$$^+HN(CH_3)_2 \cdot C_6H_4 \cdot N_2 \cdot C_6H_4 \cdot SO_3{}^-.$$

According to the views of the organic chemist there is also a quinoid rearrangement into

$$^+(CH_3)_2N : C_6H_4 : N \cdot NH \cdot C_6H_4 \cdot SO_3{}^-$$

which is without meaning in the present connection.

This method of thinking of Küster seems to me to be convincing. However, it can be used only for those amino acids that are colored and have indicator properties: thus, for example, not for aminoacetic acid. However, if, as Küster has shown, it is necessary in certain cases to assume the positively and negatively charged zwitter ion as the chief form, it becomes apparent that in many other cases also the same state of affairs occurs. If we think further that ammonium acetate in water solution occurs 99.5% as

$$NH_4^+ + CH_3COO^-$$

and only 0.5% is hydrolyzed to

$$NH_3 + CH_3COOH$$

then it seems to me to be simplest to assume that aminoacetic acid is present in water solution chiefly as

$$^+NH_3CH_2COO^-$$

We must still expect that the carboxyl group of the aminoacetic acid must have acid properties about like acetic acid, and the amino group basic properties about like ammonia. However, we will attempt to introduce the assumption that the undissociated molecules of amino acid are charged positively and negatively equally, and on this basis we will calculate the dissociation constants of the amino acid numerically.

3. According to the old view an amino acid

$$NH_2 \cdot R \cdot COOH$$

exists in water solution in three forms: as a cation

$$^+NH_3 \cdot R \cdot COOH$$

as an uncharged molecule

$$NH_2 \cdot R \cdot COOH$$

and as an anion

$$NH_2 \cdot R \cdot COO^-$$

The ratio between the three forms varies with the hydrogen ion concentration of the solution. Let A^+, A, and A^- be the concentrations of these forms, and H^+ and OH^- the concentration of hydrogen ion and hydroxyl ion. Under these conditions the acid dissociation constant k_a is defined as

$$\frac{A^- \cdot H^+}{A} = k_a \tag{1}$$

and the basic dissociation constant k_b by

$$\frac{A^+ \cdot OH^-}{A} = k_b \tag{2}$$

According to the new view an amino acid exists in solution partly as the cation $^+NH_3 \cdot R \cdot COOH$ or the anion $NH_2 \cdot R \cdot COO^-$ as above, but also as the zwitter ion $^+NH_3 \cdot R \cdot COO^-$. We will designate the concentration of this last form as A^{+-}.[1] The dissociation of the carboxyl group then follows according to the equation

$$^+NH_3 \cdot R \cdot COOH = {}^+NH_3 \cdot R \cdot COO^- + H^+$$

and for the corresponding acid dissociation constant K_A we get

$$\frac{A^{+-} \cdot H^+}{A^+} = K_A \tag{3}$$

The dissociation of the amino group occurs thus:

$$H_2O + NH_2 \cdot R \cdot COO^- = OH^- + {}^+NH_3 \cdot R \cdot COO^-$$

and for the corresponding basic dissociation constant K_B, we have

$$\frac{A^{+-} \cdot OH^-}{A^-} = K_B \tag{4}$$

If we know the old values k_a and k_b it is easy to calculate the new dissociation constants K_A and K_B, since A of the old equation is A^{+-} of the new: from (1), (2), (3), and (4) we thus obtain

$$K_A = \frac{K_{H_2O}}{k_b}, \; K_B = \frac{K_{H_2O}}{k_a} \tag{5}$$

Here K_{H_2O} means the dissociation constant of water.

If an acid or a base has the dissociation constant K, then the hydrolysis constant of the salt is known to be equal to K_{H_2O}/K. From equation (5) we also find that K_A, the new dissociation constant, *characteristic for the carboxyl group*, is identical with the hydrolysis constant which corresponds to the old basic dissociation constant k_b, and, moreover, K_B, the new dissociation constant, *characteristic for the amino group*, is identical with the hydrolysis constant which corresponds to the old acid dissociation constant k_a. By this altered understanding of the constitution of the amino acid molecules, *the constants which had previously been a function of the amino group become constants characteristic of the carboxyl group and vice versa.*

[1] In agreement with the hypothesis according to which neutral salts like NaCl or NH_4NO_3 are completely ionized, we do not consider the form

$$\begin{array}{cc} R & NH_3 \\ | & | \\ CO & . & O \end{array}$$

and in agreement with the leading view, we assume that the hydration of $-NH_2$ to $-NH_3OH$ is slight.

The rest of the body of the paper consists of applications of these ideas to specific amino acids and to methods for determining the amounts of the different ions. Bjerrum then concludes as follows:

Summary

1. The aliphatic amino acids in the undissociated condition behave almost exclusively (more than 99.5%) as salt-like zwitter ions $^+NH_3 \cdot R \cdot COO^-$. They are thus not true amino acids, but ammonium salts. A content of hydrogen or hydroxyl ions in their solutions does not mean that they are acids or bases, but only that they are hydrolyzed as salts.

The constants k_a and k_b by means of which up to now the acid and basic properties of the amino acids have been recognized are not dissociation constants, but hydrolysis constants. The true dissociation constants, which give the strength of the acidic and basic groups neutralized within the amino acid molecules, are

$$K_A = K_{H_2O} : k_b \text{ and } K_B = K_{H_2O} : k_a$$

(K_{H_2O} is the dissociation constant of water). K_A and K_B for the amino acids have values which are in agreement with their structural formulas. From the nature of the acidic and basic groups we can estimate the values of K_A and K_B, since we consider the effect of the other substituents in the usual way.

Various chemical reactions show that these substances contain no free amino groups. The physical properties are in agreement with their salt-like nature. They also behave as salts in that they raise the solubility of other salts and themselves are more easily soluble in salt solutions than in water.

2. In the aromatic amino acids there are also zwitter ions $^+NH_3 \cdot R \cdot COO^-$, as well as true amino acid molecules $NH_2 \cdot R \cdot COOH$ with free amino and carboxyl groups present (in amounts between 10–90%).

3. In the aromatic aminophenols the zwitter ion form is completely repressed.

4. It is possible to estimate the mass ratio between the salt-like zwitter ion and the true amino acid from the value of the dissociation constant of an ampholyte.

5. It is theoretically probable that for an ampholyte, $K_A \cdot K_B$ can be no smaller than $4K_{H_2O}$ ($k_a \cdot k_b$ no greater than $1/4K_{H_2O}$). It follows from this that the portion of the ampholyte that behaves as a cation and anion cannot amount to more than 50%.

6. It is pointed out that these results can be tested by study of color and solubility. This study will be reported later.

Another modification of the older ideas of the nature of acids and bases led Brönsted to a more general concept of these substances. His ideas were applied not only in inorganic chemistry, but proved to be of value also in the electronic explanation of many organic reactions.

Hantzsch was concerned especially with the reaction between a solvent and the ions dissolved in it and developed a very useful theory of ionic solutions. He had been anticipated to some extent by E. C. Franklin who had applied similar ideas to the interactions of acids with the solvent in liquid ammonia solutions, but the more common reactions with water made the work of Hantzsch well known to all chemists.

The following selection is from pages 718–721 and 728 in *Recueil des Travaux Chimiques des Pays-Bas 42*, 718–728 (1923).

Some Remarks on the Concept of Acids and Bases

J. N. BRÖNSTED

Toward a definition of acids and bases. Since the establishment of the theory of electrolytic dissociation by Arrhenius the dominant definition of acids and bases as substances that can split out hydrogen or hydroxyl ions in solution has never been seriously attacked so far as the definition of acids is concerned. We have held steadily to the idea that compound A is an acid if it is partly or completely broken down in solution according to the scheme

$$A \rightarrow B + H^+ \tag{1}$$

However, there have been attempts from various sides to modify our concept of bases. P. Pfeiffer, especially, on the basis of his important observations on aquo and hydroxo compounds in a series of metals, has presented the view that bases form salts by addition of acids, which in terms of the theory of electrolytic dissociation must lead to the idea of a definition of bases as substances that can add hydrogen ions. Although this method of treatment can be carried out convincingly here, yet in spite of its constitutive foundation it cannot serve as a direct foundation for changing the definition of a base.

The question has been treated more generally by Michaelis in his book *Hydrogen Ion Concentration*. He considers the following to be a possible definition of a base: a base is a special electrically neutral species of molecule that can bind a hydrogen ion and thus become a positive ion. However, the further developments by Michaelis are all founded on the usual definition of a base and particularly emphasize the special significance of hydroxyl ion as a constituent of bases even in nonaqueous solutions.

It is the purpose of the present small contribution to show the advantages that come from a modified definition of a base.

The formal advantages of the definition of a base as a substance that can bind a hydrogen ion are immediately apparent. In scheme (1) in which the concept of an acid (A) is established, the concept of a base (B) is equally defined and thus the reciprocal connection of acidic and basic properties is shown in the clearest and simplest way.

The advantages of scheme (1) as a basis for an equal definition of bases and acids are not merely of a formal nature, however. For example, if we express the basic properties of ammonia in one case by equation (1)

$$NH_4^+ \rightleftarrows NH_3 + H^+ \qquad (2)$$

and in another by the usual formulation

$$NH_4^+ + OH^- \rightleftarrows NH_4OH \qquad (3)$$

then, as is well known, both of these schemes are thermodynamically equivalent for an aqueous solution, i.e., we can derive identical equilibrium conditions, from the thermodynamic viewpoint, from the basic and acidic properties that appear in dilution, partial neutralization, etc. by using (2) and (3). The presence of the compound NH_4OH, that is, hydrated ammonia, and therefore the formation according to (3) of the hydroxyl ion in an ammonia solution is naturally limited to solutions in water.

This brings out the fundamental difference of the basic function as shown by (2) or (3). If we accept scheme (3) as a suitable expression for characterizing bases, we will be forced to give a special definition of a base for each special solvent. However, in principle, acid and basic properties are independent of the nature of the solvent, and the concepts of acids and bases are in fact of such a general character that we must consider it a necessary requirement of these concepts in general to formulate a pattern independent of the nature of an arbitrary solvent. Therefore we will exclude scheme (3). Scheme (2) remains for the basic property of ammonia, and for the basic function in general scheme (1) is the single foundation for an absolute definition of a base.

The result of these considerations can be made more precise in the following way: *acids and bases are substances that are capable of splitting off or taking up hydrogen ions, respectively*. The essence of this concept of defining acids and bases is once more given schematically by the expression

$$A \rightleftarrows B + H^+ \qquad (1)$$
$$\text{(acid) (base)}$$

in which nothing more is said of the properties of A and B. We will refer to A and B, that is, to an acid and a base that are related to each other by the relation given in (1), as *corresponding* acids and bases.

It follows from the form of the expression that corresponding acids and bases do not have to have the same state of electrical charge. If A is electrically neutral, as an ordinary acid molecule is, B has a negative charge, *e.g.*

$$CH_3COOH \rightleftarrows CH_3COO^- + H^+$$
$$\text{(acid)} \qquad \text{(base)}$$

where the acetate ion thus functions as a base. If A has a positive charge, B must be electrically neutral as is the case, *e.g.*, of the dissociation of the ammonium ion:

$$NH_4^+ \rightleftarrows NH_3 + H^+$$
$$\text{(acid)} \qquad \text{(base)}$$

We have a negatively charged acid, *e.g.*, in the acid oxalate ion which dissociates as follows:

$$C\overline{O}O \cdot COOH \rightleftarrows C\overline{O}O \cdot C\overline{O}O + H^+$$

etc.

It also follows from the concept of a general definition of acids and bases that ions also have to be treated as acids and bases. In principle, the electrical nature of the acid or base molecule in this view has no meaning. It would be useful from a practical point of view to be able to classify the different equilibria according to charge, and I have therefore introduced the following terminology [Table I] for this purpose:

Table I

Electrical charge	Naming of acid or base	Examples
Positive	cation acid	NH_4^+
Positive	cation base	$NH_2 \cdot C_6H_4 \cdot C_6H_4 \cdot NH_3^+$
Neutral	neutral acid	CH_3COOH
Neutral	neutral base	NH_3
Negative	anion acid	$C\overline{O}O \cdot COOH$
Negative	anion base	CH_3COO^-

Independent of the special electrical nature of the acid-base system, scheme (1) shows that the symmetry that we have seen as essential for acid and base function in the usual representation disappears in the new method of representation. However, it becomes expressed directly through the definite example of the reciprocal behavior of acids and bases.

The equilibrium formulated in scheme (1) between hydrogen ion and the corresponding acid and base can be called a simple acid-base equilibrium. By mixing two simple systems, a double acid-base system and an acid-base equilibrium result that can always be formulated as follows:

$$\text{acid}_1 + \text{base}_2 \rightleftarrows \text{acid}_2 + \text{base}_1 \qquad (4)$$

This equilibrium includes a number of important reactions such as neutralization, hydrolysis, indicator reactions, etc.

The author then shows the specific application of his theory in a number of cases. He concludes with the summary.

Summary. The chemical character of acids and bases is most simply and generally defined by the scheme

$$\text{acid} \rightleftarrows \text{base} + H^+$$

The hydroxyl ion in principle has no special position as a bearer of basic properties.

We have no logical measure for a comparison of the strengths of acids with those of bases. The usual concept of neutrality does not exist, or only by arbitrary definition. Therefore the solvent, *e.g.*, water, cannot be considered as neutral in principle.

The acid-base and reduction-oxidation equilibria are analogous:

$$\text{acid} \rightleftarrows \text{base} + \oplus$$
$$\text{reduced substance} \rightleftarrows \text{oxidized substance} + \ominus$$

In the first case the positive, in the second the negative electron is involved.

The following selection is in *Zeitschrift für Physikalische Chemie 134*, 406–412.

The Constitution of Acids and Salts and Their Chemical Alterations by Solvents

A. HANTZSCH

My studies of acids and salts, which have lasted for many years, have led me to certain conclusions. For a better understanding of the changes seen in the following work by means of molecular refraction, I will give here in compact form a summary of the most important results obtained up to now and, to anticipate the most essential general conclusions, I will explain the alterations most simply in a purely chemical way instead of assuming a physical state to explain the changes. Naturally I will not deny the effect of the latter, but it produces only secondary changes following the primary chemical alterations.

The starting point for the chemical theory comes partly from my study of the connection between constitution and color of colored salts and acids, partly from the work of K. Schaefer on the ultra-violet absorption of nitric acid and its derivatives. By extinction measurements on salts such as $[MnO_4]K$, $[CrO_4]K_2$, $[Cu(NH_3)_4]SO_4$, $[Fe(CN)_6]K_4$, and also on acids such as MnO_4H and bases such as $[Cu(NH_3)_4](OH)_2$, we recognized optical constants independent of great differences in degree of dissociation, so long as the colored complex cations and anions remained unaltered or at any rate, like most nonelectrolytes, were altered only slightly by solvate formation in different solvents, as for example, chloroplatinic acid $[PtCl_6]H_2$ and its salts, as well as the recently thoroughly studied salts of the acid $[(NH_3)_2Cr(SCN)_4]H$. Thus here the dissociation is an optically indifferent process.

The optical analysis of nitric acid, its salts and esters has also yielded the basis for the following considerations.

Constitution of Homogeneous Acids and Their Alterations by Solvents

Nitric acid is homogeneous and indifferent, nonionizing solvents like ether is optically very similar to its esters $O_2N \cdot OC_nH_{2n+1}$, but is completely different from its alkali salts $[NO_3]Me$, and thus according to A. Werner, is not a "true" acid with ionogen bound hydrogen $[NO_3]H$, but a "pseudoacid" with hydroxyl hydrogen $O_2N \cdot OH$. However, in water solution with increasing dilution it becomes increasingly similar optically to its salts, and with great dilution, identical with them; it is then (as was assumed at first) apparently changed into the true acid $[NO_3]H$, but actually, as with ammonia, it has been converted by water, a very weak basic anhydride, into a hydroxonium salt $[NO_3][H_3O]$, comparable to the ammonium salt $[NO_3][H_4N]$. This salt-forming action of water is confirmed by the fact that the solid monohydrate of the strongest acid, perchloric acid, is actually a hydroxonium perchlorate $[ClO_4]H_3O$ and has a crystal lattice corresponding to ammonium perchlorate $[ClO_4]H_4N$. However, the other strong acids appear in the homogeneous condition, like nitric acid, not to be heteropolar complexes of true acids with ionically bound hydrogen atoms as given by A. Werner, $[XO_2]H$, $[XO_3]H$, $[XO_4]H$, but to be homopolar hydroxyl compounds $OX \cdot OH$, $O_2X \cdot OH$, $O_3X \cdot OH$ whose acid hydrogen ion is thus fixed to a single oxygen atom. Thus, in general, free H ions do not exist, but only hydroxonium ions. Accordingly, all monomolecular acids are pseudoacid nonelectrolytes, but they appear as "pseudo-electrolytes" because in water they are apparently true acids, but actually they are dissolved more or less completely as their hydroxonium salts. From this we arrive at an important theoretical definition and a practical expression of their different acidities or strengths. These are not determined physically by their different dissociation constants as is stated by the dilution law of W. Ostwald for the strong acids, nearly equally strongly dissociated in water, but purely chemically by the differing strengths of their tendencies to salt formation. Indeed, since the apparently simplest salt formation by substitution

$$XH + Me \rightarrow XMe + H$$

can be exactly measured only with difficulty because of its heterogeneous system, the measurement is most simply done by means of additive salt formation with basic anhydrides (for example, amines R_3N) and especially with water, by determination of the state of equilibrium in solution

$$XH + R_3N \rightleftarrows X[HNR_3] \text{ and } XH + H_2O \rightleftarrows X[H_3O].$$

Thus the previously unknown "degrees of acidity" of the strongest acids can be determined qualitatively. This is first done statically by an indicator method, namely by study of the equilibrium

$C_6H_5N : N \cdot C_6H_4 \cdot N(CH_3)_2$
dimethylaminoazobenzene (yellow)
$$+ HX \rightleftarrows [C_6H_5 \cdot NH \cdot N : C_5H_4 : N(CH_3)_2]X$$
(salt, red, quinoid)

Second, kinetically, by measurement of the rate of decomposition of the diazoacetic ester through the nondissociated acid which is also produced primarily through additive salt formation of an aliphatic diazonium salt. The latter then decomposes spontaneously, most simply according to the following equation $XH + N_2CH \cdot$

$$COOC_2H_5 \rightarrow X[N_2CH_2 \cdot COOC_2H_5] \rightarrow N_2 + XCH_2COOC_2H_5.$$

Third, by measurement of the rate of inversion of sugars at the greatest concentration of acids possible.

Thus we can arrange the strong inorganic acids according to decreasing acidity as follows:

$$ClO_3 \cdot OH > R \cdot SO_2 \cdot OH > IH > BrH > ClH > NO_2 \cdot OH$$

For all the above acids, however, important results have been clearly shown only by the above chemical theory and they are incompatible with the results of the dissociation theory: the non-ionized strong acids act most strongly because of their great tendency to salt formation; on the other hand, in water solution the ions that are present and are the main most active components are the weakest because they dissolve as hydroxonium ions (though these are very unstable). The fact that this situation is different in weak acids, and why this is so, will be explained later.

All acids in water solution ultimately become completely saltlike, and the greater the dilution, the weaker they are. This peculiar "mass action" of water can only be explained chemically, however. as the anions of very weak silicic acid further add acid anhydride molecules, SiO_2, to become more strongly negative polysilicate ions, so the very weak positive "cation from water" that results from water and the hydrogen of the acid forming a hydroxonium ion becomes a strongly positive "polyhydroxonium cation" by further addition of water. Thus, of the acids mentioned above, which are almost equally strong (dissociated) according to the dissociation theory, only perchloric acid and apparently some of the strongest sulfonic acids like $CCl_3 \cdot SO_2OH$ form a solid hydroxonium salt with one mole of water, whereas the weakest acid, nitric acid (which according to the dissociation theory appears strongest) is only changed completely into the polyhydroxonium nitrate $NO_3[H_3O \cdot (H_2O)_n]$ by some 90 moles of water, and this then exists only in solution. This peculiarity which distinguishes hydroxonium from ammonium must also be explained chemically. The strong association of liquid water, which only becomes monomolecular at higher temperatures, as opposed to the very weak association of liquid ammonia which is not stable even at $-34°$, is also transmitted to the simple hydroxonium cations formed from water and acid, and this explains the existence of positive polyhydroxonium cations which, as will be shown later, sometimes also exist in the solid condition as hydrates of certain strong acids like $C_{10}H_{11} \cdot SO_3H \cdot 2H_2O$ and $C_6H_5 \cdot N_2 \cdot C_6H_4 \cdot SO_3H \cdot 3H_2O$, etc.

The fact that the simplest organic derivatives of water, the alcohols and ethers, are similar to water, but as weaker basic anhydrides can form alkylated hydroxonium salts only with the strongest acids and can thus serve for distinguishing their degree of acidity, is shown by giving one example only: HBr in ether actually absorbs light in the homogeneous condition just as in water and like the alkali bromides in water solution; thus it is dissolved in ether as the diethyl oxonium salt $Br[HO(C_2H_5)_2]$, while nitric acid conversely in ether, like its ester, absorbs only as a dissolved pseudoetherate $O_2N \cdot OH \ldots$ $O(C_2H_5)_2$; nitric acid is thus here a very much weaker acid than HBr, though because of its conductivity it should be the strongest acid in water solution. These facts must also be explained chemically and can be referred to two causes. The first is that the unsaturated hydrogen of the hydroxonium H_3O is more positive than the saturated alkyls of the alkylated hydroxonium salt, and the second is that (on the same grounds) water is the most strongly associated, alcohol less so, and ether not at all. Accordingly, the monoalkyl hydroxonium ions become only a little stronger by addition of alcohol, and the dialkyl hydroxonium salts $X[HO \cdot (C_2H_5)_2]$ cannot add ether at all, and thus cannot become more positive. Thus nitric acid forms only one monoetherate (isolated), while its monohydrate goes over with water into a polyhydroxonium nitrate.

The constitution of the homogeneous liquid oxygen acids is also similar to that of liquid water. Like their mother substance they are known to be associated, as hydroxyl compounds, and actually, as is well recognized, by means of the unsaturated oxygen and hydrogen atoms of the hydroxyl, and, as in associated water, traces of H-ions and OH-ions are present, or, more correctly, just as dimolar associated water forms a somewhat ionized hydroxonium hydrate by displacement of an H atom:

$$
\begin{array}{c}
\text{H} \qquad\qquad\qquad \text{H} \\
\diagup \qquad\qquad\qquad \diagup \\
\text{H---O} \qquad \text{O---H} \leftrightarrows \text{HO(H---O} \\
\diagdown \qquad\qquad\qquad \diagdown \\
\text{H} \qquad\qquad\qquad \text{H}
\end{array}
$$

so the associated strong oxygen acids also isomerize, as can again be most clearly recognized in nitric acid, partly by an analogous "disproportionation" to a heteropolar saltlike electrolyte where the dimolar associated nitric acid partly goes over to a "nitronium nitrate" and the following equilibrium results:

$$
\begin{array}{c}
\text{H} \qquad\qquad\qquad\qquad \text{[HO} \\
\diagup \qquad\qquad\qquad\qquad\qquad \diagdown \\
\text{NO}_2\text{---O} \qquad \text{O---NO}_2 \leftrightarrows [\text{NO}_3]' \qquad\qquad \text{NO]} \\
\diagdown \qquad\qquad\qquad\qquad\qquad \diagup \\
\text{H} \qquad\qquad\qquad\qquad\text{HO}
\end{array}
$$

This nitronium nitrate is dissociated in the unaltered acid, just as is hydroxonium hydrate in water; thus we have explained chemically that the homogeneous nitric acid is a relatively good electrolyte.

In the same way we also explain the apparent optical anomaly
of nitric acid that it absorbs very differently and more weakly
than its ester through its content of nitronium nitrate, since, as I
have recognized by optical analysis and molecular weight determinations, in sulfuric acid solution this is present only as a weakly absorbing, dissociated nitronium sulfate. In addition, not only do we isolate
from perchloric acid, as the strongest acid, a solid nitronium perchlorate

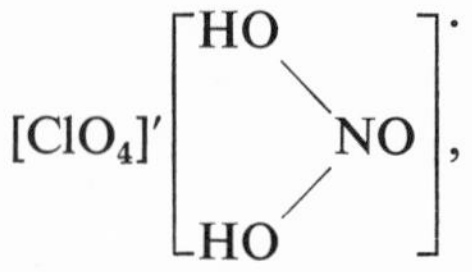

$$[ClO_4]' \left[\begin{matrix} HO \\ \diagdown \\ \diagup \\ HO \end{matrix} NO \right]^{\cdot},$$

but also, as will shortly be published, the saltlike nature of this
addition compound can be recognized by the fact that in nitro-
methane solution it behaves as a normal electrolyte and by electrolysis
nitric acid actually migrates as a cation to the cathode.

Conclusion

Homogeneous liquid oxygen acids are "pseudohomogeneous"
substances; they exist mainly as nonconducting homopolar hydroxyl
compounds which are more or less strongly associated. Secondarily
by intramolecular rearrangement they contain formed and dissociated "acidium salts" whose concentration can be determined approximately from the size of their conductivity.

The following considerations are valid for a consideration of the
transformations of the acids in water solution:

As long as water was viewed only as a passive solvent in the purely
physical theory of electrolytic dissociation, and as long as the H ion
in water solution was assumed naturally to exist in water solutions of
"free" acids, which broke up into acid ions and hydrogen ions, for
just so long we had to assume also an esterlike pseudo acid and a
saltlike true acid as an "equilibrium acid." However, since all the
studies show that the available acids must be recognized as pseudoacids $(XO_2 \cdot OH)$ exclusively, and "free" (homogeneous) true acids
almost surely do not exist, the division of acids into two different
classes is groundless. Therefore the term "true" acid with the complex formula previously assigned to it $([XO_3]H)$ must disappear
because only its oxonium salt $([XO_3]'H_3O)$ exists in its place and the
term "pseudoacid" is misleading because it depends on the assumption
of the existence of a true acid. Thus, we must once again call all of
them, even the previous "pseudoacids," simply "acids" and define them

as follows: all oxygen acids are hydroxyl compounds of negative atoms or atom complexes whose hydroxyl hydrogens can be replaced by positive metals with formation of true salts, but also by unsaturated substances like ammonia and amines, and also, which is theoretically more important, even apparently neutral oxygen compounds and "solvents" like water (in the strongest acids, alcohol and ether also) add to each other and thus form ammonium and oxonium salts. They can be defined more simply electrochemically: all homogeneous acids (halogen hydrides, oxygen acids and thio acids) in the monomolecular state are nonelectrolytes, but as evidence of their "strength" they have an increasing tendency to formation of salts, thus of electrolytes, first by replacement of hydrogen with formation of metal salts; second by addition of unsaturated compounds (such as ammonia, water, alcohol, and ether) to their hydrogen with formation of onium salts.

CHEMICAL KINETICS. With the new approach to molecules as individual particles with very specific structures, interest once again developed in the precise mechanisms by which molecules reacted. The thermodynamic approach with its statistical viewpoint had somewhat diverted interest from this branch of chemistry, but now rapid advances occurred in kinetics. The theory of chain reactions, put forward by Bodenstein in 1913, was developed by Hinshelwood, Semenov, and others during the following years. The selection from the work of Semenov shows how this concept led to a deeper understanding of explosive reactions. Nevertheless, the relatively simple collision theory of reactions was not entirely satisfactory, and the theory of the activated state as enunciated by Eyring, Polanyi, and others furnished another pillar supporting the subject of kinetics and its contributions to an understanding of chemical reactions.

The following selection is from pages 329–330 and 396–397 in *Zeitschrift für Physikalische Chemie 85*, 329–397 (1913).

A Theory of Photochemical Reaction Velocities

MAX BODENSTEIN

In an early communication there is a report of the progress of the studies of Dr. Dux on the photochemical kinetics of chlorine detonating gas. The form of the velocity equations that was observed is very unusual and its meaning has caused no little difficulty. However it has finally been found that from it and with the aid of the various measurements of photochemical reaction velocities in the literature it becomes possible to describe the process, and from this there has resulted a theory which at last is, I believe, capable of general application.

The measurements on chlorine detonating gas, in common with the results of older studies for the velocity of the reaction $H_2 + Cl_2 = 2HCl$ at constant light strength and in a homogeneous light field have yielded the equation

$$+ \frac{d[2HCl]}{dt} = k \frac{J_0[Cl_2]^2}{[O_2]}$$

with the limitation that the equation is valid only so long as there is not too little hydrogen present, the concentration of which has an effect approximately at the ratio $[H_2]:[Cl_2]$ of $1:4$. Hydrogen chloride has no obvious effect on the velocity, nor does water vapor, except perhaps if by extreme measures such a degree of drying is obtained that, as in many other reactions, there is a retardation, or even a complete stoppage. The addition of certain substances like NO_2, $NOCl_2$, NCl_3 or O_3 hinders the reaction very greatly, but these are used up in the process.

The proportionality with the strength of the incident light J_0 was shown by Bunsen and Roscoe, the inverse proportionality against the oxygen concentration was demonstrated by Chapman and MacMahon for the initial stages and by us for the whole reaction; the special action of the last mentioned gas was shown by Burgess and Chapman and by Chapman and MacMahon.

No sort of definite idea leads to these results if we assume that the chlorine molecule affected by light is brought into direct reaction with hydrogen. There must first to some extent be the complicated result of a partial process which lies between and sharply separates the original process of absorption and the later fate of the resulting substance. The process begun by the chemical action of the light absorbed in the process, as has been suggested and generally recognized for certain cases previously, is perceived as a photoelectric process, a splitting of the molecule at the expense of the energy of the absorbed light into a positive residue, an atom, or in a complicated compound substance, a molecule with a free valence position, and also a free electron. Both parts can then lead to chemical reactions, the positive residue which has a structure largely capable of a purely chemical reaction, since it can react either first with itself, or with another molecule of the same or a different substance; the electrons, since they add to molecules of the same or a different substance, thus induce secondary reactions which without this activation could not occur, or could take place only slowly.

Thus, in this sense, we can differentiate between the *primary light reaction in which the positive residue of the absorbing molecule reacts, and the secondary light reaction in which the molecules activated by the electrons play this part.*

These two types of photochemical processes are different in that by the same original light absorption process as a starting point they have entirely different behavior. The chlorine detonating gas reaction belongs to the latter class, but since the primary process is very much simpler, I will discuss it first.

A long discussion of a large number of photochemical reactions is given, and then Bodenstein summarizes as follows.

1. A theory of *photochemical reactions* can be developed on the assumption that in each one the first process is a splitting of the light-absorbing molecule into a positive residue and an electron, and both can be the source of chemical reactions.

2. The positive residue reacts almost instantaneously. The amount of substance reacting is therefore proportional to the energy absorbed, independent of impurities, concentration, and temperature. Thus, the reaction is of the first or the zero order, or it corresponds to Beer's law. The action of a quantum of energy or perhaps somewhat less thus yields a molecule of reacting substance. This process is called the "primary light reaction."

3. The electrons add to the other molecules and activate these, so that by conversion of the activated molecules to the end product they again become free for addition to new molecules. Thus they behave exactly like chemical atoms and distribute themselves according to their affinity on the molecules of the reacting substances and on the impurities, especially oxygen, which therefore have an inhibiting action in all the reactions. By the usual methods of chemical kinetics the velocity equations can be deduced for this behavior; these differ according to the velocities of the individual participants, but we always assume a clear pattern, and in certain cases this leads to the possibility of a greater temperature coefficient. According to these equations, the reaction depends not only on the energy absorbed, but also on the concentration of the participants in the reaction and the impurities; for one quantum of energy between 10^{-3} and 10^{+6} molecules react, but mostly this amounts to > 1. This behavior is called the "secondary light reaction."

4. Of the examples adequately studied in the literature, 10 belong to the first class, and 12 to the second.

5. This theory tells nothing new about the photochemical equilibria. "Catalytic" light reactions occur in both "work accumulators," especially for the first class, but also for the second.

6. The suggested ideas find confirmation in the fact that by passage of electricity through a gas and by the action of radioactive rays the reactions that occur follow the same laws. They correspond mostly to the "primary" process, but also a "secondary" process has been adequately described in the literature.

The following selection is from pages 125–129 in *Zeitschrift für Physik* *46*, 109–131 (1927).

The Oxidation of Phosphorus Vapor at Low Pressure

N. SEMENOFF

The paper begins with a discussion of various theories of oxidation of phosphorus and describes experimental results. The conclusions are then given.

We summarize our results in the following propositions:
1. Phosphorus and oxygen do not react at all with each other, or react immeasurably slowly, if the pressure of one of the participants lies below a definite critical pressure.
2. The critical pressure depends on the distance between the walls of the vessel and decreases rapidly when this is increased. It appears that at infinitely great dimensions of the vessel the reaction can occur at any small pressure of one of the reaction participants.
3. Mixing in of a neutral gas (argon) acts in the same way as an increase in the dimensions of the vessel: with increase in argon pressure (at constant phosphorus pressure) the critical pressure of the oxygen falls.
4. Increase in pressure of one of the components decreases the critical pressure of the other.

We do not place very great reliance on the accuracy of the quantitative rules that we have presented (rules I and II), but we still believe that the qualitative results formulated in the four points of the propositions are unconditionally correct.

From this we can draw the following conclusions as to the character of the reactions between phosphorus and oxygen:

I. The surface of the vessel "poisons" the reaction, since it obviously absorbs the active centers. The longer the time that the active molecule requires to reach the vessel wall, the less is the poisoning effect of that wall. Increasing the distance between the walls of the vessel or mixing in of a neutral gas makes an access to the walls difficult for the active molecules and thus increases the probability that the active molecules will enter the reaction before the activation is destroyed by the walls.

II. We view the reaction as one of the chain type: certain active centers will be stimulated by heat motion; each of them can cause a reaction (or series of reactions) which by collisions of a second type yield new centers of the same sort in a greater number, or by a collision with a wall, as perhaps also by some other type of collision or radiation in the interior of the flask, they will be destroyed. When the probability of deactivation is sufficiently large so that the statistical mean for the yield on new centers is no greater than one, a slow reaction occurs whose rate is determined by reformation of the primary centers. The probability of the deactivation depends on different conditions (pressure of the components, state and pressure of admixtures, separation of the walls, etc.) which must be continuous, but as soon as the value is reached at which the above-mentioned yield reaches the value of one and exceeds it, the number of active centers begins to increase with time and the reaction occurs explosively. Such an idea has already been developed by Christiansen and Cramer.

To illustrate these results by an example, we will carry out the calculations on the basis of some assumptions as to the mechanism of the reaction of phosphorus with oxygen, but we will not assert that these assumptions have actually been proved correct. We will also carry out the calculations approximately, since an exact calculation is very difficult and, because of the uncertainty of the assumptions, it would also be unnecessary.

We assume:

1. The active centers of the reaction are oxygen atoms (O).
2. These centers appear:

(a) because of spontaneous dissociation of the O_2 molecule. The number of centers resulting thus in unit time (n_0) can be very small,

(b) as a result of collisions of the second type between the reaction products, which have not had time to give up their energy again, and the molecules of oxygen. Here we assume that in a collision of an excited molecule of the reaction product with an oxygen molecule O_2, the latter is dissociated, but by a collision with a phosphorus molecule P_4, however, the excited molecule simply loses its energy.

To obtain a clear picture, we will assume the following scheme of the reactions:

1. $O + P_4 = P_4O' \begin{cases} P_4O' + O_2 = P_4O + O + O & \text{(a)} \\ P_4O' + P_4 = P_4O + P_4 & \text{(b)} \end{cases}$

2. $P_4O + O_2 = P_4O_2 + O$

3. $P_4O_2 + O_2 = P_4O_4' \begin{cases} P_4O_4' + O_2 = P_4O_4 + O + O & \text{(a)} \\ P_4O_4' + P_4 = P_4O_4 + P_4 & \text{(b)} \end{cases}$

4. $P_4O_4 + O_2 = P_4O_6'$

---

6. $P_4O_6 + O_2 = P_4O_{10}' \begin{cases} P_4O_{10}' + O_2 = P_4O_{10} + O + O & \text{(a)} \\ P_4O_{10}' + P_4 = P_4O_{10} + P_4 & \text{(b)} \end{cases}$

Here the sign ′ means the molecule which has excess energy immediately at its formation.

All members of the reaction behave according to the same scheme except for reaction 2 which is introduced here in order that we may pass to molecules with an even number of oxygen atoms. According to our scheme we see that an O center yields at least 11 new O centers in the case in which the intermediate reactions take place according to (a). Actually, however, they can also take place according to (b).

The probability of a collision with O_2 is obviously equal to

$$\alpha = \frac{P_{O_2}}{P_{P_4} + P_{O_2}}$$

where P_{O_2} is the pressure of O_2, and P_{P4} the pressure of P_4.

A simple calculation shows that the average number of the new O centers that occur in each reaction $P_4 + O = P_4O'$ amounts to $1 + 10\alpha$. The 1 depends on the fact that in the reaction $P_4O + O_2 = P_4O_2 + O$, a new O is generated each time, while in the other five reactions two new O centers result with the probability α.

We will now attempt to derive an equation for the reaction rate on the assumption that the reaction is stationary, that is, the reaction rate remains constant with time. It will be shown that the solution of this equation is possible under certain conditions; the limiting case where the equation fails to apply is the appearance of an explosion because here the reaction rate, assumed to be constant, becomes infinitely great.

Thus, if N is the number of primary reactions $O + P_4 = P_4O'$ in unit time, the number of newly formed O centers from collisions of the second type (through the chain) is equal to $N(1 + 10\alpha)$. With the primary centers from spontaneous reaction in a second, n_0, we obtain the whole number of new centers in unit time; $n_0 + (1 + 10\alpha)N$.

On the other hand, in unit time some O centers disappear, partly because just N primary reactions occur in which one O is destroyed and partly because a certain number are absorbed on the walls. According to our scheme there are only two possibilities for an O that becomes free inside the vessel: therefore if we denote by A the probability that as it passes through the gas mixture it is removed by a P_4, then the probability that it will reach the wall is equal to $1 - A$. Now since the number of the processes mentioned first in unit time is N, the number absorbed on the wall is $\dfrac{N}{A}(1 - A)$ and the total number of O centers which disappear is $\dfrac{N}{A}$.

If the whole process is stationary, the equation

$$n_0 + (1 + 10\alpha)N - \frac{N}{A} = 0$$

must apply; it states that the number of O centers that disappear is equal to the number of newly forming O centers. From this we get

$$N = \frac{n_0 A}{1 - A(1 + 10\alpha)}$$

Since the dissociation rate of spontaneous decomposition of the oxygen molecules n_0 is exceptionally small, the reaction rate N is also very small as long as the inequality

$$A(1 + 10\alpha) < 1$$

holds. The smaller n_0 is, however, the steeper and more sudden will be the increase in N, as soon as the expression $A(1 + 10\alpha)$ approaches the critical value of 1. At this value we get $N = \infty$, that is, the reaction cannot be stationary and an explosion occurs.

The following selection is from pages 107–108 and 109 in *The Journal of Chemical Physics 3*, 107–115 (1935).

The Activated Complex in Chemical Reactions

HENRY EYRING

Introduction

The customary procedure for calculating bimolecular reaction rates has been to estimate the number of collisions between reacting molecules by using a cross-sectional area taken from measurements on momentum transfer. Such a cross section bears no very clear relationship to the area within which two molecules must fall in order to permit exchange of partners, i.e., to transfer mass. The violence of the collisions is of different orders of magnitude for one thing, and it is quite clear that many collisions which might result in momentum transfer are not oriented properly to permit exchange of atoms. This last difficulty is ordinarily met by introducing an empirical steric or orientation factor to take care of whatever discrepancy may arise between the observed and assumed collision area. This factor is often between 1 and 10^{-1} but may be as small as 10^{-8}. We propose here to obtain explicit expressions for the reaction rates.

The ideas underlying the present calculations are the following ones. The forces between atoms are due to the motion and distribution of electrons and must be calculated, therefore, using quantum mechanics. However, after this is done the nuclei themselves can be assumed to move under the influence of these forces according to classical mechanics. It must be possible, therefore, to calculate the reaction rates by the methods of statistical mechanics (or kinetic theory), if one assumes the aforementioned forces to be known. This is what is done in the present paper using a modification of the schemes developed by Herzfeld, Tolman, and Fowler among others and more recently applied in a very interesting way to the ortho-para hydrogen conversion by Pelzer and Wigner.

Cases occur when classical mechanics does not apply to the motion of the nuclei. Zero point energy may be present for some vibrations, and it will be necessary to deal with quantized vibrations in a semiclassical way. Tunneling may occasionally play some role in the motion. In other cases, probably also of very rare occurrence, there may be jumps from one energy level to another. The latter factors may also change the results calculated by neglecting them by orders of magnitude as, e.g., in the case of N_2O. We are not concerned here with reactions in which the last two effects are important.

We now consider in more detail the nature of the surfaces and the motion which corresponds to a reaction. A group of atoms may of course arrange themselves in an infinitely large number of ways. If the energy of such a system of atoms for the lowest quantum state of the electron is plotted against the various distances between the nuclei, we obtain the potential surface which governs (except in the aforementioned cases) the motion of the nuclei.

Now a system moving on this surface will have kinetic energy which may be quantized for the different degrees of freedom in a variety of ways, consistent with the particular energy and the particular position on the surface. Low places in the potential surfaces correspond to compounds. If a particular low-lying region is separated from all other low places by regions higher than about 23 kilocalories, the compound will be stable at and below room temperature. The higher the lowest pass the higher is the temperature at which the compound is still stable. A reaction corresponds to a system passing from one low region to another. In thermal reactions the Boltzmann factor makes it certain that the reaction will proceed by way of the lowest pass. The activated state is the highest point along this lowest pass. Before considering the activated state further we discuss the general problem of constructing our partition functions for a given surface.

Equations for these are derived.

The Activated Complex

The activated state is because of its definition always a saddle point with positive curvature in all degrees of freedom except the one which corresponds to crossing the barrier for which it is of course negative. Further, the barriers are so flat near the top that tunneling may be neglected without appreciable error. A configuration of atoms corresponding to the activated state thus has all the properties of a stable compound except in the normal mode corresponding to decomposition and this mode because of the small curvature can be treated statistically as a translational degree of freedom. Thus a non-linear activated complex with n atoms ($n \gneqq 3$) has three regular translational degrees of freedom corresponding to motion of the center of mass in addition to the one corresponding to passage over the top of the barrier. It also has three rotational degrees of freedom for the molecule as a whole, and the remaining ($3n - 7$) degrees of freedom correspond to internal rotations or vibrations. A linear molecule differs from this in that one of the degrees of freedom which was a rotation is instead a bending vibration. Now the calculation of the concentration of activated complexes is a straightforward statistical problem, given the moments of inertia of the complex and the vibration frequencies. This information is given with sufficient accuracy, even by our very approximate potential surfaces, to give good values for the partition functions.

The procedure for calculating the specific rate is the following: One first calculates the concentration of activated complexes per unit length and with momentum p lying between p and $p + dp$, both these quantities taken for the degree of freedom corresponding to decomposition. This is then multiplied by the associated velocity

$p/m^\star$ and summed for all values of moments which correspond to passing over the energy barrier in the forward direction, i.e., for $p = 0$ to ∞.

Equations are then derived for specific and general cases.

An essential feature of many of the chain mechanisms assumed in studying reaction kinetics involved the intermediate formation of free radicals. Spectroscopic evidence had for a long time indicated the momentary existence of free radicals, and Gomberg at the beginning of the twentieth century actually isolated free organic radicals in certain heavy aromatic hydrocarbons; see H. M. Leicester and H. S. Klickstein, *A Source Book in Chemistry, 1400–1900* (Harvard University Press, Cambridge, Massachusetts, 1952), p. 512. In the mid-nineteenth century Kolbe believed that he had isolated simple radicals such as methyl, but it was soon realized that his radical methyl was actually the doubled molecule of ethane. Thus there was no true chemical evidence that the radicals that were assumed to take part in many reactions could actually exist. The problem was finally settled when Paneth and his co-workers in 1929 succeeded in demonstrating that free methyl could actually exist for brief but definite periods of time. The next selection shows how this was done.

The following selection is from pages 1335, 1336–1337, 1338–1340, and 1343 in *Berichte der Deutschen Chemischen Gesellschaft 62*, 1335–1347 (1929).

The Preparation of Free Methyl

FRITZ PANETH AND WILHELM HOFEDITZ

Some time ago a method was reported for the preparation of gaseous metal hydrides by glow discharge in hydrogen; it then proved necessary to replace the hydrogen by a hydrocarbon such as methane. In the case of antimony and tin it could be recognized by quantitative analysis of the resulting gaseous metal compound that the hydride actually resulted from this not very obvious method; with lead, the corresponding analysis did not succeed. In order to explain the reaction mechanism, we felt it was necessary to test whether, besides the hydride, there was not also formation of a metallic organic compound, and this led us to the question of the stability of the methyl group under the investigative conditions used. While we cannot yet say anything positive as to the mechanism of the formation of the hydrides—we will return to this point at the end of this paper—we believe we can conclude from our study that it is possible to demonstrate *the simplest organic radical with trivalent carbon, methyl, in the free state.* Since this side result of our work is of sufficient interest, we will first report on it.

A historical account is then given of early attempts to isolate free radicals.

After we had obtained evidence, by repeating the above-mentioned investigation of glow discharge in hydrogen which contained methane, that free methyl was capable of existence, we sought methods by which it could by obtained in a purer state, that is, less mixed with other hydrocarbons. We will begin by describing a study which shows *the activity of free methyl several centimeters away from the place of formation.*

If the vapor of lead tetramethyl is added to pure hydrogen or pure nitrogen and this gas mixture is conducted through a quartz tube which is heated at one point with a Bunsen burner, decomposition of the lead tetramethyl occurs with separation of lead. This separates as a gray metal mirror, brown in thinner layers, and, depending on the speed of the gas stream, in front of or behind the heated point in the tube. In our study in which we carried out the *thermal decomposition of lead tetramethyl at reduced pressure,* we used the following apparatus. [The apparatus is described.]

Under the above-mentioned conditions, by placing a lighted Bunsen burner at point II of the tube (Fig. 2) we form a lead mirror, not too heavy; the period of time for the separation is about 1–2 minutes. Then by reversing stopcocks 2, 3, and 4 (Fig. 1) the heated portion of the tube is cooled in a pure hydrogen stream.

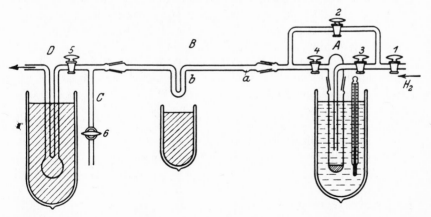

Fig. 1

Now if a new lead mirror is produced at position I in the same way, it can be seen how the old mirror at position II decreases during this process, and vanishes quantitatively from the tube, complete

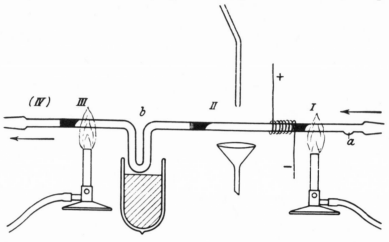

Fig. 2

purity of the reagents being assumed. The time needed for complete disappearance is in direct relation to the amount of lead contained in the mirror and is inversely proportional to the amount of lead tetramethyl that is thermally decomposed in unit time at the new separation point (I).

This effect falls off markedly with increasing separation between positions I and II but under the conditions mentioned, we could still show it at a separation of more than 30 cm.

That here there was not some thermal action of heated hydrogen was shown by the fact that it was possible to pass heated hydrogen for an hour over a lead mirror in direct proximity to the flame without any change occurring. (With direct heating, the mirror moves slowly forward in the hydrogen stream without suffering any visible amount of loss in this way.) On the other hand, we can introduce water cooling between positions I and II in the process of mirror disappearance, as Fig. 2 shows, without stopping the effect.

It seems to us to be most important to clarify the question of *what chemical compound forms when the lead mirror disappears.* It is easy to show that in this process a very stable substance is obtained which in its properties is at least extremely similar to lead tetramethyl. If a lead mirror in position II (Fig. 2) is made to disappear by the method described, and during this process the quartz tube is heated by a second burner at position III there appears at that point in proportion to the disappearance at II a new mirror, which after the end of the process approximately corresponds in strength to the mirror that disappeared at II. The study can also be so conducted that the substance that first forms with disappearance of mirror II is frozen out with liquid air at *b*, and then when the liquid air is removed, and the condensate is again vaporized, the decomposition at position III is again resumed. Moreover, by again decomposing at position III it is possible to cause the disappearance of a further mirror at position IV.

It can perhaps now be objected that by decomposition of lead tetramethyl at position I the breakdown may not be complete and some of the observed effects may be related to undecomposed or half decomposed lead tetramethyl.

We therefore studied what amount of lead methyl compound passed position I undecomposed, for which purpose we heated the tube with a second burner (about at II). We then showed that by the very strongest heating at I there was always a very slight amount of lead separated behind the second flame. This amount was certainly not sufficient to see in it the origin of the observed effect, but the explanation of its source gave another contribution to the recognition of the dissolving action.

Therefore we must raise the question of whether thermal dissociation of the lead tetramethyl permits us to observe the *consuming action* of the aggressive substance that is formed upon its "own" mirror. This question must be answered. By close observation we can see that such a lead mirror is bounded by a sharp edge on one side of the flame and on the other. While on the side of the moved flame this is limited by the flame temperature, which can also be recognized by the edge line (see Fig. 2), there appears on the other side a sharp boundary line that is remarkable for the strongly formed lead mirror and for which there is no explanation. We would expect on this side a much slower removal of the lead deposit. We now believe that we are here dealing with a second temperature boundary, and this indeed is possible from a recombination of material already split by decomposition of lead tetramethyl.

This assumption can be established by the following experiment: if the blank part of the tube behind a lead mirror (I in Fig. 2) is heated by an electric spiral to such a temperature that separation of lead occurs on the tube walls, the reformation of lead tetramethyl is hindered and thus we actually get a broader, slowly removed lead mirror. If now we allow the process of thermal dissociation to proceed again and remove the heating spiral, then the broad lead mirror will once more be reduced to the old boundary. By control with a second burner it can be shown that behind the lead mirror from the heating spiral hardly any more undecomposed lead tetramethyl is found passing through. On the other hand, one is entitled to equate the amount of lead that separated behind the second burner in the above study without the heating spiral with the amount that was missed in the study itself at the first mirror because of its limits. (The ability to dissolve lead mirrors in the cold part of the tube is not affected by the heating spiral.)

In further studies we worked mostly with the "quantitative decomposition method," that is, with the use of a heating spiral behind the Bunsen burner.

To determine whether the phenomenon is related to hydrogen in the transport gas, we replaced the hydrogen with pure nitrogen expressly prepared for the purpose. There was not the slightest difference. With commercial nitrogen, because of its oxygen content, the study was completely negative.

Collective experiments on the thermal decomposition of antimony hydride under various conditions to produce a similar effect were without results.

It is thus seen from these studies *that by thermal dissociation of lead tetramethyl a gaseous agent is formed which can dissolve a layer of lead* and convert it into a compound similar to if not identical with lead tetramethyl. This agent is *stable for only a short time*, after which its activity falls off strongly at increasing distances between the point of formation and the point of reaction. As expected, after condensation in liquid air it cannot be thawed out; its activity is then lost.

The authors show that this agent similarly dissolves mirrors of antimony and zinc metal, and that zinc dimethyl is formed from zinc. Sulfur under these conditions forms an organic sulfur compound. No ethane, ethylene, methane, or acetylene are present.

Therefore we come to the conclusion that the observations collected here can be explained only by the assumption that the aggressive substance is *the free CH_3 radical to which we must ascribe a measurable, if brief, length of life.* Under given conditions it was possible to carry free methyl over a longer distance and to carry out reactions with it far from the point of formation. The formation of zinc dimethyl, for example, can be stated as a simple addition reaction:

$$Zn + 2CH_3 = Zn(CH_3)_2$$

ARTIFICIAL RADIOACTIVITY. While chemists were busy elucidating the nature of the chemical bond—that is, studying the properties of the outer electron shells of atoms—physicists continued to investigate atomic structure and radioactive phenomena. By using increasingly powerful tools they showed that they could alter the nature of the atomic nucleus and thus transform the elements themselves. The dreams of the alchemists had been realized, but in a manner utterly foreign to alchemical thought. However, these results once more brought the chemist into the picture, for he had to prove by chemical reactions that new elements had actually been produced, and then he had to study the chemistry of the new elements.

The first successful proof of artificial transmutation came in 1934 with the work of the Joliot-Curies in France. Fermi and his co-workers in Italy showed that slowed neutron bombardment of many elements could lead to formation of new elements. Their very inclusive patent given below served as the basis for the production of the first atomic bomb.

At first it was believed that when atomic nuclei were bombarded with neutrons they always took up these neutrons to form the nuclei of heavier elements. There was thus hope of producing elements heavier than uranium. Then Hahn and Strassmann in 1939 found that results of neutron bombardment sometimes did not agree with this theory. The results that required some other explanation are given in the third of the following selections, and were at once interpreted correctly by Meitner and Frisch, as the fourth selection shows.

Two possible paths were thus available, fission or neutron capture without fission. One path led to the atom bomb, the other to the transuranium elements. McMillan and Abelson in the fifth following selection described the results of the first step on the latter path in 1940. Work after this became swallowed up in secrecy as the second world war put an end to much scientific publication. After the explosion of the first atom bomb had openly shown the results of the fission path, publication was again resumed. The selections that conclude this section showed that synthetic elements could indeed be produced in regular succession. Investigations of the transuranium elements continued actively as the first half of the twentieth century ended.

The following selection is in *Le Journal de Physique et Le Radium* [7] 5, 153–156 (1934).

I. Artificial Production of Radioactive Elements
II. Chemical Proof of Transmutation of Elements

IRENE CURIE AND F. JOLIOT

We have recently shown that certain light elements (glucinum, boron, aluminum) emit positive electrons when they are bombarded with α-rays of polonium.

Glucinum emits positive and negative electrons of comparable energies, attaining several million electron volts. We have attributed the emission of these electrons to the "internal materialization" of γ-rays of great quantum energy (5×10^6 eV) emitted by glucinum

$$^9_4\text{Be} + ^4_2\text{He} = ^{12}_6\text{C} + ^1_0\text{n} + \varepsilon^+ + \varepsilon^-$$

Aluminium, on the contrary, emits only positive electrons whose energy can attain 3×10^6 eV. The negative electrons observed are all attributable to polonium (electrons emitted by internal conversion of γ-rays) and their energy does not exceed 0.9×10^6 eV.

We have considered the positive electrons as true "transmutation electrons" whose emission intervenes in the nuclear transformation.

In the course of experiments made with a view to determining the minimum energy of α-rays exciting the positrons of aluminum we have learned that the emission is not instantaneous, but *it is only produced after some minutes of irradiation and continues for some time after stopping the irradiation.*

We irradiate a leaf of aluminium foil with α-rays from a strong polonium source for several minutes, and when we withdraw the foil it possesses an activity which decreases by half in 3 min. 15 sec.; the emitted ray, which can be observed with a counter or a Wilson apparatus, is composed of positive electrons.

Irradiated boron and magnesium also show a lasting radioactivity with periods of 14 min. and $2\frac{1}{2}$ min. respectively.

The decrease follows an exponential law.

The curves of Fig. 1 represent the logarithmic variation of intensities as a function of time.

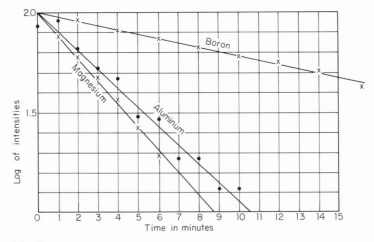

Fig. 1

We are then in the presence of new radioelements and of a new type of radioactivity with emission of positive electrons.

The initial intensity of the rays observed increases with time of irradiation t up to a limiting value of I_∞ following a law $I = I_\infty$ $(1 - e^{\lambda t})$ like, for example, the accumulation of radon in radium. We reach the activation limit after some periods of the radioactive body formation (about a quarter of an hour for aluminum, an hour for boron).

If we activate to saturation with a source of polonium of 60 millicuries, and if we immediately place the source near the counter with a thin window permitting count of the electrons, the number of counts is of the same order, about 150 per minute, for boron, aluminum, and magnesium. We can calculate by taking account of the solid angle used, that this corresponds to a yield in creation of active nuclei on the order of 10^{-6} with respect to the number of incident α-rays, as we would expect for a transmutation phenomenon.

In spite of the yields of activation which differ little for boron, magnesium, and aluminum, the experiments are more difficult with magnesium because of the more rapid decrease of the activity.

With the elements H, Li, C, Be, N, O, F, Na, Ca, Ni, Ag, no effect has been observed. For certain elements the phenomenon is probably not produced, for others the period of decrease is perhaps too short or too long, for it would then need a long irradiation.

The ray emitted by Al is absorbed for the most part in 1 gr./cm.^{2} of copper, those of B and Mg in 0.26 gr./cm.^{2}.

The rays of irradiated aluminum and boron, photographed by the Wilson method in a magnetic field, are shown to be composed solely of positrons, without negative electrons. If there are emissions of negative electrons, they should be very rare or at least their energy should be below 200,000 eV.

Here are the distribution curves observed for the energy of the positive electrons.

For Al the electrons are distributed following a continuous spectrum with a maximum intensity about 10^6 eV and an upper limit of energy close to 3×10^6 eV. For boron, the maximum intensity is about 0.5×10^6 eV, and the upper limit of energy is close to 1.5×10^6 eV.

Irradiated magnesium emits negative electrons and positive electrons, forming two continuous spectra with energy maxima about 2.2×10^6 eV and 1.5×10^6 eV respectively.

Nature of the elements formed. We can present two hypotheses as to the nature of the elements formed: the active nuclei are unstable

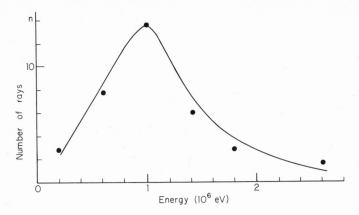

Fig. 2. Radiophosphorus.

isotopes of certain light elements or of known stable nuclei created in a state of particular excitement. The first hypothesis seems to us the more probable.

Here are the nuclear reactions that we accept in accord with our first interpretation of the positive transmutation electrons.

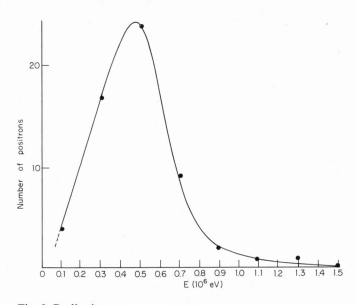

Fig. 3. Radionitrogen.

The nuclei $^{10}_{5}$B, $^{24}_{12}$Mg, $^{27}_{13}$Al undergo transmutation with capture of an α-particle and emission of a neutron

$$^{10}_{5}\text{B} \quad + {}^{4}_{2}\text{He} = {}^{13}_{7}\text{N} + {}^{1}_{0}\text{n}$$

$$^{21}_{12}\text{Mg} + {}^{4}_{2}\text{He} = {}^{27}_{14}\text{Si} + {}^{1}_{0}\text{n}$$

$$^{27}_{13}\text{Al} \quad + {}^{4}_{2}\text{He} = {}^{30}_{15}\text{P} + {}^{1}_{0}\text{n}$$

The isotopes $^{13}_{7}$N, $^{27}_{14}$Si, and $^{30}_{15}$P are not known. They are probably unstable nuclei which are destroyed with emission of positrons, giving the stable nuclei $^{12}_{6}$C, $^{27}_{13}$Al, $^{30}_{14}$Si

$$^{14}_{7}\text{N} = {}^{13}_{6}\text{C} + \overset{+}{\text{e}} \text{ [sic]}$$

$$^{27}_{14}\text{Si} = {}^{27}_{13}\text{Al} + \overset{+}{\text{e}}$$

$$^{30}_{15}\text{P} = {}^{30}_{14}\text{Si} + \overset{+}{\text{e}}$$

It is very probable that fluorine and sodium $^{19}_{9}$F and $^{23}_{11}$Na, which emit protons and neutrons under the action of α-rays give unstable isotopes $^{22}_{11}$Na and $^{26}_{13}$Al which are destroyed with emission of positrons giving the stable nuclei $^{22}_{10}$Ne and $^{26}_{12}$Mg. The period of the unstable elements is probably not favorable for observation.

The radio element, emitter of β-rays, created in irradiated magnesium is probably a nucleus of $^{28}_{13}$Al formed starting from $^{25}_{12}$Mg by capture of an α-particle and emission of a proton. The negative electrons being more numerous than the positive ones, it is probable that the period of 2 min. 13 sec. observed corresponds to this radio element.

By reason of the law of conservation of energy and of spin, it is without doubt necessary to admit that the emission of positive electrons is accompanied by that of a neutrino, as in the case of the spectrum of β-rays of ordinary radio elements, and perhaps here of an "anti neutrino" of Louis de Broglie.

Indeed, the emission of a transmutation proton of Al, for example, should follow the reaction

$$^{27}_{13}\text{Al} + {}^{4}_{2}\text{He} = {}^{30}_{14}\text{Si} + {}^{1}_{1}\text{H}$$

That of a neutron followed by that of a positive electron would lead to the same nucleus $^{30}_{14}$Si. In the second method of transmutation the emission of the proton would then be replaced by that of a neutron and a positive electron. The proton, the neutron, and the positive electron being supposed to have a spin $\frac{1}{2}$, this is possible only on condition of admitting emission of another particle with spin $\frac{1}{2}$.

If our hypotheses concerning the nuclear transformations are correct, the minimum energy of α-rays needed to create the new radio elements should be the same as the minimum energy of excitation of the neutrons.

Experiments have been made in exciting the radiation of B, Mg, and Al by α-rays slowed by thin screens. The period of the radioelements formed does not depend on the energy of the incident α-rays. We have not yet established the difference in penetration of the radiation.

The minimum energy of α-particles needed for excitation of the neutrons is 2×10^6 eV for B (1 cm. distance), 4 to 4.5×10^6 eV for Mg and Al (3 cm. distance). For Mg and Al, the limit of emission of positive electrons has been found to be the same as that of neutrons within the limits of precision of the experiments. For B we have observed the excitation of positive electrons for α-rays of about 3×10^6 eV (2 cm. distance) and it is very probable that only the lack of intensity prevents us from observing up to 2×10^6 eV.

Chemical proof of transmutation. The phenomena of artificial transmutation of elements seem to us to be certain. The physical experiments have demonstrated the existence of these phenomena and have even permitted us to conclude that the particles that produce the transmutation are captured in the nucleus as the experiments of Blackett have shown from the first for the transmutation of nitrogen for α-rays with emission of a proton.

However, the reality of transmutation has never been verified chemically, as in the case of the natural disintegration of radioactive elements. This is because the small number of atoms produced during the artificial transmutation cannot be disclosed by any procedure of analysis and consequently we cannot recognize their chemical properties.

Here, on the contrary, we have obtained by irradiation of boron, magnesium, and aluminum, different nuclei, in very small numbers, but their radioactive properties permit their detection.

We have proposed to check the hypothesis that we have suggested on the nature of these elements by determining their chemical characteristics.

Transmutation of boron. Boron, composed of grains very difficult to attack, is badly adapted to experiment. We have irradiated boron nitride (nitrogen has no effect). Boron nitride, BN, is decomposed by hot soda and the nitrogen is liberated in the form of ammonia. This operation can be carried out in a few minutes. We showed that boron loses its activity. The ammonia that was evolved was recovered in a narrow tube which we measured in a Hoffmann electrometer in an ionization chamber closed by a narrow piece of aluminum foil. Taking account of the decrease of activity during the operation we established that a great part of the activity was found in the tube. The radioelement showed the chemical properties of nitrogen; it was liberated in the form of nitrogen or in the form of ammonia carried along by the inactive ammonia.

Transmutation of aluminum. A thin sheet of irradiated aluminum is dissolved in HCl. The aluminum salt, dried immediately, is almost completely inactive. The hydrogen evolved can be recovered in a narrow tube at a distance and we have established that it has caught the activity. It is necessary to act very quickly because of the rapid decrease in activity; we can carry out the operation in 3 minutes.

The radioelement which should have the properties of phosphorus has entered the gaseous state in the form of a phosphorus hydride produced by the nascent hydrogen. If we dissolve Al in an oxidizing medium $HCl + HNO_3$, the activity remains with the aluminum.

However, the above reactions are produced in the same manner if the radioelement had the properties of silicon, for in this case silicon hydride would be formed.

We can also dissolve the irradiated aluminum, add sodium phosphate, and precipitate by a zirconium salt. The zirconium phosphate which precipitates in a weakly acid solution carries the acidity. It is thus probable that it indeed acts like a phosphorus isotope.

For magnesium we have not verified the chemical nature of the elements formed which in our view should be isotopes of silicon and aluminum.

We propose to call the new radioelements which emit positrons or β-rays *radionitrogen, radioaluminum, radiosilicon, radiophosphorus.*

The above experiments give chemical proof 1, that the element formed by transmutation is different from the initial element; 2, that the α-particle has been captured in the nucleus.

Conclusions. It is probable that a certain number of nuclei, isotopes of known elements, are radioelements which do not exist in nature because of their instability, but which can be created by transmutation of ordinary elements by means of various irradiating particles: protons, deutons, α-rays, neutrons, and perhaps still others. We may believe that these radioelements are not all emitters of positrons or β-rays but that certain of them emit heavier particles. Perhaps there also exist elements derived from others which constitute true unknown radioactive families.

The same radioactive element can without doubt be created by several different nuclear reactions.

Cockroft, Gilbert, and Walton, following our experiments, having tried to create new radioelements by bombarding with protons, have obtained by irradiation of carbon a radioelement, an emitter of positrons with a period of 10.5 minutes; these authors suppose that it is related to the radionitrogen that we have created starting from boron and they explain the difference in period by a different state of excitation. This interpretation seems improbable to us and we think that it relates to still another radioelement.

The study of these phenomena cannot fail to add an important contribution to the problem of stability of nuclei.

Moreover, the energies and intensities actually obtained in the producing tubes for accelerated particles allow us to consider close the moment when we will be able to create by means of these particles radioelements with an intensity of radiation superior to that of preparations of natural radioelements, usable for medical application or for other purposes. These radioelements will not only be emitters of positrons, but also of γ-radiation from annihilation of positrons, let us say 2 quanta of 500,000 eV per positron emitted. They will then constitute powerful sources of penetrating radiation.

We thank Mme. Pierre Curie for the interest she has taken in this work and M. Preiswerk for the efficient aid he has rendered.

The following patent selection includes seven claims.

Patented July 2, 1940   2,206,634
United States Patent Office

Process for the Production of Radioactive Substances

ENRICO FERMI, EDOARDO AMALDI, BRUNO
PONTOCORVO, FRANCO RASETTI, AND EMILIO SEGRÈ,

Rome, Italy, assigners to G. M. Giannini and Co., Inc., New York, N.Y., a corporation of New York

Application October 3, 1935, Serial No. 43,462
In Italy October 26, 1934

This invention relates to the production of isotopes of elements from other isotopes of the same or different elements by reaction with neutrons, and especially to the production of artificial radioactivity by formation of unstable isotopes.

It has been known for many years that, although each chemical element has always the same atomic number of charge, it may exist in different forms having different atomic weights. These forms of the elements are referred to as isotopes.

It has also been known that radio-active elements, by disintegration or breakdown occurring in their nuclei are spontaneously converted into various isotopes of other elements. Thus, for example, the radio-active element uranium may be converted into lead of atomic weight 206, while the element thorium may be converted into a different isotope of atomic weight 208.

It has long been known that such spontaneous disintegration of radio-active elements is accompanied by emission of alpha, beta, and gamma rays, that is to say, of the helium nucleus, electrons, and electromagnetic radiation of extremely short wave length.

In more recent years it has been demonstrated that isotopes of various elements could be converted into other isotopes of the same or different elements by bombardment with alpha particles, diplons, protons or gamma rays of very high energy, and that the isotopes thus produced may be unstable so as to decompose with features similar to those of the naturally radioactive bodies. That is to say, radioactive isotopes may, in this way, be artificially produced.

Accordingly, it is an object of the present invention to provide a method and apparatus by which nuclear reactions can be carried on with high efficiency and with the heavier as well as with the lighter elements. A more specific object of the invention is to provide a method and apparatus for artificially producing radioactive substances with efficiency such that their cost may be brought below that of natural radioactive materials.

Our invention is based upon the use of neutrons instead of charged particles for the bombardment and transformation of the isotopes.

All of the prior work on nuclear reactions has been done with high energy particles and every effort has been bent toward increasing the energy of the particles as the means of extending and making more efficient the nuclear reactions. We have now discovered that effort in this direction is sound only when charged particles are used which require tremendous energy to break through the potential barrier surrounding the nucleus; and that if, instead of charged particles, neutrons are used for the nuclear reactions, the greatest efficiencies are in some cases attained with low energy or "slow" neutrons, *e.g.*, of the order of a few hundred electron volts, or even much less down to a small fraction of an electron volt.

Neutrons when produced in any ordinary manner, *e.g.*, by the action of radon on beryllium or of polonium on beryllium or by bombardment of atomic nuclei with artificially accelerated particles, might have a very wide range of energies but high average energy.

These energies range up to several million volts. It is necessary, therefore, if the greatest efficiency of reaction is to be attained, to reduce by artificial means the energy of these neutrons. We describe below a method for slowing down fast neutrons.

We have demonstrated that the absorption of slow neutrons is anomalously large as compared with that of the faster or higher energy neutrons. The simplest explanation for most cases is to admit that the neutron is captured by the nucleus with formation of an isotope heavier by one mass unit. If this heavier isotope is unstable a strong induced radio-activity may be expected. This occurs, for example, with silver and iridium which go over into radio-active isotopes. In other cases it is found that no activation, or at least no strong activation, follows an anomalously large absorption. This is the case with many elements, *e.g.*, yttrium and cadmium. In these cases the formation of a stable nucleus upon the capture of the neutrons is to be expected.

In some cases the absorption of the slow neutrons results in the emission of a relatively strong gamma-radiation with energy corresponding to the binding energy of the neutron. This gives a reliable source of very hard gamma rays, even harder than the naturally produced gamma rays, *e.g.*, from radium.

In view of these considerations it is obviously desirable to convert as many as possible of the available neutrons into the slow or low energy condition in which they may be readily captured by the nuclei of the substance being reacted. We have found that it is possible to achieve the desired results by passing the neutron radiation against or through a screen of suitable material.

The materials which have been found best suited to this purpose are those containing hydrogen (including all its isotopes, but the light isotope which predominates in natural occurrence being most efficient) and especially water and the hydrocarbons, such as paraffin for example. Other materials, as for example beryllium, carbon, silicon, lead, show this effect to a lesser degree. Other materials, of which iron is an example, do not produce a similar effect to any practical extent, probably because of a relatively large absorption of the neutrons when their energy is reduced.

The increase in activity of the neutrons by such substances is apparently due to two effects both resulting from collisions of the neutrons. In the first place it is readily shown that an impact of a neutron against a proton reduces, on the average, the neutron energy by a factor of $1/e$. From this it follows that ten impacts reduce the energy to about $1/20,000$ of its original value. Assuming the initial energy to be 4.10^6 electron volts, the energy after ten impacts would be about 200 electron volts and 20 impacts would reduce the energy of the neutron down to a value corresponding to thermal agitation. Thus the first important effect is probably the reduction of the energy of the faster neutrons by impact and the efficiency of hydrogen for this purpose is probably due to the low mass of the hydrogen nucleus. Although we refer to the nucleus, because almost the entire mass is represented by the nucleus, it will be understood that the impact for slowing down may be, and for reasons of economy ordinarily will be, with atoms, *i.e.*, combined nuclei.

The second probable effect is the scattering and reflection of the neutrons.

Hydrogen is so much more effective than any of the other elements for reducing the energy of neutrons that it will ordinarily be used. It must not be overlooked, however, that the elements having a lesser effect offer possibilities for control of the neutron energy. Where neutrons of initially lower energy are used or where their use requires a higher energy than in the reactions with which we are here especially concerned, the less effective elements may be used singly or combined with elements of different energy reducing power.

The density of the energy reducing or scattering substance has also been found to be an important factor. This follows, likewise, from the theoretical explanation given above. If the energy reduction and scattering of the neutrons is due to impact with atomic nuclei, the probable frequency of such impacts will be directly dependent upon the number of atoms in a given space. For this reason such substances ordinarily should be used in liquid or solid (*i.e.*, non-gaseous) form and, so far as is practicable, substances will be chosen having as high as possible a proportion of hydrogen in the molecule. Here again, the gaseous state under various pressures, and substances having less hydrogen offer the possibility for accurate control if less than the maximum slowing of neutrons is desirable.

It will be readily understood from what has been said above that the greatest effect is attained if the source of neutrons and the substance being irradiated are both surrounded by the energy reducing and scattering material. This could easily be accomplished in many cases by immersing the neutron source in a solution or emulsion of the substance being bombarded. We have illustrated diagrammatically in Figures 1 and 2 [not included here] arrangements by which this may be accomplished.

In Figure 1 a cylindrical paraffin block 10 is provided with a hole 11 into which is inserted a source of neutrons, *e.g.*, a tube containing radon and beryllium. The material being irradiated is placed above the source on the paraffin block as shown at 12 and is covered by a second paraffin block 13 having a central opening 14 to accommodate the material being irradiated. For the treatment of small amounts of materials the block 10 may be, for example, about 24 centimeters in diameter and about 14 centimeters in height with the neutron source about 2 centimeters under the upper surface. It will observed that these dimensions give radial thickness of the material surrounding the neutron source approximately equal to the mean free path in the substance of the high energy neutrons.

Where the substances to be irradiated are soluble in or can be suspended in water or a hydrocarbon or other energy reducing or dispersing substance, etc., may be formed and the substances irradiated therein by immersing the neutron source directly into the solution etc. [sic] (See Fig. 2.)

The hydrogen which serves to reduce the energy of the neutrons may also be in chemical combination with the substance being irradiated.

Figure 2 is a diagrammatic illustration of a neutron irradiating device in which the substance being irradiated is dissolved or dispersed in the energy reducing or dispersing material. A suitable vessel 20 is provided for holding the solution or dispersion 21 and into this is immersed the neutron source 22.

Instead of the radon beryllium source, any other source of neutrons may be used, as for example neutron tubes as developed by Oliphant and as more recently developed by the laboratories of the General Electric Company and the Westinghouse Electric and Manufacturing Company or cyclotrons as developed by Lawrence. In such tubes deuteron oxide (heavy water), which may be separated by known methods from naturally occurring water, is bombarded with deuterons accelerated in an electric field produced by a grid tube. The deuteron nucleus is disintegrated with the emission of neutrons.

Obviously the apparatus can be endlessly modified, the essential being the combination of the energy reducing substance near the substance being irradiated, and a suitable source of neutron radiation.

A tabulation of the results of various irradiations carried out is given. The description of the irradiation of uranium reads as follows:

92. *Uranium.* We have also studied the influence of hydrogenated substances on the induced activities of this element. (Periods 15 seconds, 40 seconds, 13 minutes, 100 minutes.) The result was that while the activities corresponding to the first, third and fourth period are slightly increased by water, no increase was found for the activity corresponding to the 40-second period.

Chemical evidence seems to indicate that the carriers of the 13- and the 100-minute activities were not isotopes of any of the known heaviest elements, and that they were probably due to transuranic elements.

The precipitation of the activity with a sulphide was repeated, precipitating several metals (silver, copper, lead, mercury); the acidity of the solution (hydrochloric acid) was about 20 %; sometimes slightly varied in order to facilitate the precipitation of the sulphide of the metal used. The yield in activity of the precipitate was generally good—about 50 %—and varied according to the conditions of the precipitation. Nitric acid lowers the yield of the reaction very much. The usual high yield of the sulphide reaction is also obtained in presence of a hydrofluoric solution of tantalum. We also made a test in order to see whether the induced activities presented a reaction which is given by von Grosse as the most characteristic of proto-actinium.

We dissolved in a 25 % hydrochloric acid solution uranium oxide which had been purified and irradiated; we added to the solution zirconium nitrate and phosphoric acid; the precipitate of zirconium phosphate was inactive. After the separation of zirconium we precipitated a sulphide from the filtered solution, and collected the activity in the sulphide with the usual yield. According to von Grosse and Agruss, this reaction must be considered a proof by the non-identity of the carrier of the activity with a protoactinium isotope. The 15-second, 13-minute, and 100-minute activities are probably chain products, with atomic number 92, 93 and 94 respectively and atomic weight 239.

From the above tabulation it is apparent that the increase in activities by the hydrogen containing substances, etc., is particularly applicable to those nuclear reactions in which the neutron is captured with the formation of a heavier isotope of the same element; and the present invention makes possible numerous reactions of this type which could not be appreciably carried out without the use of our invention. . . .

Although we have herein described our invention in detail and specified particular examples of apparatus and processes and various modifications thereof, and have proposed various theoretical explanations, it is to be understood that these are not binding nor exhaustive but are intended rather for the assistance of others skilled in the art to enable them more easily to apply our invention under widely varying conditions encountered in actual practice and to change and modify the particular embodiments and examples herein described as may be necessary or desirable under such varying conditions. The theoretical statements and explanations are, of course, not conclusive and our invention is in no way dependent upon their correctness. We have found them helpful and give them for the aid of others, but our invention will be equally useful if it should prove that our theoretical conclusions are not altogether correct.

The following selection is from pages 11–12 and 12–14 in *Die Natur-wissenschaften 27*, 11–15 (1939).

The Detection and Behavior of the Alkaline Earth Metals Which Result from the Irradiation of Uranium by Neutrons

O. HAHN AND F. STRASSMANN

In a preliminary communication which recently appeared here it was reported that by irradiation of uranium with neutrons, in addition to the separately described transuranium elements of Meitner, Hahn, and Strassmann, elements 93 to 96, a number of other disintegration products resulted which evidently owed their formation to two successive α-ray disintegrations from the transient uranium 239. In such a disintegration the element with the nuclear charge 92 must give one with the nuclear charge 88, thus a radium. In that communication we proposed as a preliminary disintegration scheme 3 such radium isotopes with estimated half lives, and their disintegration products, three isomeric actinium isotopes which in turn evidently changed into thorium isotopes.

At the same time we made the unexpected observation that with α-ray disintegration the thorium-forming radium isotopes resulted not only with fast, but with slow neutrons.

The conclusion that the starting members of these three new isotopic series were radium isotopes was based on the fact that these substances could be separated with barium salts and showed all the reactions characteristic of the element barium. All the other known elements, beginning with the transuraniums through uranium, protoactinium, thorium, to actinium have properties different from barium and can easily be separated from it. This also applies to the elements below uranium, bismuth, lead, polonium, ekacesium.

Thus, if barium itself is left out of consideration, only radium remains.

In what follows we will describe briefly the separation of the isotope mixture and the obtaining of the individual members.

The activity behavior of the individual isotopes shows their half lives and permits finding the disintegration products which result from them. However, in this communication the latter are not yet described separately, because of the very complex processes—there are at least three and apparently four series with three substances—the half lives of all the disintegration products cannot yet be completely established.

As the carrier of the "radium isotopes" we always used natural barium. Most logical was the precipitation of barium as the barium sulfate which along with the chromate is the most difficultly soluble barium salt. However, from previous experience and some preliminary studies, the separation of the "radium isotopes" with barium sulfate was discarded, for the precipitate carried down along with slight amounts of uranium not inconsiderable amounts of actinium and thorium isotopes, the then supposed disintegration products of the radium isotopes and therefore this permitted no purification of the initial members. Instead of the sulfate precipitate with its quantitatively very great surface we therefore chose barium chloride, which is very difficultly soluble in strong hydrochloric acid, as the precipitating material, a method that has proved the best.

Because of the difficulty in understanding the formation of radium isotopes from uranium by bombardment with slow neutrons, it was especially necessary to determine the chemical nature of the newly formed artificial radioelements. By the separation of individual analytical groups of elements from the solution of irradiated uranium, besides the large group of transuraniums, there was always an activity from the alkaline earths (carrier Ba), from the rare earths (carrier La), and from the elements of the fourth group of the periodic system (carrier Zr). We next studied more thoroughly the barium precipitation, which evidently included the starting members of the observed isotopic series. It will be shown that the transuraniums, protoactinium, thorium, and actinium can always be easily and completely separated from the activity which precipitates with barium.

1. For this purpose, the transuraniums were separated together from an irradiated uranium by hydrogen sulfide along with platinum sulfide, and were then dissolved in aqua regia. Barium chloride was precipitated from this solution by hydrochloric acid. The platinum was once more precipitated from the filtrate of the barium precipitate using hydrogen sulfide. The barium chloride was inactive, the platinum sulfide still had an activity of about 500 particles/minute. A corresponding study with long lived transuraniums had the same result.

2. A precipitate of barium chloride from 10 g. of non-irradiated uranyl nitrate which was in equilibrium with $UX_1 + UX_2$ (thorium and protoactinium isotopes) and had an activity of about 400,000 particles/minute showed an activity of about 14 particles/minute and thus was practically inactive, that is, neither uranium nor protoactinium precipitated with the crystalline barium chloride.

3. Finally, we precipitated from a solution of an actinium preparation ($MsTh_2$) with 2500 particles/minute a barium chloride precipitate which showed about 3 particles/minute and thus was practically inactive.

In a similar way we carefully tested the strongly active barium chloride precipitate from irradiated uranium; the sulfide precipitate from neutral, weak acetic acid, or weak mineral acid solutions of the active barium was practically inactive, while the lanthanum and zirconium precipitates had only the activity whose origin from the activity of the barium precipitate could easily be recognized.

The simple precipitation with $BaCl_2$ from strong hydrochloric acid solution naturally permits no separation between barium and radium. Thus, on the basis of this overall count the activity that separates with the barium salt can come only from radium, if barium itself is left out of consideration as too improbable.

We will now consider briefly the activity curve obtained with the barium chloride, which indicates the number of "radium isotopes" and also permits a determination of their half lives.

Figure 1 shows the activity behavior of the active barium chloride after four day irradiation of uranium. Curve a gives the measurement over the first 70 hours; curve b the values measured for the same preparation continued over 800 hours. The scale of the lower curve is ten times less than that of the upper one. The initial rapid decrease gradually becomes slower and after about 12 hours changes to a slow increase. After about 120 hours a very gradual fall in activity begins again; it takes place exponentially with a half life of around 13 days.

The behavior of the curve shows clearly that several substances must occur here. However, we cannot say without more information what these substances are: whether several "radium isotopes" or a "radium isotope" with a series of disintegration products determine the activity behavior.

We could anticipate here that the three "radium isotopes" mentioned in the first communication would be confirmed. They were given the preliminary designations radium II and radium III and radium IV (concerning the supposed radium I, see below).

Their recognition and the report of their half lives is briefly presented in the following figures.

The next section of the paper deals with determination of the half-lives of these isotopes. The paper then continues.

The scheme given in our first report must now undergo certain

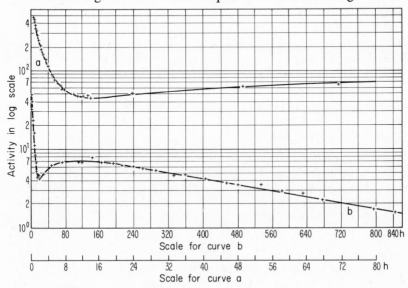

Fig. 1. The three Ra-isotopes after long irradiation. a = Ra (irradiated four days) measured over 70 hours. b = upper curve on scale 1:10 measured over 800 hours.

corrections. The following scheme shows the changes as calculated and gives for the initial members of the series the more accurately determined half lives:

$$\text{"Ra I"?} \xrightarrow[<1 \text{ min.}]{\beta} \text{Ac I} \xrightarrow[<30 \text{ min.}]{\beta} \text{Th?}$$

$$\text{"Ra II"} \xrightarrow[14\pm 2 \text{ min.}]{\beta} \text{Ac II} \xrightarrow[\sim 2.5 \text{ hrs.}]{\beta} \text{Th?}$$

$$\text{"Ra III"} \xrightarrow[86\pm 6 \text{ min.}]{\beta} \text{Ac III} \xrightarrow[\sim \text{several days}]{\beta} \text{Th?}$$

$$\text{"Ra IV"} \xrightarrow[250-300 \text{ hrs.}]{\beta} \text{Ac IV} \xrightarrow[<40 \text{ hrs.}]{\beta} \text{Th?}$$

The large group of "transuraniums" as yet has no recognizable connection with these series.

The disintegration series given in the foregoing scheme are doubtless to be considered correct in their *genetic* relations. We have also been able to recognize some end members indicated at the end of the isotopic series as "thorium." However, since we have not been able to give exact data for the individual half lives, we have in general given up the idea of identifying them.

Now, however, we must speak of some new researches which because of the strange results we have hesitated to announce. In order to produce beyond doubt evidence for the chemical nature of the initial members of the series which are separated with barium and which have been called "radium isotopes," we have carried out fractional crystallizations and fractional precipitations with the active barium salts in the manner known for enriching (or diminishing) the radium in barium salts.

Fractional crystallization of barium bromide strongly increases the radium; not too rapid separation of crystals of barium chromate does so still more; barium chloride enriches less strongly than the bromide; barium carbonate somewhat diminishes it. The corresponding studies we have made with our active barium preparations, purified from disintegration products, *were without exception negative: the activity remained uniformly divided in all fractions of the barium,* at least as far as we can tell within the not too small experimental error. We then made a pair of fractional studies with the radium isotope ThX and with the radium isotope $MsTh_1$. They behaved exactly as would be expected from all previous experiences with radium. Then the "indicator method" was applied to the mixture of purified long-lived "Ra IV" with pure, radium-free $MsTh_1$: the mixture with barium bromide as the carrier was fractionally crystallized. *The $MsTh_1$ was enriched, the "Ra IV" was not,* but its activity with an equal barium content of the fraction remained equal. We have come to the conclusion: our "radium isotopes" have the properties of barium; as chemists we must properly say that the new substances behave not as radium, but as barium; here elements other than radium or barium do not come into question.

The paper concludes with attempts to establish the nature of the disintegration products.

The following selection is from page 239 in *Nature 143*, 239–240 (1939).

Disintegration of Uranium by Neutrons.
A New Type of Nuclear Reaction
LISE MEITNER AND O. R. FRISCH

On bombarding uranium with neutrons, Fermi and collaborators found that at least four radioactive substances were produced, to two of which atomic numbers larger than 92 were ascribed. Further investigations demonstrated the existence of at least nine radioactive periods, six of which were assigned to elements beyond uranium, and nuclear isomerism had to be assumed in order to account for their chemical behavior together with their genetic relations.

In making chemical assignments, it was always assumed that these radioactive bodies had atomic numbers near that of the element bombarded, since only particles with one or two charges were known to be emitted from nuclei. A body, for example, with similar properties to those of osmium was assumed to be eka-osmium ($Z = 94$) rather than osmium ($Z = 76$) or ruthenium ($Z = 44$).

Following up an observation of Curie and Savitch, Hahn and Strassmann found that a group of at least three radioactive bodies, formed from uranium under neutron bombardment, were chemically similar to barium, and therefore, presumably isotopic with radium. Further investigation, however, showed that it was impossible to separate these bodies from barium (although mesothorium, an isotope of uranium, was readily separated in the same experiment), so that Hahn and Strassmann were forced to conclude that *isotopes of barium ($Z = 56$) are formed as a consequence of the bombardment of uranium ($Z = 92$) with neutrons.*

At first sight, this result seems very hard to understand. The formation of elements much below uranium has been considered before, but was always rejected for physical reasons, as long as the chemical evidence was not entirely clear cut. The emission, within a short time, of a large number of charged particles may be regarded as excluded by the small penetrability of the "Coulomb barrier," indicated by Gamov's theory of alpha decay.

On the basis, however, of present ideas about the behavior of heavy nuclei, an entirely different and essentially classical picture of these new disintegration processes suggests itself. On account of their close packing and strong energy exchange, the particles in a heavy nucleus would be expected to move in a collective way which has some resemblance to the movement of a liquid drop. If the movement is made sufficiently violent by adding energy, such a drop may divide itself into two smaller drops.

In the discussion of the energies involved in the deformation of the nuclei, the concept of surface tension of nuclear matter has been used and its value has been estimated from simple considerations regarding nuclear forces. It must be remembered, however, that the surface tension of a charged droplet is diminished by its charge, and a rough estimate shows that the surface tension of nuclei, decreasing with increasing nuclear charge, may become zero for atomic numbers of the order of 100.

It seems therefore possible that the uranium nucleus has only small stability of form, and may, after neutron capture, divide itself into two nuclei of roughly equal size (the precise ratio of sizes depending on finer structural features and perhaps partly on chance). These two nuclei will repel each other and should gain a total kinetic energy of c. 200 MeV, as calculated from nuclear radius and charge. This amount of energy may actually be expected to be available from the difference in packing fraction between uranium and the elements in the middle of the periodic system. The whole "fission" process can thus be described in an essentially classical way, without having to consider quantum-mechanical "tunnel effects," which would actually be extremely small, on account of the large masses involved.

The paper concludes with speculations of possible mechanisms.

The following selection is in *The Physical Review 57*, 1185–1186 (1940).

Radioactive Element 93

EDWIN McMILLAN AND PHILIP HAUGE ABELSON

Last year a nonrecoiling 2.3 day period was discovered in uranium activated with neutrons, and an attempt was made to identify it chemically, leading to the conclusion that it is a rare earth. Impressed by the difficulties raised by this identification, the authors independently decided that the subject was worth further investigation. In Berkeley it was found that: (1) If a layer of $(NH_4)_2U_2O_7$ with about 0.1 mm. air equivalent stopping power, placed in contact with a collodion film of 2 mm. air equivalent, is activated by neutrons from the cyclotron, the 2.3 day period appears strongly in the uranium layer, and not at all in the collodion, which shows a decay curve parallel to, and 1/7 as strong as, that of a paper "fission catcher" behind it. One day after bombardment the uranium layer has five times the activity of the fission catcher. This shows that the 2.3 day period has a range of <0.1 mm. air and an intensity larger than all the long period fission products together. (2) When a thin layer of uranium is bombarded with and without cadmium around it, the fission product intensity is changed by a large factor, while the

2.3 day period and the 23 minute uranium period are only slightly changed, and their ratio remains constant. Also absorption of resonance neutrons by uranium changes these two periods in the same ratio, suggesting a genetic relation between them, and the consequent identification of the longer period with element 93. In Washington it was found that the 2.3 day period probably does not behave consistently as a rare earth, since attempts to concentrate it chemically with the rare earths from activated uranium failed, although it is known to have an intensity large compared with that of the rare earth fission products.

At this stage of the investigation one of the authors (P. H. A.) came to Berkeley on a visit, and a combined attack was made. With pure 2.3 day substance from thin uranium layers, the chemical properties were investigated, and a very characteristic difference from the rare earths was soon found; namely, the substance does not precipitate with HF in the presence of an oxidizing agent (bromate in strong acid). In the presence of a reducing agent (SO_2) it precipitates quantitatively with HF. Cerium was used as a carrier. This property explains the erratic nature of previous chemical experiments in which the oxidizing power of the solution was not controlled. Further chemical experiments showed that in the reduced state with a thorium carrier it precipitates with iodate, and in the oxidized state with uranium as sodium uranyl acetate. It also precipitates with thorium on the addition of H_2O_2. It precipitates in basic solution if carbonate is carefully excluded. These properties indicate that the two valence states are very similar to those of uranium (U^{++++} and UO_2^{++} or $U_2O_7^{--}$), the chief difference from that element being in the value of the oxidation potential between the two valences, such that the lower state is more stable in the new element. It is interesting to note that the new element has little if any resemblance to its homolog rhenium; for it does not precipitate with H_2S in acid solution, is not reduced to the metal by zinc in acid solution, and does not have an oxide volatile at red heat. This fact, together with the apparent similarity to uranium, suggests that there may be a second "rare earth" group of similar elements starting with uranium.

The final proof that the 2.3 day substance is the daughter of the 23 minute uranium is the demonstration of its growth from the latter. For this experiment activated uranium was purified twice by precipitation as sodium uranyl acetate, which was dissolved in HF and saturated with SO_2. Then equal quantities of cerium were added at twenty-minute intervals and the precipitates filtered out. The first precipitate, made immediately after purification, carried all the fluoride-precipitable contaminations and was discarded; its weakness indicated a very good purification. The activities of the others are plotted in Fig. 1.

A preliminary study of the radiations from 93^{239} shows that it emits continuous negative beta-particles with an upper limit of 0.47 Mev, and a weak complex spectrum of low energy gamma-rays

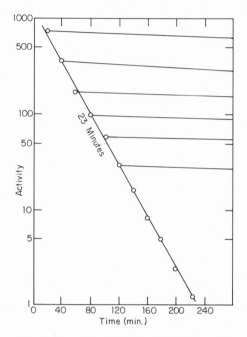

Fig. 1. Growth of 2.3-day 93^{239} from 23-minute U^{239}. The points indicate the activities of successive fluoride extractions, plotted at the times of extraction. Decay measurements were made a day later on the first six fractions, and the resulting slopes are shown on the plot.

(<0.3 Mev) and probably X-rays. The question of the behavior of its daughter product 94^{239} immediately arises. Our first thought was that it should go to actinouranium by emitting an alpha-particle. We sought for these by preparing a strong sample (11 millicuries) of purified 93 and placing it near a linear amplifier in a magnetic field to deflect the beta-particles. From the experiment we conclude that, if alpha-particles are emitted, their half-life must be of the order of a million years or more; the same experiment showed that if spontaneous fission occurs, its half-life must be even greater. We wish to express our gratitude to the Rockefeller Foundation and the Research Corporation, whose financial support made this work possible.

The following selection is in *The Physical Review 69*, 366–367 (1946).

Radioactive Element 94 from Deuterons on Uranium

G. T. SEABORG, E. M. McMILLAN, J. W. KENNEDY, AND A. C. WAHL

Jan. 28, 1941[1]

We are writing to report some results obtained in the bombardment of uranium with deuterons in the 60-inch cyclotron.

The uranium was bombarded in the form of U_3O_8 and the deuterons had to pass through a 2-mil thickness of aluminum foil before hitting the uranium target. The carefully purified element 93 fraction contained a beta-activity whose aluminum absorption curve (taken on an ionization chamber connected to an FP-54 tube and also on a Lauritsen electroscope) was distinctly different from the absorption curve of a sample of the 2.3 day 93^{239} (formed from uranium plus neutrons) taken under identical conditions. The upper energy limit of the beta-particles from this new 93 activity is about 1 MeV, compared with about 0.5 MeV for 93^{239}. The ratio of gamma-ray to beta-particle ionization is about five times larger than for 93^{239}. The initial part of the absorption curve of this 93 from uranium plus deuterons is very similar to the initial part of the absorption curve of 93^{239}. Of course the production of 93^{239} is expected in the deuteron bombardment of uranium from the reaction $U^{238}(d,n)93^{239}$. It is impossible to deduce from the absorption curve the relative intensities of the new 93 and of 93^{239}, since the initial parts of the individual absorption curves of these two activities might well be nearly identical. The rate of decay of the high energy beta-particles (0.5–1 Mev) and gamma-rays from the 93 of uranium plus deuterons was determined. This gave a half life of about 2 days for the new 93. This activity is probably to be assigned to 93^{238}, 93^{236}, or 93^{235} formed in the reactions $U^{238}(d,2n)93^{238}$, $U^{235}(d,n)93^{236}$, or $U^{235}(d,2n)93^{235}$, respectively.

---

[1] This letter was received for publication on the date indicated but was voluntarily withheld from publication until the end of the war.

The growth of alpha-particles, which might be due to the element 94 daughter of the 2 day 93, was then looked for. We did observe the growth of alpha-particles in the very carefully purified, as well as in the semi-purified 93 fractions, and the growth curves indicate a half-life of roughly 2 days for the parent of the alpha-emitter. The final alpha-particle count amounts to several hundred counts per minute for a bombardment of 200 microampere-hours. The work was done with a proportional type counter. We plan to re-determine the alpha-particle growth curve more accurately using an ionization chamber and linear amplifier with the help of a magnetic field to bend out the very strong beta-particle background. The alpha-particles have a range of approximately 3.9 cm. in air.

This alpha-activity is chemically separable from uranium and 93. The chemical experiments so far indicate a similarity to thorium and the activity has not yet been separated from thorium. More chemical experiments definitely must be performed before it can be regarded as proved that the alpha-particles are due to an isotope of element 94.

The following selection is in *The Physical Review 69*, 367 (1946).

Radioactive Element 94 from Deuterons on Uranium

G. T. SEABORG, A. C. WAHL, AND J. W. KENNEDY

March 7, 1941[1]

We should like to report a few more results which we have found regarding the element 94 alpha-radioactivity formed in the 16 MeV deuteron bombardment of uranium. We sent a first report of this work in a Letter to the Editor of January 28, 1941. We have in the meantime performed more experiments in order to study the chemical behavior of this alpha-radioactive isotope. The radioactivity can be precipitated, in what is probably the $+4$ valence state, as a fluoride or iodate by using a rare earth or thorium as carrier material. How ever, in the presence of the extremely strong oxidizing agent per-sulfate ion ($S_2O_8^{--}$), plus Ag as a catalyst, this radioactive isotope is oxidized to a higher valence state which does not precipitate as a fluoride. The oxidizing agent bromate ion (BrO_3^-) is not sufficiently powerful to oxidize it to this higher valence state and hence the radioactivity comes down as a fluoride even in the presence of bromate

---

[1] This letter was received for publication on the date indicated but was voluntarily withheld from publication until the end of the war.

ion. With the help of persulfate ion it has been possible to separate quantitatively this radioactivity from thorium, by using the beta-active UX_1 as an indicator for thorium. These experiments make it extremely probable that this alpha-radioactivity is due to an isotope of element 94. The experiments are being continued.

The following selection is from pages 1128–1129 and 1134 in *The Journal of the American Chemical Society 70*, 1128–1134 (1948).

The Chemical Properties of Elements 94 and 93[1]

GLENN T. SEABORG AND ARTHUR C. WAHL

This report describes the chemical experiments which we have performed on elements 94 and 93 and the chemical properties which we have deduced from these experiments.

Although the chemical experiments have been under way for 94 since December, 1940, when element 94 was discovered, and for 93 since somewhat earlier than this, the investigation has not been a very systematic one. In the case of element 93, we have repeated most of the experiments reported by McMillan and Abelson in their original publication and have confirmed their results. It has been of paramount importance to develop as quickly as possible methods of isolating in very thin precipitates elements 94 and 93 from large amounts of uranium in order to study the properties of 94^{239}, and, therefore, the experiments have been of a very practical and explora-tory nature. It is only recently that we have begun a systematic investigation of the chemical properties; the description of these experiments is included also.

The experimental results and techniques are then reported in detail; they are summarized as follows.

Summary[2]

The chemical properties of elements 94 and 93 have been studied by means of the tracer technique using the radioactive isotopes 94^{238} and 93^{239}. Plutonium is suggested as the name for element 94

[1] This article was mailed as a secret report from Berkeley, California, to the "Uranium Committee" in Washington, D.C., on March 21, 1942. The experimental work was done throughout all of 1941 and the early part of 1942. . . .
[2] Summary was written at the time of publication, since the original report contained no summary.

following the convention used in the naming of neptunium (element 93) and uranium. The chemical symbols Pu and Np are suggested for plutonium and neptunium. In the reduced states the precipitation reactions of neptunium and plutonium are similar to those of the tripositive rare earths and actinium, and of the quadripositive cerium, thorium and uranium. Neptunium and plutonium resemble actinium, thorium and +4 uranium in that their fluorides, iodates and hydroxides are insoluble in water; their sulfides are soluble in acid; and their metals are electropositive. Neptunium and plutonium exhibit a higher oxidation state with properties similar to those of uranium of oxidation state +6.

Probably the reduced state of both elements has an oxidation number of +3 or +4 and the formulas of the fluorides are NpF_3 and PuF_3 or NpF_4 and PuF_4. For both elements the standard oxidation-reduction potential from the metal to the reduced ionic strength is greater than +0.5 V. For the reduced to the oxidized ionic state the standard potential for neptunium is about −1.35 v. and for plutonium, −1.0 to −1.4 v. Probably PuO_2 and NpO_2 are the oxides formed by electrodeposition.

There is practically no resemblance in chemical properties between neptunium and plutonium and rhenium and osmium. The chemical properties of neptunium and plutonium indicate that a "rare earth" type group of elements is starting at the upper end of the periodic table, and from the present data we can just as well consider the group to be starting with actinium or thorium, rather than with uranium which has previously been suggested as the starting point.

Part III   Organic Chemistry

At the beginning of the twentieth century organic chemistry was a well-established branch of the science with an extensive array of general synthetic methods and a proved set of procedures for determining the structures of the compounds with which it dealt. It is true that the methods of structural determination were often very laborious and time-consuming, so that the structures of most of the more complex natural products were still unknown, but the organic chemist felt sure that his well-tested methods would ultimately reveal them. Most organic chemists felt content with the path they followed, and seldom turned aside from it.

Such a state of affairs could not long continue in the developing atmosphere of coöperation that was characteristic of the new century. The concepts of electronic structure and chemical bonding that developed from the theories and methods of the physicist had to be applied to the structures of organic compounds, and when they were, they opened new vistas to the physicist himself. No doubt to the surprise of many an organic chemist, the discoveries of physical chemistry were at once applicable to his work. And for the physical chemist, the structural determinations of organic chemistry turned out to validate much of his work. Thus the old barriers broke down and physical and organic chemists began to coöperate, to the mutual advantage of both. The results of such coöperation have been shown in a number of the selections already given in Part II.

The more rapid determinations of structure now made possible soon permitted the determination of structure and the synthesis of a considerable number of complex compounds of biological importance. This brought the chemist and the biologist closer together, and this in turn resulted in the rapid rise of biochemistry as a new branch of science. The results of this coöperation will be shown in Part IV.

SYNTHETIC METHODS

A large number of general synthetic methods had been developed by the end of the nineteenth century. However, one of the most versatile and important was first described as the new century opened. This was the Grignard synthesis. It had been foreshadowed by the use of a number of zinc organic compounds in organic reactions, but, due to their extreme reactivity, these compounds were difficult to handle. The replacement of zinc by magnesium opened the way for the preparation of a vast number of new compounds of many different classes. The first step in this direction was taken by Barbier, but it was Victor Grignard who revealed the full possibilities of the method.

A second general method of wide usefulness was discovered by Diels and Alder in the third decade of the century. The diene synthesis that they worked out permitted the synthesis of many compounds, often closely related to natural substances. The next two selections show the early stages of the development of these reactions.

The following selection is in *Comptes Rendus Hebdomadaires des Séances de l'Académie des Sciences 130*, 1322–1324 (1900).

Some New Organometallic Compounds of Magnesium and Their Application to the Synthesis of Alcohols and Hydrocarbons

V. GRIGNARD

In continuation of the synthesis of dimethyl heptenol by M. Barbier for which this scholar has applied the method of Saytzeff, replacing zinc by magnesium, I proposed to study some advantages which this substitution could present. In the course of these investigations I have discovered a series of organometallic compounds of magnesium which has permitted me to modify greatly the method of Wagner-Saytzeff, with great advantage to the rapidity and regularity of operation and, in general, to the yield obtained.

Methyl iodide attacks magnesium turnings only very slowly in the cold, but if a little anhydrous ether is added, a reaction begins immediately and quickly becomes extremely lively. It is then necessary to cool and add an excess of ether. Under these conditions solution of the magnesium occurs rapidly, and a very fluid and colorless liquid is finally obtained without any appreciable deposit.

If the ether is driven off, there remains a grayish mass, confusedly crystalline, which absorbs moisture very rapidly with warming and deliquescence. However, the great advantage of the compound that is obtained is that it is unnecessary to isolate it. Actually, if a molecule of an aldehyde or a ketone is added to the preceding ether solution which contains very exactly one atom of magnesium dissolved by a molecule of methyl iodide, a lively reaction usually occurs, and finally, by decomposing the resulting compound with acidulated water the corresponding secondary or tertiary alcohol is isolated with a yield of about 70 per cent.

I have established that hydrobromic and hydriodic esters of aliphatic saturated monoatomic alcohols up to C_5, as well as benzyl bromide, give the same reaction, and it is very likely that it would occur with many other halogen esters.

For reasons I will explain later, I believe I can attribute to the organometallic compounds that I have obtained the formula RMgI or RMgBr, R being an aliphatic or aromatic alcoholic residue. The reactions that I have described above can then be explained in the following manner

$$CH_3I + Mg = CH_3MgI$$

$$CH_3MgI + RCHO = RCH\begin{matrix} \nearrow OMgI \\ \searrow CH_3 \end{matrix}$$

$$RCH\begin{matrix} \nearrow OMgI \\ \searrow CH_3 \end{matrix} + H_2O = RCH(OH)CH_3 + MgIOH$$

I have prepared some secondary and tertiary alcohols, of which some were already known but which it was interesting to prepare again to assure the generality of the method. With the aliphatic halogen esters the results have always been excellent; they are much poorer with benzyl bromide due to the relatively abundant formation of bibenzyl.

Here Grignard describes the experimental details of the preparation of phenylisobutyl carbinol, dimethylphenyl carbinol, and dimethylbenzyl carbinol.

When unsaturated aldehydes and ketones in which the double bond is near the functional group are employed, the alcohol formed is often unstable; it dehydrates when distilled, even in a vacuum, and only a diethylenic hydrocarbon is obtained.

Thus, by the action of mesityl oxide on the methyl iodide of magnesium I have obtained a hydrocarbon boiling at 92–93° at 750 mm., which corresponds to the formula

$$CH_3\text{—}\underset{\underset{CH_3}{|}}{C}{=}CH\text{—}\underset{\underset{CH_3}{|}}{C}{=}CH_2$$

which is 2,4-dimethyl-2,4-pentadiene. (Analysis given.)

I will continue the study of the applications of these new organo-metallic compounds.

The following selection is from pages 912–913 in *Zeitschrift für Angewandte Chemie 42*, 911–918 (1929).

The "Diene Synthesis," an Ideal Synthetic Principle for Organic Substances

O. DIELS

Diels discusses various important methods of organic synthesis and the place of isoprene in nature. He then continues:

It will naturally not be asserted that only isoprene can be made responsible for the formation of these and other metabolic products of the plant organism, but it should be recognized that this hydrocarbon contains an essential structure for smooth occurrence of an organic synthesis, namely a system of conjugated double bonds, and this is also characteristic of other "dienes." Therefore we cannot help but feel that in the *living organism* the building principle of the dienes, or, as I may call the complex of these processes, the *"diene synthesis" may also perhaps play as meaningful a part as the aldol condensation*, or other synthetic pathways that have sometimes been considered.

Observations and experiments that I can report today appear to me to be supports that are important in establishing the correctness of this conjecture. They are the result of many years of investigation that I have carried out with K. Alder and in which a large number of younger chemists have assisted.

We feel we have successfully established that the "dienes," of which isoprene itself is one type, *are capable of an astonishingly large number of surprising syntheses which occur under the mildest conditions.* We cannot doubt, on the basis of our observations, that they play an important role *as significant synthetic principles in true organic syntheses even in the organism.*

These studies did not indeed at first arise from any special considerations, but a short description of their historical development will show that they are by no means the result of a lucky accident.

Studies with *diimide*

$$HN\!\!=\!\!NH$$

which were carried out from many angles acquainted me with the esters of *azodicarboxylic acid*

$$RO_2C\!\!-\!\!N\!\!=\!\!N\!\!-\!\!CO_2R.$$

Next I observed that these added to *amines* of all types in accordance with the nature of the amines, whether primary, secondary, or tertiary, to give addition products of various types which could be used in interesting reactions.

In the course of further investigations it was then proved that *enols* and compounds such as malonic ester which tended to enolization could also combine with the azoesters. In addition, more complicated substances, such, for example, as *naphthylamines* or *naphthols*, could combine smoothly with the azoesters.

It was shown that we did not have "molecular compounds" in any of these reaction products by the results of a closer study of their transformations.

Thus we finally came to the opinion that we should test experimentally *the tendency of the azoesters to add to hydrocarbons.* We could expect that for such a study we should use strongly unsaturated substances, and therefore it was with some *alkylated butadienes* that a beginning was made. The typical addition in this case took place exceptionally vigorously and smoothly. From this discovery it was recognized that the essential feature of the ability of the azoesters to add to other substances was not the presence of a definite atom group like —NH$_2$, —OH, —SH, or others, but the specific reason was *an unsaturated condition of the molecule concerned, definite in type and degree of intensity.*

This idea obtained positive support when the investigation of *cyclopentadiene* was carried out

$$
\begin{array}{l}
HC\!\!=\!\!CH \\
\quad\diagdown \\
\quad\quad CH_2, \\
\quad\diagup \\
HC\!\!=\!\!CH
\end{array}
$$

a substance on which many investigators had made studies and had given purely speculative suggestions.

The addition of azoesters in this case gave us compounds whose structure could be definitely established by hydrogenation and subsequent conversion to the known 1,3-diaminopentane:

$$
\begin{array}{ccc}
\overset{\textstyle CH}{\diagup\big|\diagdown} & \overset{\textstyle CH}{\diagup\big|\diagdown} & \overset{\textstyle CH-NH_2}{\diagup\big|} \\
HC\quad CH_2\quad N-CO_2R & HC_2\quad CH_2\quad N-CO_2R & H_2C\quad CH_2 \\
\|\qquad\big|\qquad\big| \quad\rightarrow & \big|\qquad\big|\qquad\big|\quad\rightarrow & \big|\qquad\big| \\
HC\qquad\big|\qquad N-CO_2R & HC_2\qquad\big|\qquad N-CO_2R & H_2C\qquad\big| \\
\diagdown\big|\diagup & \diagdown\big|\diagup & \diagdown\big| \\
\overset{}{\underset{\textstyle CH}{}} & \overset{}{\underset{\textstyle CH}{}} & \overset{}{\underset{\textstyle CH-NH_2}{}}
\end{array}
$$

In this reaction for the first time there was obtained a system with a methylene bridge, one which, it is true, also *contained nitrogen;* but it followed from my new studies with Dr. Alder and other coworkers that we learned to prepare a large number of *nitrogen-free rings with built-in methylene, ethylene, and other bridges.* The essential step for further development of the diene synthesis, namely *the transfer of the observations made with the azoesters to suitable nitrogen-free systems* was carried out by a study of the older work of Albrecht [1906], a student of Thiele. He had made the observation that cyclopentadiene could combine with 1 or 2 molecules of quinone and had attributed to the two products of this reaction, though with reservations, the formulas

From the experiments and observations on the azoesters we were convinced from the first of the incorrectness of the Albrecht formulas, and the results of our investigations confirmed this. The addition of cyclopentadiene to quinone takes place in the 1,4-position, so that the Albrecht formulas must be replaced by the structures

This result also appears to be clear since the molecule of the azo-esters is very similar formally to quinone

$$
\begin{array}{ccc}
& O & & & O \\
& \| & & & \| \\
& C & & & C \\
& \diagup \quad \diagdown & & \diagup \quad \diagdown \\
RC & & N & HC & & CH \\
\| & & \| & \| & & \| \\
RC & & N & HC & & CH \\
& \diagdown \quad \diagup & & \diagdown \quad \diagup \\
& C & & & C \\
& \| & & & \| \\
& O & & & O
\end{array}
$$

According to this principle we have further succeeded by the addition of simple "dienes" of the type of butadiene or alkylated butadienes, and also *cyclic* dienes, to α-naphthoquinone in building up numerous *homologs of anthraquinone*. There is no limit to the number of possible syntheses according to this principle; and *since these reactions in general occur spontaneously, or in any case without the participation of any other agency*, it seems to me to be reasonable to think that nature itself in many cases also uses this method to build up more complicated derivatives of anthracene and other hydrocarbons.

The rest of the paper is devoted to further examples of the diene synthesis.

POLYMERS

As the century advanced and the coöperation of physical and organic chemists increased, it became possible to work with substances of greater and greater complexity. Previously, when a synthesis led to the formation of a "tar," the chemist simply discarded the non-crystalline material and started over again. Now even these amorphous and high-molecular-weight substances began to attract interest. Herman Staudinger in 1920 gave the first clear discussion of the nature of polymers and soon introduced the term "macromolecules" for the large polymerization products. Somewhat later Wallace Carothers made the classification of polymers more definite, and his work led to many of the industrial applications of resins and polymers that supplied a whole new group of materials of the greatest practical importance. The next three selections illustrate these developments.

The following selection is from pages 1073–1077 and 1081–1082 in *Berichte der Deutschen Chemischen Gesellschaft 53*, 1073–1085 (1920).

On Polymerization

H. STAUDINGER

Some time ago G. Schroeter offered interesting views on the composition of polymerization products, especially on the constitution of polymeric ketenes. These compounds were to be considered molecular compounds and not cyclobutane derivatives, as had been assumed previously, since, according to Schroeter's investigations, these polymeric ketenes differed in essential ways from the cyclobutane derivatives that could be obtained by synthesis from derivatives of acetone dicarboxylic ester.

The same views on the composition of polymerization products had already been expressed in 1909 by H. Hildebrand in a dissertation from the laboratory of Thiele, proposed in a study on the polymerization of *asym*-diphenyl ethylene. The dimolecular polymerization product should not be tetraphenyl cyclobutane, but rather a molecular compound produced by the partial valences in an unsaturated molecule.

$$2(C_6H_5)_2C:CH_2 \rightarrow (C_6H_5)_2C\text{---}CH_2$$
$$CH_2 . C(C_6H_5)_2$$
$$\text{and not } (C_6H_5)_2C\text{---}CH_2$$
$$CH_2 . C(C_6H_5)_2$$

Such assumptions are very appealing today in organic chemistry, after a large number of well-characterized compounds such as the quinhydrones have been interpreted in the studies of Pfeiffer as molecular compounds held together by secondary valences. Nevertheless, I believe that from the existing observational material, such assumptions as to the origin of polymeric products do not have to be made; it is much more likely that different types of polymerization products, as I hope to show in what follows, *can be explained satisfactorily by normal valences*, and as long as possible the properties of the compounds can continue to be expressed straightforwardly in organic chemistry by normal valence formulas.

Before I enter upon the special question of the constitution of polymeric ketenes, I would like in what follows to give some general views on polymerization that I have developed in recent years on the basis of a number of studies, and which have already been set down in part in the dissertations of L. Lautenschläger and E. Suter.

General Remarks on Polymerization Processes

Ideas of "polymerization processes" and "polymerization products" have not been used in the same way in chemistry, as the remarks of A. Franke in Weyl's *Methoden der organischen Chemie* have shown. Holleman calls polymerization processes those in which two or more molecules of a single substance are so linked that they can again be regenerated. As will subsequently be shown in detail, this latter criterion for a polymerization process is not completely essential. According to their constitution, the polymerization products can exhibit entirely different methods of decomposition.

Polymerization processes in the wider sense are all processes in which two or more molecules combine into a product of the same composition, but with a higher molecular weight. However, these processes can be divided into two subgroups.

1. In one we find polymerization processes in which the polymerization products *still have the same type of linking of atoms* as the monomolecular substance.

Examples of this are: the formation of hexaphenyl ethane from triphenyl methyl, the formation of paraldehyde from acetaldehyde, of cyclobutanedione derivatives from the ketenes; here also belong the conversion of styrene to metastyrene, of isoprene to rubber, and of formaldehyde to paraldehyde. We suggest calling these processes *true polymerization processes* and the polymerization products from these *true polymerization products*.

2. We also frequently find polymerization processes which take place with more or less strong displacement of the atoms, so that the polymerization product no longer shows the original linkage type of the atoms that occurred in the monomolecular substance. Here we find aldol polymerization, benzoin formation, the polymerization of formaldehyde to glycol aldehyde and sugar, and also the polymerization of the nitriles and of cyanamide to dicyandiamide, etc.

Further examples of this are the formation of distyrene from styrene, of diisobutylene from isobutylene, and of diacrylic acid ester from acrylic acid ester.

These reactions will be called *false polymerization processes* or *condensing polymerization processes*. They take place analogously to the true condensation processes by which molecules of different composition are combined in a similar way. These processes have often been called condensation (cf. benzoin formation). The products of this group I might call *false polymerization products* or *condensed polymerization products*.

A comparison of the polymerization of crotonic ester to dicrotonic ester and of cinnamic acid to α-truxillic acid shows clearly the difference between these two types of polymerization.

$$2\ CH_3 \cdot CH : CH \cdot COOC_2H_5 \rightarrow CH_3 \cdot CH \cdot CH_2 \cdot COOC_2H_5 \qquad \text{false}$$
$$\underset{|}{\qquad\qquad\qquad\qquad\qquad\qquad} \text{polymerization}$$
$$CH_3 \cdot CH : C \cdot COOC_2H_5$$

$$2\ C_6H_5 \cdot CH : CH \cdot COOH \rightarrow C_6H_5 \cdot CH \cdot CH \cdot COOH \text{ [sic]} \qquad \text{true}$$
$$\underset{|}{\qquad\qquad\qquad\qquad\qquad\qquad} \text{polymerization}$$
$$COOH \cdot CH \cdot CH \cdot C_6H_5$$

In what follows we will consider only the true polymerization processes. Such processes can occur in molecules which have an unsaturated atom (an example of this is the polymerization of triphenyl methyl to hexaphenyl ethane), or—and this is by far the most important case—which have an open bond; finally, unstable ring systems have a tendency to go over to a stable higher molecular product through polymerization.

The true polymerization process of substances with open bonds can lead to ring systems with 4-, 6-, or even 8-member rings, or can form polymerization products with very high molecular weight.

On the basis of previously known material it is not clear under what conditions ring formation will occur and when high molecular products will result. Slight constitutional changes very often produce different courses of polymerization. For example, cinnamic acid polymerizes to truxillic acid, while cinnamic acid ester goes over to a high molecular product.

Phenyl ethylene (styrene) changes to the high molecular metastyrene, while the *asym*-diphenyl ethylene gives a cyclobutane derivative. Butadiene derivatives, finally, can go over to the dimolecular polymerization product, and indeed, into cyclobutane derivatives or into a cyclohexene ring, or they can be polymerized to high molecular products.

In the ethylene compounds, finally, as E. Suter has shown in his dissertation, there is no connection between constitution and tendency to polymerization.

From this we can draw some entirely general conclusions as to *the stability of the polymerization products and their tendency to depolymerization*. Four-member rings in general are more unstable than six-member rings, and actually in recent years there have been a great many observations made in the study of ketenes on the decomposition of four-member rings. This has given a far-reaching confirmation to the Baeyer strain theory. As already mentioned earlier, the tendency to decomposition depends on the type of ring member; heterocyclic four-member rings, especially if they contain several heteroatoms, as a rule are not as stable as cyclobutane derivatives where there are four firm carbon bonds. Also, the stability especially of the cyclobutane derivatives is strongly modified by substituents, and the ring system can be greatly weakened, for example, by the introduction of several phenyl groups or carbonyl residues. We thus make the same observation here as for open carbon chains, for which it is known that the strength of the bonds is reduced by phenyl substitution. It is also known that molecules are unstable when two or more carbonyl groups are located on one carbon atom.

In comparison with the four-member rings, six-member rings, chiefly the isocyclic six-member rings, are stable; in heterocyclic rings, splitting occurs more often.

In high molecular polymerization products the stability is also very strongly changed by the composition and the substituents.

Whether smooth depolymerization to the monomolecular substance occurs depends in all cases not only on the decomposition temperature of the polymerization product, but also on the stability of the monomolecular substance.

As will be shown in what follows, all the stable polymerization products known up to now when considered from this viewpoint can be represented by formulas with normal valences.

A discussion of 4-, 6-, and 8-member rings follows. The paper then goes on.

High Molecular Polymerization Products

Very often in polymerization processes high molecular products are formed whose constitution has not yet been solved. These products are amorphous, colloidal bodies. They are insoluble in the monomolecular substances and separate out immediately in polymerization. This can be seen in the formation of paraldehyde from liquid formaldehyde, and here also belongs the polymerization of vinyl bromide; we have here the group of polymerization processes that Kronstein calls euthymorphic polymerizations.

On the other hand—and this is very often the case—these high molecular polymerization products may dissolve colloidally in the monomolecular substance. The colloids can be separated by addition of other solvents or by distillation of the monomolecular substance. The gel thus obtained is either soluble by fresh addition of monomolecular substance and is thus a reversible gel—here belongs metastyrene according to the work of Stobbe—or else the gel may be insoluble in the monomolecular substance after its separation, as is apparently the case for some sorts of rubber.

For all these colloids, naturally, no molecular weight can be given, and there is no sense in carrying out a molecular weight determination with such substances. Certain freezing point depressions or boiling point increases may be observed if some of the monomeric dispersion medium, which is often very difficult to separate, still adheres to the polymeric substance. The molecular weight found in this way is subject to remarkably large variations in the values found. If we carry out the molecular weight determinations with pure substances, free from monomolecular starting materials, there is no, or very little, alteration in the freezing or boiling points of the solvent, as has been recognized for pure styrene by Stobbe and Posniak, and for malonic acid anhydride by Staudinger and Ott.

If we wish to represent the formation and constitution of such high molecular substances, we can assume that first a combination of unsaturated molecules has occurred similar to that in the formation of four- and six-member rings, but that perhaps for some steric reason four- and six-member ring closure has not occurred, and now numerous, even hundreds, of molecules have combined together until equilibrium conditions between the large molecules occurs, and this may depend on temperature, concentration, and solvent.

The remainder of the paper is made up of applications of these ideas to paraformaldehyde and rubber.

Four years later Staudinger made his ideas more definite in another paper from which the next extract is taken.

The following selection is from page 1206 in *Berichte der Deutschen Chemischen Gesellschaft 57*, 1203–1208 (1924).

On the Constitution of Rubber (*Sixth Paper*)

H. STAUDINGER

A homogeneous molecularly dispersed compound is therefore characterized by the fact that its molecules are equally large; their size can be determined by known methods in the vapor state or in solution. In this case, for an organic compound there is no difficulty in principle in carrying out a definite structural determination and thus establishing the manner in which each atom is linked in the molecule. The matter is different with colloids, whose size is not exactly known. The molecules of rubber which are believed to be identical with the colloidal particles are not homogeneous, and it is at once apparent that they have entirely different sizes and that these can be changed, by temperature for example. The different physical states of rubber can therefore be explained; naturally they depend on the fact that the assemblages of primary particles can undergo alterations to secondary particles.

However, it is very important here to use the idea of the molecule, though it varies very greatly depending on the molecularly dispersed system used; if we call the colloidal particles the molecules of rubber, we can say that the individual isoprene residues which make up the colloidal particles are held together by normal chemical bonds and that in the structural sense we are dealing with very long carbon chains. The polymerization of isoprene to these long chains, according to this idea, goes on until a sufficiently large, little reactive and thus strongly saturated molecule, the colloidal particle, has been formed. If only a few isoprene molecules combine, saturation with ring closure occurs, and we then have a low molecular disperse *polyterpene*. For those colloidal particles in which the molecule is identical with the primary particle and in which the individual atoms of the colloidal molecule are linked by normal valences, we propose to differentiate the type by the term *macromolecules*.

The following selection is from pages 2548–2550 and 2558–2559 in *The Journal of the American Chemical Society 51*, 2548–2559 (1929).

Studies on Polymerization and Ring Formation. I. An Introduction to the General Theory of Condensation Polymers

WALLACE H. CAROTHERS

Polymerization frequently leads to substances of very high molecular weights, and the problem of the structure of high polymers is attracting a great deal of attention, especially because such important materials as rubber, cellulose, proteins and resins either are high polymers or have certain properties which are common to high polymers.

The conditions which Berzelius was concerned to recognize by the term polymer were the presence of the same atoms in the same proportions in compounds having different molecular weights. These conditions are satisfied by the members of a great many thousand pairs of compounds which are not now regarded as polymers. Thus, of the compounds paracetaldehyde, butyric acids and hydroxycaproic acids, only the first would now be considered a polymer of acetaldehyde, although there is nothing in the conditions of the Berzelius definition to exclude the others. Hence, whatever the term polymer may mean now, it does not mean precisely what Berzelius intended, and the conditions which he set up are not sufficient to define it. In current attempts to define this term it is still stated that a polymer and its monomer must have the same atoms in the same proportions. But this condition is not satisfied by the polyoxymethylenes (see Table 1 [not included here]) which are universally considered to be polymers of formaldehyde. It seems desirable, therefore, to attempt to formulate a definition which will be in so far as possible in accordance with both the current usage and the essential facts.

The structures of a good many polymers, including some of very high molecular weights, are known either completely or in part and an examination of their formulas shows some interesting relationships (see Table I). They are characterized by a recurring structural unit, so that if this is represented by —R—, the structure of these polymers may be represented in part by the general formula —R—R--R—R—R—R—R—R—, etc., or $(—R—)_n$. In this formula n may be small as in paracetaldehyde ($n = 3$), or it may be very large as in the polyoxymethylenes. The end valences may be united as they are in paracetaldehyde to form a ring, or they may be saturated by univalent groups such as H— and —OH to form an open chain of the type $H(—R—)_n OH$ as they are in α-polyoxymethylene. It seems probable that cellulose and silk fibroin are of this type, and in any event it may be observed that no high polymer is certainly known to be cyclic. There are polymers which do not conform to the type $(—R—)_n$ but those which do will be called linear whether the chain is open or closed; and the subsequent discussion is concerned only with these.

The structural units —R— are bivalent radicals which, in general, are not capable of independent existence. The presence of a recurring structural unit is, of course, characteristic of most organic compounds (*e.g.*, —CH$_2$— in aliphatic compounds), but in the case of polymers there exists a molecule, the monomer, corresponding to the structural unit, and from which the polymer may be formed or to which it may be degraded.

Examination of the formulas of Table I will show that two types of polymers may be distinguished. In the first type, which includes paracetaldehyde, rubber, polystyrene and polyoxymethylenes, the molecular formula of the structural unit is identical with that of the monomer, *i.e.*, the formula of the structural unit, —R—, is isomeric with that of the monomer. In the second type, which includes the polyethylene glycols, cellulose and silk fibroin, the molecular formula of the structural unit differs from that of the monomer by H_2O, *i.e.*, the monomer is H—R—OH. The transformation of polymers of the first type into their monomers is brought about simply by heating, and the reverse transformation (polymerization) occurs spontaneously or by the action of catalysts. In the second type, degradation to the monomer occurs by hydrolysis, and if the reverse process were to take place it would require the elimination of water among many molecules. This would be polyintermolecular condensation.[1]

These two classes will be distinguished as (1) addition or A polymers. The molecular formula of the monomer is identical with that of the structural unit. The monomer can be obtained from the polymer by thermolysis or the polymer can be synthesized from the monomer by self-addition. (2) Condensation or C polymers: the molecular formula of the monomer differs from that of the structural unit. The monomer can be obtained from the polymer by hydrolysis or its equivalent or the polymer can be synthesized from the monomer by polyintermolecular condensation. Polymerization then is the chemical union of many similar molecules either (A) without or (C) with the elimination of simpler molecules (H_2O, HCl, NaCl, NH_3, etc.).

Assuming that polyintermolecular condensation exists, the above examples and definitions and their implications provide ample reason for referring to the process as a type of polymerization. These examples, of course, do not provide any proof that this process as distinct from and independent of A polymerization does exist. This proof will appear incidentally in the following discussion, which is concerned with the general principles involved in the formation of condensation polymers.

Many examples of C polymerization are discussed. The paper then continues.

The process of polyintermolecular condensation finds no mention in treatises on polymerization. This may be due to the fact that

---

[1] The term condensation is used here to name any reaction which occurs with the formation of a new bond between atoms not already joined and which proceeds with the elimination of elements (H_2, N_2, etc.) or of simple compounds (H_2O, C_2H_5OH, NH_3, NaBr, etc.). Examples are the Wurtz reaction, Friedel-Crafts reaction, esterification, etc.

such a process is not admitted to exist, or that it is not admitted to be polymerization. The examples cited above, and others to be described later, prove that such a process does exist, and that it may result in the formation of very large molecules. Whether it is to be regarded as polymerization or not will depend upon the definition which is adopted for that term. The definitions offered above include it as a special type of polymerization. This classification finds more to justify it than the analogies which are recognized in these definitions.

The process of A polymerization (the only type which appears to have been generally recognized) results in the formation of large molecules from small; and it has come about that any process which has this result is called polymerization. Since, however, A polymerization is by definition a process of self-addition, chemists have often been misled to the assumption that condensation leads directly only to small molecules, and that if large molecules are formed from small as the apparent result of condensation, this is due to the intervention of some unsaturated molecules capable of undergoing A polymerization. It is quite certain, however, that in many such cases (*i.e.*, in all cases of true C polymerization) no such intermediate products occur. This is a matter of important practical implications. The reactions involved in the formation of A polymers must, in the nature of the case, be for the most part reactions which are peculiar to the process of polymerization. For this reason the mechanism of A polymerization still remains somewhat obscure. Hence, the mere assumption that unsaturated intermediates intervene in a reaction which leads to high polymers contributes little to one's understanding of the mechanism of the process, or the structure of the product. In those cases in which this assumption is wrong its use leads one to regard as complicated and mysterious a process which may be simple and obvious. C polymerization merely involves the use in a multiple fashion of the typical reactions of common functional groups. Among bifunctional compounds these reactions may proceed in such a way as to guarantee the structure of the structural unit, —R—, in the polymer, $(—R—)_n$, formed. It is one of the immediate objects of the researches to be described in subsequent papers to discover how the physical and chemical properties of high polymers of this type are related to the nature of the structural unit.

NATURAL COMPOUNDS

Another branch of organic chemistry that developed rapidly in the twentieth century was the proof of structure and the synthesis of many

natural products, some of great biological and pharmacological importance. The difficulties involved in the study of these compounds in the
nineteenth century had been great, not only because many of them had
complicated structures, but also because of their occurrence in small
amounts in very complex mixtures. The technical developments of
separation and microanalysis shown in Part I now made it possible to
isolate and study these substances, and the newer methods of structure
determination, such as the various types of spectral analysis, the study
of spreading of films on liquids, the improvements in laboratory apparatus, and more sophisticated synthetic methods, all combined to give rapid
progress in the study of natural organic products.

Proteins. The first great achievement in determining structure and then
synthesizing came in the field of the proteins. Emil Fischer, a master of
organic techniques, had already shown the essential nature of the carbohydrates, see H. M. Leicester and H. S. Klickstein, *A Source Book in
Chemistry, 1400–1900* (Harvard University Press, Cambridge, Massachusetts, 1952), p. 499. Now, in the first decade of the new century,
Fischer proved the essential structure of the proteins and carried out the
synthesis of an artificial polypeptide. Not for another thirty years was any
marked further progress made in protein chemistry, and then only when
the powerful new tools of the ultracentrifuge and electrophoresis had been
perfected.

The following selection is in *Zeitschrift für Angewandte Chemie* 20,
913–917 (1907).

Proteins and Polypeptides

EMIL FISCHER

Chemical discoveries of an unusual type, such as the discovery
of new elements with wonderful properties or the artificial preparation
of long-used, important substances of the plant and animal kingdoms,
are quickly told to the great public today by the busy daily press and
arouse keen hopes for an awakening of an interest in chemical research in wide general circles.

Nevertheless, in spite of all this, the deepest part of our science
has not become altogether popular. This is much less so than for
the closely related physics, and very much less so than for the descriptive sciences. This is partly because of its peculiar abstractions with
their complicated formulas, and also because of its almost distinc-
tively difficult language.

Though I have the chance at today's session to present a scientific topic in popular terms, I cannot conceal from myself the difficulties of the task, and you must recognize my good intentions in choosing to speak of something of which everyone knows and of which we possess a great supply. I refer to a major constituent of our own bodies, that chemical structure with which organic life is most closely bound. Its common name is egg white. The chemists expand its meaning because they know there are many substances like egg white. To avoid misunderstanding they call these proteins, a name derived from the Greek proton, the first.

The number of natural proteins seems to be very large: we already know some 40 quite different individuals. These include, besides the white part of eggs, the casein of milk, gelatin, some constituents of blood, muscle, hair, nails, skin, grains and other plant seeds, and finally, clothing materials like wool and silk. We have shown you a fairly complete collection of such substances which since 1901 have been studied partly by myself and partly by my colleague, Dr. Abderhalden. The most noteworthy and rarest is the so-called spider silk which comes from a large spider in Madagascar and not only equals ordinary silk in luster and filament strength, but is also distinguished by a beautiful orange color.

The elementary composition of the proteins is fairly simple, since they contain besides carbon, hydrogen, and oxygen, which are found in almost all products of the plant and animal kingdoms, only nitrogen and often also sulfur. Their chemical constitution is not as well understood, since they and their numerous derivatives offer the most complicated picture that nature has produced.

The starting point for a judgment of their structure up to now has been merely a decomposition process, the so-called hydrolysis.

They can be acted upon by hot acids or alkalis, and also by digestive juices. For instance, if we leave a small piece of hard-cooked egg white in the juice of an animal stomach and warm to 37°, in the course of several hours the egg white disappears because it is changed into the easily soluble peptones. The process is not complete here, since the peptones in the intestine undergo a further hydrolysis, the final products of which are the so-called amino acids. Since these also result from the proteins by splitting them with hot acids, alkalis, or ammonia, we can consider them the actual building blocks of the proteins.

The individual amino acids known to Fischer are then described.

These amino acids are for the most part available for synthesis, especially the optically active forms that occur exclusively in the proteins.

The artificial synthesis of the proteins themselves thus seems to be essentially the task of arranging these amino acids in the correct sequence of the right acids by splitting out water once more to bind them together.

I have therefore occupied myself for five years with finding suitable methods for this purpose, and in fact I have succeeded in obtaining products by the combination of different amino acids that are very similar first to peptones, and then, by continued synthesis, to proteins.

For these artificial substances, which are distinguished from the natural ones in that they are recognized as chemical individuals, I have chosen the collective name "polypeptides." According to the number of amino acids they are divided into di-, tri-, tetrapeptides, etc.

In order to give an idea of the method of carrying out their synthesis, I will describe the formation of an octadecapeptide, which is composed of 15 molecules of glycine and three molecules of optically active *l*-leucine.

As the starting material for this we used glycine on the one hand, and on the other, *d*-leucine, that is, the optical antipode of the natural amino acid. Why this must be used to obtain derivatives of natural *l*-leucine will be explained later.

Glycine is known to be converted through its ester into the glycine anhydride discovered by Curtius and Goebel

$$
\begin{array}{ccc}
 & CH_2\!\!-\!\!CO & \\
 & \diagup \qquad \diagdown & \\
NH & & NH \\
 & \diagdown \qquad \diagup & \\
 & CO\!\!-\!\!CH_2 & \\
\end{array}
$$

This last is the simplest representative of the diketopiperazines whose history began about 60 years ago with the discovery of leucine imide. I have so simplified its preparation that obtaining large amounts offers no difficulty.

The diketopiperazines stand in simple relation to the dipeptides and can be converted to them by partial hydrolysis. This occurs most easily with glycine anhydride using alkalis, since it suffices to shake the powdered substance with a small excess of dilute sodium hydroxide at ordinary temperature for 10–15 minutes in order to obtain complete solution and at the same time conversion into the dipeptide. In this way we obtain glycyl-glycine

$$NH_2CH_2CO \cdot NHCH_2COOH$$

which is not only the simplest, but also the oldest polypeptide.

To generate a tripeptide from this requires a new reaction that depends on coupling with acyl halide. Thus, the dipeptide is shaken in alkaline solution at low temperature with chloroacetyl chloride and the resulting chloroacetyl glycyl-glycine

$$ClCH_2CO \cdot NHCH_2CO \cdot NHCH_2COOH$$

by standing for several days with strong aqueous ammonia is changed into diglycyl-glycine

$$NH_2CH_2CO \cdot NHCH_2CO \cdot NHCH_2COOH.$$

This behavior is capable of many variations and we will return to it in later phases of our special synthesis.

From the tripeptide, a peculiar condensation leads rapidly to the hexapeptide. The methyl ester is necessary for this. It is obtained as the hydrochloride by leading hydrogen chloride into a mixture of diglycyl-glycine and methyl alcohol and can be set free from the salt without difficulty.

The condensation of the ester is carried out rapidly and very smoothly by heating to 100°, by which procedure there occurs first melting and then solidification. The product is the methyl ester of the hexapeptide, and the process corresponds to the scheme:

$$2NH_2CH_2CO \cdot NHCH_2CO \cdot NHCH_2COOCH_3 =$$
$$CH_4O + NH_2CH_2CO \cdot (NHCH_2CO)_4 \cdot NHCH_2COOCH_3$$

The pentaglycyl-glycine which results from the methyl ester by saponification with alkali

$$NH_2CH_2CO \cdot (NHCH_2CO)_4 \cdot NHCH_2COOH$$

is an amorphous, difficulty water-soluble, colorless powder, but with mineral acids it forms well-crystallized salts.

For further building we need besides this hexapeptide another fairly complicated substance that bears the name of bromoisocaproyl-diglycyl-glycine, and for the preparation of which we use the previously mentioned d-leucine. For this purpose it must first be converted to α-bromoisocaproic acid, and this takes place by treatment of its cold hydrobromic acid solution with bromine and nitrogen oxides. The process corresponds to the conversion of aspartic acid into active halosuccinic acid which was carried out in a similar way by Tilden and Marshall, and at almost the same time by P. Walden.

The optical activity is retained in this reaction, but, as I recently recognized, there is a change in configuration, the so-called Walden inversion. The active α-bromoisocaproic acid thus no longer corresponds to the *d*-leucine that was used, but to the optical antipode, and can then be used to convert this into the polypeptide.

For this purpose the acid is next converted in the usual way with phosphorous pentachloride into the corresponding chloride $BrCH(C_4H_9)COCl$ and this is combined with amino acids or polypeptides in alkaline solution.

In the present particular case I have coupled it with diglycyl-glycine, from which the following optically active compound resulted: *d*-α-bromoisocaproyl-diglycyl-glycine

$$BrCH(C_4H_9)CO \cdot (NHCH_2CO)_2 \cdot NHCH_2COOH$$

This substance is now recognized as a very useful material for building up high molecular polypeptides. Thus, it can be converted in turn into the chloride

$$BrCH(C_4H_9)CO \cdot (NHCH_2CO)_2 \cdot NHCH_2COCl$$

For this purpose it must be prepared in a special way by crystallization from alcohol, and a special type of acid chloride formation is required which consists in the combined use of phosphorous pentachloride and acetyl chloride. However, by employing these conditions the process occurs very smoothly and the isolation of the very difficulty soluble chloride causes no trouble. Fortunately, in spite of its high molecular weight, it is still reactive enough to combine with polypeptides in ice cold, very dilute alkali solution.

Therefore its coupling with the above-mentioned pentaglycyl-glycine offers only a mechanical difficulty that is caused by the very strong foaming of the alkali solution. This can be overcome with glass beads and strong shaking of the liquid. As in a ball mill the glass beads break up the clumped chloride and also disperse the foaming liquid so strongly that there is a close contact with the undissolved chloride.

Under such conditions the coupling proceeds so smoothly that the yield of *d*-α-bromoisocaproyl-octaglycyl-glycine

$$BrCH(C_4H_9)CO \cdot (NHCH_2CO)_8 \cdot NHCH_2COOH$$

is 70% of the theoretical yield.

For the conversion of the new bromine compound into the corresponding decapeptide we can no longer use aqueous ammonia which is so useful in simpler cases. Dry liquid ammonia here performs the service better. It is enough to shake the insoluble bromine compound with it in a closed flask for several days to carry out a complete reaction. The purification of the decapeptide, which is called *l*-leucyl-octaglycyl-glycine

$$NH_2CH(C_4H_9)CO \cdot (NHCH_2CO)_8 \cdot NHCH_2COOH$$

also offers no special difficulty, since it can be reprecipitated from dilute alkali solution by acetic acid.

Fortunately in this high molecular polypeptide the reactivity of the amino group is little weakened. Therefore the coupling with bromoisocaproyl-diglycyl-glycyl chloride can be repeated under similar conditions. The resulting *d*-α-bromoisocaproyl-triglycyl-*l*-leucyl-octaglycyl-glycine

$$BrCH(C_4H_9)CO \cdot (NHCH_2CO)_3 \cdot NHCH(C_4H_9)CO \cdot$$
$$(NHCH_2CO)_8 \cdot NHCH_2COOH$$

is likewise very difficultly soluble in water and therefore is precipitated from alkaline solution by hydrochloric acid. However, its purification raises a new difficulty, the removal of which has caused much trouble.

Thus if we use for the coupling molecular amounts of the components, as we did successfully in all previous cases, a considerable amount of the decapeptide remains unaltered and on acidification this precipitates with the bromo compound, even when a marked excess of hydrochloric acid is added. The same thing happens every time the product is dissolved in alkali and again precipitated.

With this difficulty, not only the purification of the bromo compound, but also the further synthesis would have failed, if we had not finally been successful by using an excess of chloride (3 to 4 moles) to bring about almost complete coupling of the decapeptide.

By this method it has been possible to obtain pure bromoiso-caproyl-triglycyl-*l*-leucyl-octaglycyl-glycine.

Its amination by liquid ammonia takes place still more easily than in the previous example because it is completely soluble in the liquid. Even after a short time, the start of the reaction is seen by separation of the tetradecapeptide *l*-leucyl-triglycyl-*l*-leucyl-octa-glycyl-glycine

$$NH_2CH(C_4H_9)CO \cdot (NHCH_2CO)_3 \cdot NHCH(C_4H_9)CO \cdot$$
$$(NHCH_2CO)_8 \cdot NHCH_2COOH$$

With this product the same coupling followed by amination of the bromo compound is repeated once more and the product is then an octadecapeptide *l*-leucyl-triglycyl-*l*-leucyl-triglycyl-*l*-leucyl-octa-glycyl-glycine

$$NH_2CH(C_4H_9)CO \cdot (NHCH_2CO)_3 \cdot NHCH(C_4H_9)CO \cdot$$
$$(NHCH_2CO)_3 \cdot NHCH(C_4H_9)CO \cdot (NHCH_2CO)_8 \cdot NHCH_2COOH$$

We would remain uncertain of the composition of this high molecular substance, since the elementary analyses no longer give decisive results, if the bromo compound did not form an easy and definitive control. I must call it real luck that the synthesis has to be carried out in this way, since on the one hand purification of the substance is possible, and on the other, a clear idea of the molecular size and structure of the end product is established. This is the more gratifying since the properties of this substance exclude determination of the molecular weight by physical methods. In this, just as in the chemical reactions, it shows a great similarity to the natural proteins. If we had first encountered it in nature we would indeed think that it should be classed in the group of proteins. I believe I can say, however, that though present-day methods suffice in principle for building up the proteins, we must expressly mention that this artificial substance is in no way identical with any natural material.

In my experience, we must assume the opposite, that nature never creates long chains of the same amino acids, but favors the mixed forms in which the amino acids change from member to member. Thus it becomes possible to introduce as many building blocks into the same molecule as we find by the hydrolysis of most natural forms. If we wish to reproduce these artificially, for any synthesis we will have to proceed as with other natural substances and make a closer study of peptones and albumins. We will also have to continue to separate these into chemical individuals and to identify them with the artificial products.

From these large fragments we would then have to try to build up higher systems and to compare these with the natural products.

In order to carry out such studies we would surely have to commit ourselves to a very laborious project that would apparently take much more time than for the syntheses carried out up to now, but to me there seems to be no serious reason to doubt its final accomplishment.

We can only raise the question of whether the necessary trouble will find a corresponding reward. No competent judge would ever believe that a practical synthesis of foodstuffs could be realized, since plants that can prepare proteins from the constituents of the atmosphere and the earth are so cheap, and no rational manufacturing process for these substances could be developed.

However, we must seek the uses of protein synthesis in scientific, and preferably in biological field. It is to be expected that by combined synthetic and analytical studies the whole group of chemical methods will make possible the explanation of metabolism in animals and plants that the physiologists seek.

And chemistry will not be relegated by this to the role of hand-maiden, but will doubtless also find for itself a great new field of independent investigation and probably also of industrial development.

I am thinking here chiefly of the study of enzymes and enzymatic processes which occur in the organism and which are certainly closely connected with the metamorphoses of the proteins.

As soon as we understand these in a way somewhat similar to what we know today of the changes in benzene and its derivatives we will develop new branches of chemical manufacture that will still further surpass the present great fermentation industry.

In brief, with some optimism we can expect that from the ever closer connection of organic chemistry with biology we will find a great and lasting new source of inspiration which will be placed too highly by destiny ever to sink to a subordinate branch of our science.

NUCLEIC ACIDS. The nucleic acids were early recognized as an interesting group of compounds with a very complex structure, but there was no inkling of their biological functions. Nevertheless, P. A. Levene was able to demonstrate their essential structure very early in the century, as the next selection shows. It was only after the middle of the century that their role in heredity and in enzyme formation became known.

The following selection is from pages 2474–2476 in *Berichte der Deutschen Chemischen Gesellschaft 42*, 2474–2478 (1909).

Yeast Nucleic Acid

P. A. LEVENE AND W. A. JACOBS

As is known, the complicated nucleic acids are composed of purine bases, pyrimidine bases, carbonhydrates, and phosphoric acid. The simpler ones—inosinic acid and guanylic acid—consist only of a purine base, a carbohydrate group, and phosphoric acid. No views of the more exact constitution of the substances have recently been firmly established by experiment. The opinion of Schmiedeberg, according to which the basic substance of nucleic acids was to be regarded as a nucleotin, was based mainly on speculative grounds. A year ago, Levene and Mandel expressed the idea that the more complicated nucleic acids are built of many fragments that have the composition of the simple nucleic acids, inosinic and guanylic acids. A study of inosinic acid was then in progress in this laboratory; according to this its constitution can correspond to the following scheme:

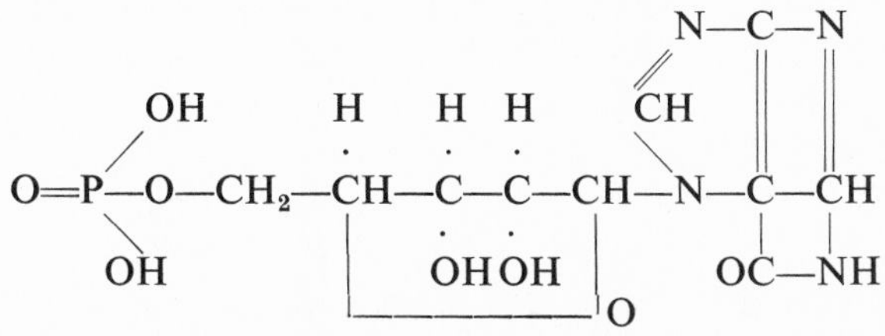

On the same grounds, guanylic acid must then have the following composition:

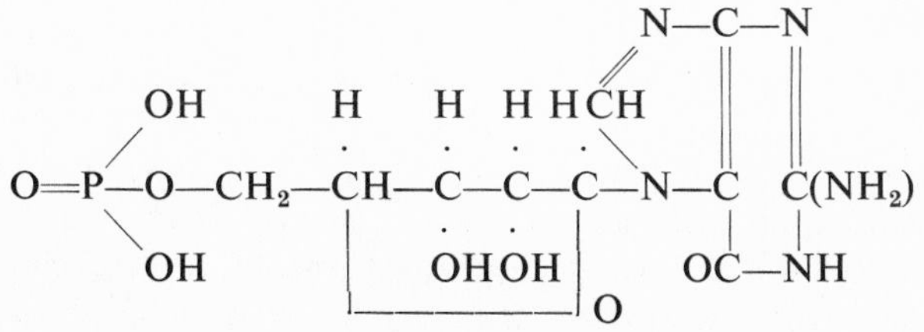

Levene and Mandel have called complexes of this order *mono-nucleotides*, the more complicated nucleic acids should then be built of several such components, somewhat according to the scheme:

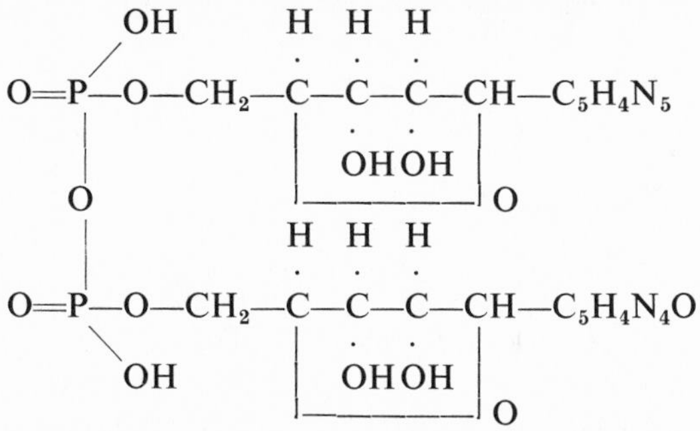

Since then this view of the constitution of inosinic acid has been experimentally established by the work of Levene and Jacobs and of Haiser and Wenzel. We have recently succeeded in recognizing an analogous composition for guanylic acid. There was left unexplained only the position of the hydroxyl group through which the sugar and the phosphoric acid were connected. The binding of the purine base must be assumed with Burrian to occur in position 7.

Some time ago Levene presented evidence for the assumption that yeast nucleic acid has a composition of the same nature as that of thymus nucleic acid. He based this on the fact that by partial hydrolysis with dilute mineral acids complexes were obtained which were apparently composed of pyrimidine bases, a pentose, and phosphoric acid, while by alkaline hydrolysis glycoside-like substances were obtained. At that time, isolation of these substances in pure crystalline form was not successful; but now it is possible to obtain such substances and study them more exactly. We propose the general name "nucleosides" for them. Two such nucleosides are already well known: inosine which Haiser and Wenzel discovered in carnine and which we recognized as a component of inosinic acid, and the guanosine which we discovered and which is a component of guanylic acid.

We have now succeeded in obtaining guanosine also by the hydrolysis of yeast nucleic acid. To obtain this substance in good yield we split the substance in the most neutral solution possible. This discovery also indicates that yeast nucleic acid consists of several nucleotides which are composed of guanylic acid.

By splitting yeast nucleic acid we obtain in the mother liquors from guanosine several similar substances in amorphous form. They are phosphorus free and yield by hydrolysis with dilute mineral acids pentoses and bases. We are now occupied with working these up.

This discovery also gives us information as to the nature of the pentose that occurs in yeast nucleic acid. On the basis of the investigations of Neuberg and his co-workers the pentose in the nucleic acids has been identified as *l*-xylose. In the study of inosinic acid we first encountered a contradiction between the results of Neuberg and our findings on the rotation of the phenyl osazones; later we were able to recognize definitely that the Neuberg view of the nature of the pentose in inosinic and guanylic acids was incorrect. We have now succeeded in obtaining this pentose in crystalline form. We had provisionally called it carnose; but now we find we must correct ourselves; it corresponds to *d*-ribose. We have also succeeded in obtaining the same pentose from guanosine of yeast nucleic acid. By direct splitting of yeast nucleic acid with dilute acid we have also formed the left-rotating pentose, but its isolation involves much difficulty and loss, so that from 30 g. of nucleic acid we have obtained only about 0.35 g. of pure sugar, in this case non-crystalline. We also mentioned in previous communications that we encountered similar difficulties in the hydrolysis of inosinic and guanylic acids.

ALKALOIDS. The essential oils, alkaloids, and other products synthesized by plants had long been of interest to the chemist and some of them had been synthesized in the laboratory by methods that often employed reagents and drastic conditions that obviously could not exist in a living plant. In 1917 Robert Robinson suggested a number of methods by which alkaloids could be formed in biosynthesis. The following selection illustrates some of these suggestions, and the path thus proposed was then followed by Robinson and his students in such a fruitful manner that in later years the mechanisms of a large number of phytochemical reactions became clear.

The following selection is from pages 876–882 in *Journal of the Chemical Society 111*, 876–899 (1917).

A Theory of the Mechanism of the Phytochemical Synthesis of Certain Alkaloids

ROBERT ROBINSON

Although in recent years, largely owing to the investigations of Pictet and his collaborators, there has been a due recognition of the importance of the role played by formaldehyde in the production of alkaloids in plants, and although it is generally admitted that the amino acids and carbohydrates are the most probable starting points for the majority of phytochemical syntheses, yet little progress has been made in ascertaining the nature of these processes or even in the less ambitious task of formulating possible mechanisms based on laboratory analogies. The details of the schemes which have been suggested, with but few exceptions, involve reactions for which little or no parallel exists in synthetical organic chemistry under conditions approximating to those obtaining in a plant. Thus Pictet's view of the mechanism of the synthesis of nicotine was founded on observations of pyrogenic reactions of pyrrole derivatives, and Winterstein and Trier seek to replace this hypothesis by another, according to which the base results from the oxidation of a mixture of pyridine and N-methylpyrrolidine. Similar ideas have been advanced by Windaus and Knoop to explain the formation of xanthine by the oxidation of a mixture of carbamide and methylglyoxaline and of histidine by an analogous process applied to glycine and methylglyoxaline.

There has thus been a tendency to explain the results observed by the assumption that plants have at their command enormously powerful reagents that are able to cause substances, the properties of which have been investigated with considerable care, to undergo transformations which cannot be induced in the laboratory. To a certain extent, and especially in regard to oxidation and reduction, this must be true, but it is probable that this aspect has been exaggerated and that an equally important cause of the variety and complexity of syntheses in plants resides in the highly reactive nature of the substances which function as intermediate products.

The point of view reached in the present communication is due to a development of ideas which owed their inception to the hypothesis that the synthesis of tropinone recently described, on account of its simplicity, is probably the method employed by the plant, and confirmation of this theory was sought and found in the structures of hygrine and cuschygrine, which stand to one another in the same relation as styryl methyl ketone (benzylideneacetone) to distyryl ketone (dibenzylideneacetone). Having found it desirable to proceed from ornithine in order to reach the bases of the pyrrolidine group, it was obviously interesting to inquire as to whether similar methods applied to the homologous lysine would lead to naturally occurring piperidine compounds. This proved to be the case, and the investigation was then extended to include the more important of the alkaloids, the constitutions of which have been determined. In the schemes given in the sequel, linking of carbon to carbon is traced to two processes only, namely, the aldol condensation and the very similar condensation of carbinol-amines, resulting from the combination of an aldehyde or ketone and ammonia or an amine, and containing the group $\cdot\dot{C}(OH)\cdot\dot{N}\cdot$, with substances containing the group $\cdot\dot{C}H\cdot CO\cdot$.

The latter reaction has been investigated chiefly in connexion with cotarnine and similar pseudo-bases, and the production of anhydrocotarnineacetone (I) may be cited as a typical example:

$$C_8H_6O_3\!-\!CH\cdot OH \qquad\qquad\qquad C_8H_6O_3\!-\!CH\cdot CH_2\cdot CO\cdot CH_3$$
$$\mid \qquad\qquad \mid \quad + CH_3\cdot CO\cdot CH_3 \rightarrow \quad \mid \qquad\qquad \mid$$
$$CH_2\cdot CH_2\cdot NMe \qquad\qquad\qquad\quad CH_2\cdot CH_2\cdot NMe$$
$$\text{(I)}$$

The condensing agent employed by Liebermann and Kropf in this case is unnecessary, and the reaction proceeds to completion in aqueous solution and at the ordinary temperature. In fact, these pseudo-bases are substances which enter into a variety of condensations with the greatest facility, and a large number of substances have been prepared in this way, and in most cases in good yield.

Employing these admissible methods it is possible in each instance to obtain the alkaloid skeleton, and the further modifications are usually made by means of oxidations or reductions and by elimination of water with the formation of an aromatic nucleus or occasionally of an ethylene derivative. The more important starting points employed are ammonia and formaldehyde, ornithine (arginine) and lysine and degradation products of carbohydrates. Of the latter, citric acid is suggested as the source of acetone residues, which it supplies in the form of acetonedicarboxylic acid as the result of oxidation. Seekamp has observed the formation of acetone by the photochemical decomposition of a 5 per cent aqueous solution of citric acid containing 1 per cent of uranium oxide, and it can scarcely be doubted that the dicarboxylic acid was an intermediate product. The author does not, however, wish to emphasize unduly this theory of the source of the acetone residues, and it is interesting to note that Lippmann found that acetonedicarboxylic acid was obtained during the spontaneous decomposition of calcium trisaccharate. Further, a reactive acetone derivative may be found in diacetylacetone or other "polyketen," the formation of which in plants has been discussed by Collie, and in that case the acetyl groups would be removed by hydrolysis subsequent to the condensations. However, the occurrence of the carboxyl group in ecgonine suggests that in the synthesis of cocaine it is a carboxylated acetone derivative which is the forerunner of the alkaloid. Except in the cases of hygrine and tropinone, the carboxyl groups have been omitted from the acetone rests for the sake of simplicity in representation. As a starting point for both quinoline and *iso*quinoline bases, it has been found convenient to assume the intervention of acetylglycollaldehyde (II) or Δ^{α}-butene-$\alpha\beta$-diol-γ-one, a substance which has not yet been isolated. It may readily be derived from a pentose or methylpentose by loss of water and oxidation, as shown below, and it is perhaps significant that a methylpentose, quinovose, occurs in a state of combination as quinovin in cinchona-bark.

$$OH \cdot CH_2 \cdot CH(OH) \cdot CH(OH) \cdot CH(OH) \cdot CHO$$

$$\Big|-H_2O \qquad\qquad CH_3 \cdot CH(OH) \cdot CH(OH) \cdot CH(OH)$$
$$\downarrow \qquad\qquad\qquad\qquad \downarrow \text{Oxidation} \qquad\qquad\quad \cdot CH(OH) \cdot CHO$$
$$CH_3 \cdot CO \cdot CH(OH) \cdot CH(OH) \cdot CHO$$
$$\qquad \downarrow \text{Oxidation}$$
$$CH_3 \cdot CO \cdot CH(OH) \cdot CHO \rightleftharpoons CH_3 \cdot CO \cdot C(OH):CH \cdot OH$$
$$(II)$$

The Pyrrolidine Group

It has recently been demonstrated by Hess that the methylation of an amine with the aid of formaldehyde is accompanied by oxidation, amino-alcohols yielding methylaminoketones. The methylating and oxidizing action of formaldehyde on ornithine might therefore yield a carbinol-amine of the pyrrolidine series in accordance with the equation

$$NH_2 \cdot CH_2 \cdot CH_2 \cdot CH_2 \cdot CH(NH_2) \cdot CO_2H + CH_2O =$$

$$NHMe \cdot CH_2 \cdot CH_2 \cdot CHO \left[\rightarrow \begin{array}{c} CH_2 \cdot CH(OH) \\ | \qquad\qquad >NMe \\ CH_2 - CH_2 \end{array} \right] + NH_3 + CO_2$$

Naturally, the possibility is not excluded that the oxidation of the amino acid is preceded by the formation of a hydroxy-acid and ammonia and alcohols may in all cases be intermediate between amines and the aldehydes obtained by oxidation.

Further oxidation accompanying methylation might attack both ends of the molecule, with the production of succindialdehyde and methylamine, as shown below:

$$[NH_2 \cdot CH_2 \cdot CH_2 \cdot CH_2 \cdot CH(NH_2) \cdot CO_2H + 2CH_2O =$$

$$CHO \cdot CH_2 \cdot CH_2 \cdot CHO \left[\rightarrow \begin{array}{c} CH_2 \cdot CH(OH) \\ | \qquad\qquad >NMe \\ CH_2 \cdot CH(OH) \end{array} \right] + 2NH_2Me + CO_2]$$

After condensation with acetonedicarboxylic acid and elimination of carbon dioxide, hygrine (III), cuschygrine (IV), and tropinone (V) are obtained. The synthesis of the latter base by means of the reaction here assumed to occur in nature was accomplished in dilute aqueous solution at the ordinary temperature. Willstätter has already given reasons for supposing that the synthesis of atropine and its congeners and of cocaine is preceded by that of tropinone, and it is now possible to add that the carboxyl of cocaine is the result of partial decomposition of tropinonedicarboxylic acid, possibly occasioned by the formation of the methyl ester or of an acid salt. In the latter case, the process resembles that which Bandrowski employed for the preparation of propiolic acid from acetylenedicarboxylic acid. The question of the synthesis of benzoic and tropic acids is not examined here, since there is no evidence from accompanying hydroaromatic compounds as to how these may be derived from the carbohydrates.

The condensation product (VI), which forms the source of hygrine, may also be the progenitor of nicotine (VIII), and the reactions necessary involve condensation with formaldehyde and ammonia to a piperidone (VII) containing the nicotine skeleton, after which there are alternative ways of expressing the remaining stages.

Similar mechanisms for formation of piperidine, quinuclidine, and isoquinoline groups and of a number of individual alkaloids are discussed in the remainder of the paper.

$$
\begin{array}{cc}
\text{NMe} & \text{CO}_2\text{H} \\
\diagup\diagdown & | \\
\text{CH}_2 \quad \text{CH}\cdot\text{OH} & \text{CH}_2\cdot\text{CO}\cdot\text{CH}_2\cdot\text{CO}_2\text{H} \rightarrow \\
| \qquad | & \\
\text{CH}_2\text{—CH}_2 &
\end{array}
$$

$$
\begin{array}{cc}
\text{NMe} \quad \text{CO}_2\text{H} & \text{NMe} \\
\diagup\diagdown \quad | & \diagup\diagdown \\
\text{CH}_2 \quad \text{CH}\cdot\text{CH}\cdot\text{CO}\cdot\text{CH}_2\cdot\text{CO}_2\text{H} \rightarrow & \text{CH}_2 \quad \text{CH CH}_2\cdot\text{COMe} \\
| \qquad | & | \qquad | \\
\text{CH}_2\text{—CH}_2 & \text{CH}_2\text{—CH}_2 \\
\qquad\text{(VI.)} & \qquad\text{(III.)}
\end{array}
$$

$$
\begin{array}{ccc}
\text{NMe} & \text{CO}_2\text{H} \quad \text{CO}_2\text{H} & \text{NMe} \\
\diagup\diagdown & | \qquad\quad | & \diagup\diagdown \\
\text{CH}_2 \quad \text{CH}\cdot\text{OH} & \text{CH}_2\cdot\text{CO}\cdot\text{CH}_2 \quad \text{HO}\cdot\text{CH} \quad \text{CH}_2 \rightarrow \\
| \qquad | & | \qquad | \\
\text{CH}_2\text{—CH}_2 & \text{CH}_2\text{—CH}_2
\end{array}
$$

$$
\begin{array}{cc}
\text{NMe} & \text{NMe} \\
\diagup\diagdown & \diagup\diagdown \\
\text{CH}_2 \quad \text{CH}\cdot\text{CH}_2\cdot\text{CO}\cdot\text{CH}_2\cdot\text{CH} \quad \text{CH}_2 & + 2\text{CO}_2 + 2\text{H}_2\text{O} \\
| \qquad | \qquad\qquad\qquad\qquad | \qquad | & \\
\text{CH}_2\text{—CH}_2 \qquad\qquad\qquad \text{CH}_2\text{—CH}_2 & \\
\qquad\qquad \text{(IV.)}
\end{array}
$$

$$
\begin{array}{ccc}
\text{CH}\cdot\text{OH CH}_2\cdot\text{CO}_2\text{H} & \text{CH—CH}\cdot\text{CO}_2\text{H} & \text{CH—CH}_2 \\
\diagup\quad| & \diagup\quad| & \diagup\quad| \\
\text{CH}_2 \quad | & \text{CH}_2 \quad | & \text{CH}_2 \quad | \\
| \quad \text{NMe} \quad \text{CO} \rightarrow & | \quad \text{NMe CO} \rightarrow & | \quad \text{NMe CO} \\
\text{CH}_2 \quad | & \text{CH}_2 \quad | & \text{CH}_2 \quad | \\
\diagdown\quad| & \diagdown\quad| & \diagdown\quad| \\
\text{CH}\cdot\text{OH CH}_2\cdot\text{CO}_2\text{H} & \text{CH—CH}\cdot\text{CO}_2\text{H} & \text{CH—CH}_2 \\
& & \text{(V.)}
\end{array}
$$

Ecgonine

CH—CH·CO$_2$K(Me)

↓ Reduction ↓

Tropine ψ-Tropine

↓   ↓

Benzoyl ecgonine ⟵^{Reduction}

CH$_2$

NMe CO

CH$_2$

Hyoscyamine,
Tropaatropine,
etc., Cocaine

Cocaine

CH—CH$_2$

LARGE RINGS. A new field of organic chemistry of both practical and theoretical significance was opened when L. Ruzicka found that the naturally occurring perfume bases muscone and civetone were made up of very large rings. He developed methods for the synthesis of such rings, as illustrated in the following selection. These new products were thus made

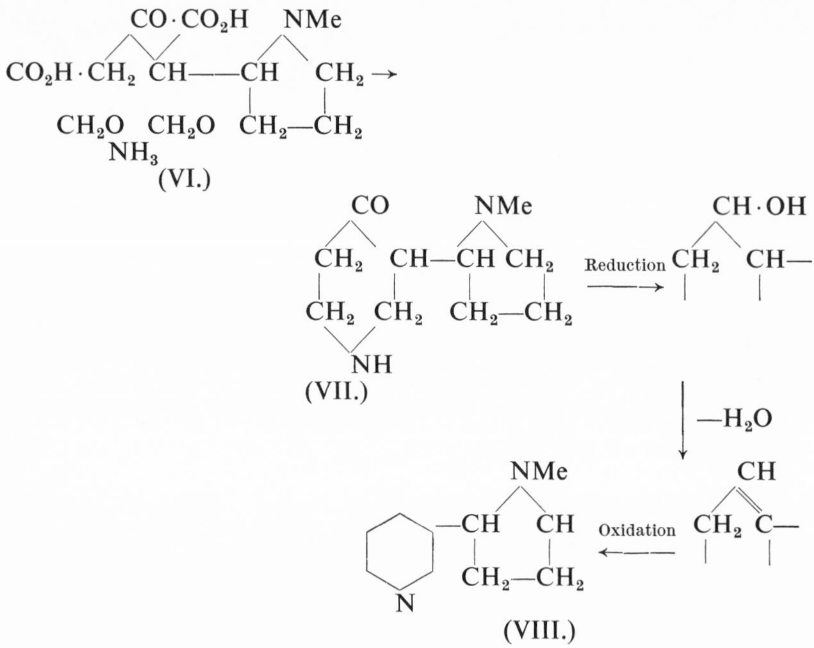

$$CO_2H \cdot CH_2 \quad \overset{\overset{\displaystyle CO \cdot CO_2H \quad NMe}{\diagup}}{CH} \overset{}{——} CH \quad CH_2 \rightarrow$$

$$\underset{NH_3}{CH_2O} \quad CH_2O \quad CH_2—CH_2$$

(VI.)

$$\overset{\overset{\displaystyle CO \quad NMe}{\diagdown \diagup}}{CH_2} \quad CH—CH \; CH_2 \quad \text{Reduction} \quad \overset{\overset{\displaystyle CH \cdot OH}{\diagup}}{CH_2} \quad CH—$$

$$CH_2 \quad CH_2 \quad CH_2—CH_2 \quad \xrightarrow{\hspace{1cm}}$$

$$\underset{NH}{\diagdown \diagup}$$

(VII.)

$$\Big| \; —H_2O$$

$$\overset{\overset{\displaystyle NMe}{\diagup}}{\bigcirc —CH} \quad CH \quad \text{Oxidation} \quad \overset{\overset{\displaystyle CH}{\diagup}}{CH_2} \quad C—$$

$$\underset{N}{} \quad CH_2—CH_2 \quad \xleftarrow{\hspace{1cm}}$$

(VIII.)

available to the perfume industry. At the same time the limitations imposed on chemistry by the strain theory of Baeyer (Leicester and Klickstein, *Source Book*, p. 465) were removed and new theoretical developments could follow.

The following selection is from pages 249–252 in *Helvetica Chimica Acta 9*, 249–264 (1926).

Knowledge of Carbon Rings.
II. Synthesis of Carbocyclic Ketones with Ten- to Eighteen-member Rings

L. RUZICKA, M. STOLL, AND H. SCHINZ

After the results of the demonstration of the constitution of civetone, which is a carbocyclic seventeen-membered ring, it was of interest to test whether higher-membered carbon rings could also be obtained synthetically. A nine-member carbon ring had perhaps been produced synthetically. The slight yield of a ketone from distillation of the calcium salt of sebacic acid as contrasted to the yield, always above 30%, obtained in the formation of cyclohexanone and cycloheptanone from the calcium salts of the corresponding dicarboxylic acids made the assumption quite probable that higher-membered carbocyclic ketones would be obtained only in vanishingly small yields if they were obtained at all.

Although we know numerous methods for the synthesis of five- and six-member carbon rings from aliphatic compounds, these partially fail even when passing to a seven-member ring, and for direct passage in the aliphatic series to eight- and nine-membered rings, according to present knowledge, we can consider only the reaction mentioned above.

We have studied various reactions for preparing higher-member carbon rings and we will report on these in detail later. In the work which follows we will describe a method for the whole series of polymethylene dicarboxylic acids from nonan-1,9-dicarboxylic acid to heptadecan-1,17-dicarboxylic acid. Orienting studies showed us that the yields of ketones from the dicarboxylic acids in part were greatly dependent on the metal which was used for salt formation. Another still more important fact resulted from the metal used. Wallach had already noted that the cyclooctanone resulting from the calcium salt of azelaic acid was contaminated by other ketones. By the use of certain metals, among others, of thorium, not only was the yield of ketone raised, but also a purer ketone, free from contaminants, was obtained.

The polymethylene dicarboxylic acids needed for this study were not all easily available, and their preparation required considerable expenditure of time and materials. The preparation of such acids in the Hochschule laboratory presented difficulties which could scarcely be overcome, and therefore we must thank Dr. Ph. Chuit who prepared the dicarboxylic acids at the factory of the firm of M. Naef & Co. in Geneva.

By the decomposition of the thorium salts of polymethylene dicarboxylic acids we obtained cyclic ketones in all the cases studied. The decomposition was carried out in a vacuum, and the main reaction took place between about 350–400°. Along with the ketones there formed chiefly a mixture of various kinds of compounds, from which the ketones could be isolated by fractional distillation and conversion to the semicarbazones. The semicarbazones obtained in this way were not individuals, but by repeated recrystallizations the melting point was raised steadily to its highest value. These high-melting semicarbazones (all above 180°) were derivatives only of pure polymethylene ketones. By splitting with oxalic acid or hydrochloric acid the ketones themselves could be obtained from them.

The following table [I] gives the melting points of the pure ketones and semicarbazones and the boiling points of the ketones.

Table I

	M.p. of ketone	B.p. of ketone	M.p. of semicarbazone
10 ring	?	100° (12 mm)	200°
11 ring	?	110° (12 mm)	200°
12 ring	59°	125° (12 mm)	226°
13 ring	32°	138° (12 mm)	207°
14 ring	52°	155° (12 mm)	197°
15 ring	63°	120° (0.3 mm)	187°
16 ring	56°	138° (0.3 mm)	180°
17 ring	63°	145° (0.3 mm)	191°
18 ring	71°	158° (0.3 mm)	184°

In the 10 and 11 rings the available amounts of pure semicarbazones were too small to determine the melting points of the ketones regenerated from them reliably. The yield of cyclic ketones which was 1.5% in the nine ring fell in the 10 ring to a minimum of about 0.1–0.2% and then with increasing number of ring members rose almost continuously, and indeed proportionally, to the 18-ring compound; even with the first members, the yield of cyclononane was again reached, and then was considerably exceeded. Later we will report these quantitative relationships in more detail when more results are available.

Cyclolheptadecanone was identical with dihydrocivetone. The constitution of all the polymethylene ketones which we obtained was shown by oxidation with chromic acid to the normal polymethylene dicarboxylic acids with the same number of carbon atoms, which were identical with the synthetic compounds.

All the pure ketones prepared (from the 12-ring up) are solid and show, like civetone, a camphor or camphor-like looking mass. The odor of the ketones from 10 to 12 rings is clearly like camphor.

Cyclotridecanone has only a slight characteristic odor like cedar wood, which is often found for compounds of similar molecular size (for example, pseudoionone and numerous sesquiterpene alcohols). The higher ketones also have a certain cedar-like odor when in concentrated form, as, for example is the case with ionenes and in mucone and civetone. On dilution, however, these ketones from the 14 to the 18 ring have the typical musk odor, and indeed the first members, the 14 and 15 rings, resemble muscone and the higher, civetone, while cyclohexadecanone forms a transition. Cyclopentadecanone is the most similar to muscone in odor. In contrast to this, the aliphatic ketones with the same number of carbon atoms have a fatlike odor which is not very characteristic.

By the synthesis of these ketones the way is opened for the preparation of odor carriers for natural muscone and civetone. Moreover, it has been shown that *the ability of carbon atoms to act as members of rings is not nearly as limited as we were inclined to assume on the basis of carbon compounds known previously.* It was premature previously to conclude on the basis of a lack of well-established experimental evidence that carbon can act as a ring member in rather large rings in a way similar to long-chain aliphatic compounds. Such an assumption is not justified from the present material either and we plan further experimental tests of all the complex questions raised here. Naturally it is clear on the basis of the facts given here and also from the customary views on the ease of formation of carbon rings that the conditions which are decisive for the formation of a carbon ring must be greatly revised. We will report in more detail on this in connection with further experimental results.

Experimental results are then given.

CHOLESTEROL COMPOUNDS. The alcohol cholesterol had been known for many years to exist in animal cells, but discovery of its structure eluded the skill of the organic chemists until the early 1930's. Many chemists worked on this problem, and a number of others attempted to determine the structure of the natural bile acids. Gradually it came to be realized that all these compounds were related, and the combined attack of the various groups led in 1932 to the recognition that the older formula for the multi-ring skeleton that had been assumed as a basis for most of the work was incorrect. Since a knowledge of the correct formula was essential, the work that revealed it, shown in the first of the following selections, at once also made possible determination of the structures of all the other steroids. These included the bile acids, hormones, and vitamins. As an illustration of the speed with which this was accomplished the paper of Butenandt on the sex hormones is quoted. This was published in the same year as the paper of Wieland and Dane. Thus the two next selections show not only the method of the organic chemist in solving complex problems, but also how rapidly the results could then be applied to related compounds.

The following selection is from pages 268–275 in *Hoppe-Seylers Zeitschrift für Physiologische Chemie 210*, 268–281 (1932).

Studies on the Constitution of the Bile Acids.
XXXIX. Concerning 12-Hydroxycholanic Acid

HEINRICH WIELAND AND ELISABETH DANE

By the exclusion of other possibilities, the previous development of the structural question has led to the assumption that the two C atoms not yet provided for in the total structure of the molecule are arranged as $HC \cdot CH_3$ groups in ring III, a seven-membered ring. In order to investigate this assumption further experimentally we have tried to learn the nature of this ring free of the disturbing influence of neighboring groups. We have utilized as the model the methods that have been in use in the study of rings I and II. Here knowledge of the hydroxycholanic acids (3 and 7) and the corresponding keto acids has made it possible to determine the pattern of these rings by oxidative ring splitting or by bromination and related reactions. Ring III has not yet been studied by these methods, since no suitable bile acid derivatives are known that are substituted only in ring III. Then at almost the same time Borsche and Todd and Wieland and Deulofeu obtained the β-cholenic acid $C_{24}H_{38}O_2$ from apocholic acid; it is fairly certain that its double bond is in ring III, but in a position that up to now could not be successfully used for constitution determination. Above all, it was not suitable for the preparation of the desired compound which by splitting of ring III would give the expected tricarboxylic acid.

In order to obtain a cholanic acid substituted only in ring III, it was necessary to replace the oxygen that was substituted in another ring of a known bile acid by hydrogen. Experience has shown that secondary OH groups in positions C_3, C_7, and C_{12} are dehydrogenated to carbonyl groups at different rates; it seems that the rate decreases in the order C_{12}—C_3—C_7. The secondary alcohol group on C_7 shows the lowest reactivity, not only toward chromic acid, but also in ester formation and other reactions. This gradation suggests a method of partial dehydrogenation which can permit dihydroxy (and also trihydroxy) cholanic acids to be converted to hydroxyketo acids. For this purpose, we may consider the transformation of anthropodesoxycholic acid (3,12-dihydroxycholanic acid), 7,12-dihydroxycholanic acid, and finally, hyodesoxycholic acid (3,13-dihydroxycholanic acid). In this way we can pass from desoxycholic acid to 3-keto-7-hydroxycholanic acid.

Then if we have available a hydroxyketocholanic acid with a substituent on ring III, two methods for reaching the goal are possible: the method of Windaus and Borsche, and that developed in this laboratory in studies on bile acids. If OH is present in ring III and CO in another position, we can obtain, usually in very good yield, the hydroxycholanic acid (A), substituted only in ring III, if we use deoxidation of the CO group through the semicarbazone by the Kishner-Wolff method. If the CO is in ring III and the OH outside of it, thermal decomposition in which water is split out can give a ketocholenic acid which by catalytic hydrogenation can then be converted to the hydroxy acid substituted in ring III (B).

$$
\begin{array}{cccc}
\overset{H}{\underset{HO}{\diagdown}}C\Big|Ring\ III & \overset{H}{\underset{HO}{\diagdown}}C\Big|Ring\ III & OC\Big|Ring\ III & OC\Big|Ring\ III \\
\xrightarrow[\text{Wolff}]{\text{Kishner-}} & \xleftarrow[\text{hydrogenation}]{\text{catalytic}} & \xleftarrow[\text{decomp.}]{\text{therm.}} & \\
\overset{|}{\underset{|}{OC}} & \overset{|}{\underset{|}{H_2C}} & -CH{=}CH- & CHOH-CH_2- \\
A & & & B
\end{array}
$$

In the second process, which leads to the same goal, the difference in hydrogenation rate of the keto acids is used. It has long been known that in the reduction of dehydrocholic acid (3,7,12-triketo-cholanic acid) only the keto group of C_3 is hydrogenated (to the so-called reductodehydrocholic acid = 3-hydroxy-7,12-diketocholanic acid) and Borsche has also carried out this reaction with catalytically activated hydrogen on dehydrocholic acid and also on dehydrodesoxycholic acid (3,7-diketocholanic acid).

7,12-Diketocholanic acid, which we can obtain in excellent yield by a slight alteration of the previous method, can be hydrogenated without difficulty to 7-keto-12-hydroxycholanic acid whose semicarbazone is split smoothly to the well-crystallized 12-hydroxycholanic acid (I), the goal of this investigation.

We had expected that the 12-hydroxycholanic acid by thermal decomposition would split out water to form a cholenic acid which would contain the double bond between C_{12} and C_{13}, so that it could be smoothly hydrogenated to the cholanic acid in a manner similar to the cholatrienic and choladienic acids obtained from cholic acid and desoxycholic acid. However, this was not the case. We isolated instead a cholenic acid that was absolutely stable toward catalytically activated hydrogen and that agreed so closely in all properties with

the cholenic acid obtained by splitting out water from apocholic acid that we were forced to consider this to be structurally the same as our acid. Slight variations could indicate spacial isomerism such as is found between apocholic acid and the hydrogenation product of dihydroxycholadienic acid, the so-called β-apocholic acid.

We could at first see no explanation for this unexpected result. Then we remembered that thermal splitting of cholic acid does not lead to apocholic acid, whose formation was found by Boedecker to occur from the action of sulfuric acid or zinc chloride on cholic acid.

Next we turned to oxidative splitting of ring III. 12-Hydroxy-cholanic acid is split very smoothly by nitric acid to the expected tricarboxylic acid $C_{24}H_{38}O_6$ (II). This makes known the third of the isomeric tricarboxylic acids of the bilianic acid type. The other two acids were obtained in an analogous way from lithocholic acid (3-hydroxycholanic acid) with opening of ring I to give the so-called lithobilianic acid (III), and from 7-hydroxycholanic acid with opening of ring II to give the acid called iso-lithobilianic acid. By decomposition of the side chain ring IV was split to etiobilianic acid (IV). We will call the new tricarboxylic acid, the third of the isomers, by the short name of thilo-bilianic acid, by transposition of "litho."

Thermal decomposition of lithobilianic acid gives the next lower five-membered ring ketone which in agreement with the analogous results of Windaus on cholesterol can be considered an indication that the CO_2H groups in the 1,6- (perhaps also the 1,7-), but certainly not the 1,5-positions come together, and ring I thus consists of more than 5 C atoms. Isolithobilianic acid, which comes from the opening of ring II, splits out only water and no CO_2 when heated; it thus forms no cyclic ketone, from which the conclusion has been drawn on the basis of the Blanc rule that ring II has five members.

Now to our great surprise we found that thilobilianic acid also did not give a cyclic ketone, but only a well-crystallized anhydride. For ring III, however, we have discussed in our last work a seven-carbon compound, a cycloheptane structure, on the basis of new developments of the structural problem. The six-member structure of this ring is experimentally well established by our previous deductions and most forcefully by the evidence presented by Borsche of the nature of cilianic acid which arises from the oxidation of bilianic acid with alkaline permanganate through a benzilic acid rearrangement on ring III.

By study of the tricarboxylic acid from splitting of six-member ring III we come to the definite result, so important for investigation of the constitution of bile acids and steroids, that *the Blanc rule for dicarboxylic acids derived from condensed ring systems has no general validity*. It is practically useful in cases in which both carboxyls are in one and the same ring in the compound. Confidence in the correctness of this idea is based on the work of Windaus and von Hückel on the behavior of cyclohexane propionic and acetic carboxylic acids in thermal decomposition, where no exceptions to the rule were found. On these grounds we also conclude that the results from the study of thermal decomposition of etiobilianic acid (IV) are firmly established. This acid corresponds completely to the model of a simple cyclohexane acetic carboxylic acid. Ring IV is therefore certainly a five-member ring.

In the case of lithobilianic acid (III) the transformation of the acid into a cyclic ketone and all the degradation reactions carried out likewise determine that ring I is composed of more than five members.

On the other hand, according to the behavior of thilobilianic acid we do not seem to come to closure of a five-membered ring in a 1,6-dicarboxylic acid, where the four C atoms lying between the two carboxyl groups belong to rings bound together, as is expressed in formula II. To be sure, if we take an example in the aromatic series, the thermal conversion of diphenic acid to its anhydride and not to

III   IV

fluorenone has not been sufficiently considered up to now. Diphenic acid anhydride distills at 270° and about 40 mm. as a colorless oil which crystallizes immediately. No trace of yellow fluorenone is apparent. The ketone appears first above 320°.

Now that firm proof of the denial of the Blanc rule has been shown for the field of saturated rings, the only argument for the idea that ring II is five membered disappears. One of us previously perceived the "beautiful error" in the structural picture of a five-membered ring and in several earlier communications left open the possibility of a six-member ring for the structure of ring II (V).

V   VI

Scheme V was then given up, since it did not seem to agree with a degradation reaction carried out by Windaus on cholesterol. The decomposition of the diketodicarboxylic acid $C_{23}H_{34}O_6$ to a tetra-carboxylic acid $C_{16}H_{24}O_8$ (VI) that followed later was likewise not derived from V.

The position of the constitutional question is now this, that on the basis of the experiments carried out up to now, the way is open for a discussion of a modified formulation of the bile acid skeleton. We

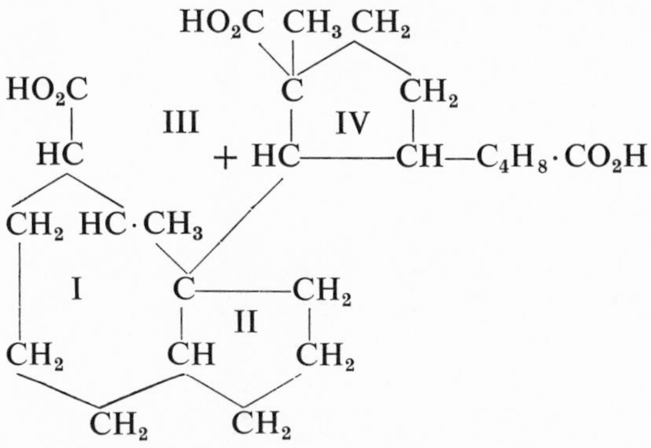

$$HO_2C \quad CH_3 \quad CH_2$$

I, II, III, IV, VII structure

$$HO_2C \quad HC \quad | \quad III \quad + \quad HC{-}{-}{-}{-}CH{-}C_4H_8 \cdot CO_2H \quad IV$$

VII

$$C_4H_8 \cdot CO_2H$$

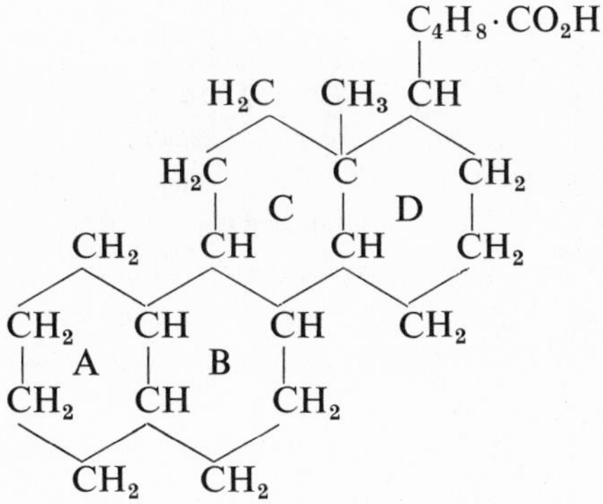

VIII

$$C_4H_8 \cdot CO_2H$$

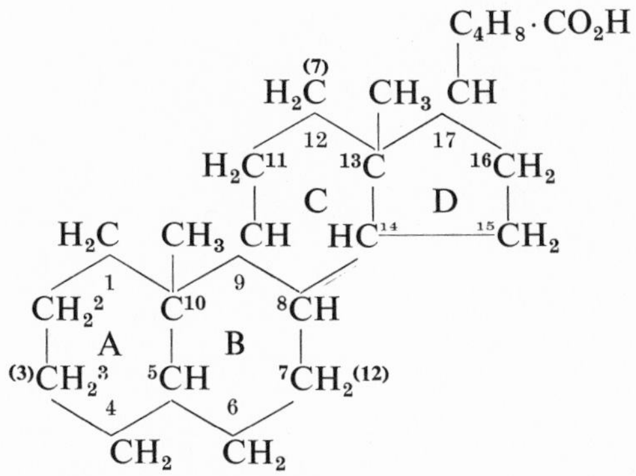

IX

are now free from a firm attachment to the idea of a five-member ring system for II. It is indeed true that the denial of the Blanc rule in thilobilianic acid does not contradict the presence of a five-member ring in this system. We must draw a second conclusion from the behavior of the new tricarboxylic acid in its thermal decomposition: our conjecture that a seven-member ring occurs in ring III becomes improbable with the recognition of the anhydride formation. There would hardly be a reason for a supposed 1,7-dicarboxylic acid (VII) to be converted to an anhydride and not a cycloketone.

Several weeks ago O. Rosenheim and H. King, starting from the firmly established Diels formation of chrysene by thermal dehydrogenation of cholic acid with selenium and of cholesterol with palladium charcoal, have introduced consideration of the skeleton of a perhydrogenated chrysene, VIII, as the basis for the structure of both substances. The difference from the previously discussed formula is that ring II is six membered and ring IV is also enlarged to a six-member ring. We regard the Rosenheim proposal as a very valuable suggestion. It permits explanation of most of the reactions already studied, especially if ring B is set equal to ring III of the previous formula, and ring C to ring II. The C atoms 3, 7, and 12 in formula IX are shown by boldface numbers to correspond to the places indicated. The ring III of the older cholesterol formulation which is recognized as identical with ring II of the bile acids is then ring B. We do not agree with Rosenheim in the enlargement of ring IV (D) to a six-member ring, and further, on grounds to be reported later, we are of the opinion that the still-missing CH_3 will be one of the carbon atoms common to rings A and B. We are now occupied with the experimental evidence for the constitution IX which we consider very probable.

The experimental portion of the paper follows.

The following selection is in *Zeitschrift für Angewandte Chemie 45*, 655–656 (1932).

The Chemistry of the Sex Hormones

A. BUTENANDT

(Reported at a meeting of the Deutsche Chemische Gesellschaft and Deutsche Bunsengesellschaft, Mainz, September 27–29, 1932.)

As has already been reported in this Journal, two of the already known sex hormones have been obtained in crystalline form and this has made possible an exact physiological, physical, and chemical study of the follicular hormone of the female and the testicular hormone of the male.

1. The follicular hormone. This hormone has been characterized in pure condition by the two physiological properties of a "female sex hormone" developed in the animal kingdom: it produces estrus and influences the growth and development of the female sex characteristics; in the plant kingdom it hastens the development of already present blossoms and fruit; although the specificity of this action has still not been completely studied, the definite effect of this hormone on plants shows for the first time the possibility of understanding the significance of the occurrence of the follicular hormone in the plant kingdom; it has been shown in work with Dr. H. Jacobi that the estrus-producing substance that occurs in the plant kingdom is identical with the animal hormone. The crystalline hormone was prepared from plant material (extract from hearts of palms). The closer study of the follicular hormone crystallizate from pregnancy and mare's urine has shown that there is a whole series of substances that develop the properties of the follicular hormone; however, they all belong to the same class of substances and are related closely to each other, some being isomers; but they are differentiated from each other by their physical and chemical properties and by the degree of physiological activity. The most important representatives are the α-follicular hormone $C_{18}H_{22}O_2$ and the follicular hormone hydrate $C_{18}H_{24}O_3$; the first is a hydroxyketone, the last a triol which by splitting of water from two neighboring alcoholic hydroxyl groups becomes the hydroxyketone; both substances contain an acid hydroxyl group in the same type of combination. In a study with U. Westphal I have shown the degree of saturation of the follicular hormone by catalytic hydrogenation to an assured saturated hexahydro derivative, and by measurements of molecular refraction we have shown without doubt that in the follicular hormone there are only three double bonds and therefore the saturated parent hydrocarbon $C_{18}H_{30}$ has the structure of a four-ring system. From the optical behavior of the hormone, the character of the three double bonds, and the acid hydroxyl group we must conclude that these double bonds occur in a benzene ring which carries the hydroxyl group: the four-ring system which basically belongs to the hormone thus contains a benzene ring and three saturated rings. By the preparation of a phenol dicarboxylic acid $C_{18}H_{22}O_5$, Marrian and Doisy have recognized that the carbonyl group of the hormone and the alcoholic hydroxyl group of the hydrate occur in one of the saturated rings; J. D. Bernal and N. K. Adam have shown from crystallographic and roentegenographic measurements on the hormone crystallizate

and from the results of spreading studies that the functional groups of this hormone stand at opposite ends of the molecule. Along with Dr. Pavilides, J. Stormer, and H. Weidlich, dehydrogenation and degradation studies have been carried out, leading to the preparation of the aromatic parent substance of the hormone through a zinc dust distillation: it has the composition $C_{18}H_{14}$ (m. p. 243°) and contains a condensed four-ring system with the supposed arrangement I.

From the assumption that the hydrocarbon stands close to the basic system of the hormone, we are able to develop formulas of types II and III for the hormone and the hormone hydrate according to the present ideas of their constitution.

2. The testicular hormone, which was prepared in crystalline form from male urine with K. Tscherning, is so difficult to obtain that up to now 25 mg. altogether has been available; on the basis of this, the reported results must be considered today to be preliminary and, as has been mentioned before, we still require a final answer as to whether the crystallizate which melts at 178° and with a total dose of 1 to 1.2 given four times in two days produces a 30 to 35% growth in a cock's comb is the chemically pure hormone. The crystallizate repeatedly isolated in the same way shows a close resemblance to the follicular hormone in its properties: it is likewise a hydroxyketone, but it has a saturated character and since it has no acid properties, according to the more recent analyses and a study of the acetate (m.p. 160°), it apparently has the composition $C_{19}H_{30}O_2$, though the formula $C_{18}H_{28}O_2$ is not excluded. This composition shows that

in the testicular hormone also there are very evidently four rings which all have a saturated character. On the assumption that the testicular hormone has the same basic ring structure as the follicular hormone, we can assign to it the working hypothetical formula of type IV.

The formulas proposed here show a close apparent connection of both hormones to the steroids and bile acids of formula V; they can then be interpreted as "oxidation products" by the degradation of the side chain and aromatization of one ring with loss of a methyl group. This assumptions seems established and experimentally testable as a working hypothesis, since the "intermediate products" of this degradation were isolated as accompanying substances of the hormone, so that in its constitution we assigned for pregnandiol, $C_{21}H_{36}O_2$, the formula VI, an alcohol $C_{19}H_{32}O_2$ (m.p. 232°) the proposed constitution VII, and a hydroxyketone $C_{19}H_{30}O_2$ (or $C_{18}H_{30}O_2$), m.p. 176.5°, isomeric with the testicular hormone, which can likewise belong to the type formula IV. The aromatization of a ring with splitting off of methane here finds its parallel in the transition from ergosterol $C_{28}H_{44}O$ to neoergosterol $C_{27}H_{40}O$.

PORPHYRINS. Another field in which a basic structural determination led to far-reaching results was the elucidation of the prophyrin ring structure and the eventual synthesis of various porphyrins. The importance of this discovery lay in the fact that the major pigment of the plant kingdom and the major pigment of the animal kingdom both contained this ring in their active part. Chlorophyll and hemin are certainly the most important porphyrins, but, as the next selection shows, many other sources for porphyrin compounds occur in nature. The early work of Willstätter and the synthetic work of Hans Fischer led to a very complete understanding of porphyrin chemistry. The next selection illustrates some of the methods and significance of this work.

The following selection is from pages 7–11 in *Verhandlungen der Deutschen Gesellschaft für Innere Medizin 45*, 7–27 (1933).

Hemin and Porphyrins

HANS FISCHER

The blood pigment hemoglobin is a compound substance that can be broken down by different methods into its components: pigment and protein. Teichmann first observed this splitting in a microscopic preparation by the addition of glacial acetic acid-sodium chloride to blood; Schalfejeff, Nencki, Piloty, Willstätter and others have carried the method over to a large scale, so that the Teichmann crystals are available in kilogram lots. The Swedish investigator Mörner has also also worked out a method of splitting with alcoholic sulfuric acid by which the ester of hemin is formed.

Hemin has the formula $C_{34}H_{32}O_4N_4FeCl$. Numerous variations of this arrangement of atoms are possible. By the analytical degradation methods of Nencki, Küster, Piloty, Willstätter, H. Fischer, and their students, the pyrrol nature of hemin has been recognized and a far-reaching view of its constitution has been obtained. If hemin is deprived of its iron, porphyrin results, a substance that has a sensitizing action, as Hausmann has shown. Porphyrins are also obtained from chlorophyll by various reagents, so that a brief discussion of the leaf pigment is necessary. In contrast to the unity of hemin, chlorophyll can be separated into two components, a and b. The b component has one more oxygen atom. Chlorophylls a and b are dicarboxylic acids. One carboxyl group is esterified with phytol, the second with methyl alcohol. Phytol is a high molecular alcohol whose constitution was demonstrated by the studies of Willstätter on the one hand and Gottw. Fischer on the other, according to the following formula:

$$C_{20}H_{40}O = CH_3-CH-CH_2-CH_2-CH_2-CH-CH_2-CH_2-$$
$$\quad\quad\quad\quad\quad | \quad\quad\quad\quad\quad\quad\quad\quad\quad | $$
$$\quad\quad\quad\quad\quad CH_3 \quad\quad\quad\quad\quad\quad\quad\quad CH_3$$
$$CH_2-CH-CH_2-CH_2-CH_2-C=CH-CH_2OH$$
$$\quad\quad\quad | \quad\quad\quad\quad\quad\quad\quad\quad\quad | $$
$$\quad\quad\quad CH_3 \quad\quad\quad\quad\quad\quad\quad\quad CH_3$$

The second carboxyl group is esterified with methyl alcohol. Both components contain complexly bound magnesium. If suitable leaf material is treated with methyl alcohol, then by the action of an enzyme, the Willstätter chlorophyllase, esterification occurs and methyl chlorophyllides a and b are formed; they are well crystallized and according to Willstätter have the formulas

methyl chlorophyllide a $C_{32}H_{30}ON_4Mg(COOCH_3)_2 + \frac{1}{2}H_2O$
methyl chlorophyllide b $C_{32}H_{28}O_2N_4Mg(COOCH_3)_2 + \frac{1}{2}H_2O$

By treatment with hydrochloric acid we obtain the crystalline

pheophorbide a $C_{32}H_{32}ON_4(COOCH_3)(COOH)$

pheophorbide b $C_{32}H_{30}O_2N_4(COOCH_3)(COOH)$.

With oxalic acid and other acids chlorophyll can lose its complexly bound magnesium. We thus obtain the noncrystalline pheophytins which still have the ester groups contained in chlorophyll and have the properties of a wax.

Alkaline saponification of all these substances gives

phytochlorin e $C_{34}H_{36}O_6N_4$ or

phytorhodin g $C_{34}H_{34}O_7N_4$.

The chlorin forms from the a component, the rhodin from the b component. Neither contains any ester groups.

A principal difference between hemin and chlorophyll is the type of metal bound as a complex. Hemin contains iron, chlorophyll, magnesium, and to this we ascribe the different functions of the two pigments. Thus chlorophyll by its magnesium content mediates the synthetic processes of the plant, especially the assimilation of carbonic acid, while hemin or hemoglobin can regulate by its iron content the gas exchange and breakdown processes in animals. Perhaps in the latter process the Keilin cytochrome also plays a part where apparently a protein component is added to the hemin by a firm chemical bond on the vinyl group. Hoppe-Seyler first produced porphyrins from chlorophyll by the action of alcoholate under pressure, a reaction that was later studied in detail by Schunck, Marchlewski, and especially by Willstätter and his students. Thus phyllo, pyrro-, and rhodoporphyrins were isolated in crystalline condition but with a lower carbon content than the original chlorophyll, and which therefore had to be assumed to be degradation products.

By mild reducing agents, especially by the action of hydrogen iodide-glacial acetic acid, it was possible to obtain porphyrins with 34 carbon atoms, and thus to maintain the number of C-atoms in chlorophyll. The number of carbon atoms in chlorophyll and in hemin thus is equal. It was further apparent that the porphyrin ring was at the end of chlorophyll.

Porphyrins are widely distributed in nature, and in porphyria, a disease aggravated by light, humans excrete large amounts of porphyrins. It has previously been assumed that, as we will hear, the hematoporphyrin was the prophyrin most like that of hemin. This view can be refuted. At least two porphyrins are excreted, uro- and coproporphyrin which both occur in the urine (one of them, coproporphyrin, had already been observed by Hammarsten in sulfonal poisoning), and coproporphyrin is chiefly in the feces. This coproporphyrin does not always occur in urine. In rare cases an iso-coproporphyrin is observed; it will be discussed later. Interestingly enough, uroporphyrin also occurs in the quill feathers of African birds of the turaco species, in which it exists as a complex copper salt.

Closely related to uroporphyrin is the conchoporphyrin which is apparently contained in mussel shells as the calcium salt; uropor-phyrin can also be isolated from pearl mussel shells.

Coproporphyrin is especially widely distributed; in normal urine traces occur, and also in yeast along with hemin. Yeast can be forced to produce more coproporphyrin without change in hemin content by unfavorable growing conditions. The yeast thus is placed in a state comparable to human porphyria.

A porphyrin (ooporphyrin) is also obtained from the spots on the egg shells of birds that nest in the open. By putrefaction of blood pigment, as we can confirm, an identical porphyrin is obtained, Kämmerer's porphyrin, which Hijmanns van den Bergh and Grote-pass regularly found in human red blood cells. Prolonged putrefaction of hemoglobin produces deuteroporphyrin. This process also takes place in blood vessels of the human gastrointestinal tract.

Chlorophyll in the gastrointestinal tract of ruminants loses its complexly bound magnesium, its phytol, and its methyl alcohol; it is then decarboxylated and changed to protophorbide, then to phylloerythrin which is a characteristic porphyrin. Invertebrate animals such as silkworms also show degradation of chlorophyll. However, here no porphyrins are formed, but phyllobombycin which apparently belongs to the group of purpurins. Phyllopurpurin which is found as a by-product is identical with purpurin 18-trimethyl ester. The constitutional explanation of these biological products was given because it would be expected that their constitutional determination would be an indication of the constitution of hemin and chlorophyll.

The establishment by W. Küster of the oxidative formation of hematinic acid (1), which by decarboxylation gave methyl ethyl maleinimide (2), was basic for consideration of the constitution of hemin.

$$H_3C \underline{\qquad} CH_2CH_2COOH \qquad\qquad H_3C \underline{\qquad} C_2H_5$$

	1			2	
O	NH	O	O	NH	O

Hematinic acid   Methyl ethyl maleinimide

The reductive splitting of hemin gave the following pyrrol derivatives with basic and acidic natures, which, as can be seen, are very similar in their relationships. If the acid products of splitting are decarboxylated, they form the basic ones.

Hemopyrrol Bases

H_3C————C_2H_5
H_3C 3 H
NH
Hemopyrrol

H_3C————C_2H_5
4 CH_3
H
NH
Cryptopyrrol

H_3C————C_2H_5
H_3C 5 CH_3
NH
Phyllopyrrol

H_3C————C_2H_5
6 H
H
NH
Opsopyrrol

Hemopyrrol Acids

H_3C————CH_2CH_2COOH
H_3C 7 H
NH
Hemopyrrol
carboxylic acid

H_3C————CH_2CH_2COOH
8 CH_3
H
3 NH
Cryptopyrrol
carboxylic acid

H_3C————CH_2CH_2COOH
H_3C 9 CH_3
NH
Phyllopyrrol
carboxylic acid

H_3C————CH_2CH_2COOH
10
H H
NH
Opsopyrrol
carboxylic acid

The acid portions yield by oxidation Küster's hematinic acid (1), the basic ones methyl ethyl maleinimide (2). Thus their constitutions were firmly established in general; exact proof was furnished by synthesis and we will not go into this more closely. Synthesis made these products available in any amount. The yield of bases and acids from hemin is so large that we must conclude there are four pyrrol rings in the molecule, which also agrees with the molecular weight determinations.

Even in 1912 W. Küster proposed a constitutional formula which gave an essentially correct picture for hemin. We give this formula as it has today been recognized by synthesis and follow with a review of the analytical results not through historical, but through logical development.

Four pyrrol rings (respectively a pyrrol, a maleinimide, and two pyrrolene rings) are joined through four methine groups. The

11

successive sequence of single and double bonds gives the color. The FeCl group is bound as a complex in the molecule, substituting on two NH groups.

Details of interrelated syntheses leading finally to hemin are then given.

CAROTENOIDS AND VITAMIN A. The carotenoids were another group of natural plant pigments whose structure baffled organic chemists for nearly a hundred years. The method of chromatography developed by Tswett (p. 23) largely for the purpose of isolating such pigments and chlorophylls was neglected for some twenty years. After the full possibilities of chromatography had been realized, the isolation of pure carotene permitted Karrer to determine the basic carotenoid structure. The close relationship between carotene and vitamin A quickly became apparent and determination of the structure of the vitamin was possible even before it had finally been isolated in the pure state. The following selection illustrates not only the methods employed in studying a highly reactive and complex organic compound, but also the synthesis of one of the vitamins. The isolation and synthesis of these structurally varied and biologically very important compounds were triumphs of organic chemistry in the first half of the twentieth century.

The following selection is from pages 21–30 in *Chemical Reviews 14*, 17–30 (1934).

The Chemistry of Vitamins A and C

PAUL KARRER

The paper opens with a review of vitamin C chemistry.

I now proceed to my next subject, vitamin A. This is one of several vitamins necessary for the proper growth of the animal. It therefore is called the fat-soluble growth factor. However, deficiency of vitamin A not only produces loss in weight, but also hemeralopia, xerophthalmia, degeneration of nerve fibers, skin diseases, and affections of the mucous membrane, etc.

The history of vitamin A is still young, but has nevertheless been full of interesting episodes. Osborne and Mendel, McCollum and Davis were the first who associated the presence of factor A in cod-liver oil and butter. Hopkins found that cod-liver oil loses its curative qualities if air is bubbled through it. Then came Steenbock and his school with their thorough and important investigations. They examined numerous plants and their extracts, also food stuffs, as to their vitamin A content. They brought out the interesting fact that only such vegetable and similar products had a vitamin A effect, as were rich in certain yellow pigments, the so-called carotenoids. From this they concluded that vitamin A must stand in some relation to these pigments. Steenbock tested carotene for vitamin A effect, and claimed that it had curative properties. Drummond repeated these tests, and found that it was ineffective. He drew the conclusion that Steenbock's positive results must have been due to some foreign substance accompanying the carotene, and for years this remained the generally accepted opinion.

In 1927 von Euler was able to harmonize these contradictory statements. Drummond had used a vitamin A-free diet plus carotene. von Euler's investigations established the important fact that the above ration had indeed no vitamin A curative effect. The cause of this, however, was not inefficiency of carotene, but the fact that this ration was not only devoid of vitamin A, but also of vitamin D. Vitamin A however can only exert its curative powers in presence of vitamin D and the other vitamins. von Euler therefore added carotene and vitamin D to the ration used by Drummond and now the curative effects were the same as of good cod-liver oil, which as you know is rich in both of these vitamins.

These new facts, however, were not generally accepted. It was argued that cod-liver oil, a rich source of vitamin A, does not contain any carotene, but some other substance with an absorption spectrum totally different from that of carotene. Th. Moore finally solved the riddle. The liver is the storage house for vitamin A. Moore found that the vitamin A content of the liver decreases rapidly and finally disappears completely, if animals are kept on a vitamin A-free diet. After an addition of carotene to the diet, the vitamin A content increases again rapidly. The explanation is, that carotene is a provitamin of the A factor which means that it is transformed by the organism into the vitamin.

Von Euler and our own investigations have shown that of all naturally occurring carotenoids, only the carotenes have this provitamin A effect. Vegetable carotene is hardly ever homogeneous. It is a mixture of two or more isomeric forms, known as α-, β-, γ-, and possibly even still another one. The γ-carotene of Kuhn is present only in traces; β-carotene is always the main component and can perhaps occur without any of the others. The amount of α-carotene varies greatly, from traces to 20 or more per cent. The separation of these various isomeric carotenes from each other was a tedious and not very satisfactory process. Fractionation by crystallization, adsorption on specially prepared aluminum hydroxide or Fuller's earth, give a certain degree of purification and enrichment of one of the components. To get a complete separation, the process must however be repeated over and over again. In search of better adsorbents we recently found that calcium hydroxide or calcium monoxide are greatly superior. The process is carried out like a chromatographic analysis. One adsorption suffices to bring about a clean separation of α-carotene from β-carotene, and α-carotene is now a readily accessible substance. α-, β-, and γ-carotene have slightly different melting points and solubilities. Their absorption spectra also show different lines. Only α-carotene is optically active. (See Table 1).

Table I

	Melting point	Maxima of absorption (cs$_2$)			$[\alpha]_{844}$
		$\mu\mu$			
α-Carotene $C_{40}H_{56}$	183°C	509,	477,	448	+323°
β-Carotene $C_{40}H_{56}$	183°C	520,	485,	450	Inactive
γ-Carotene $C_{40}H_{56}$	174°C	533,	496,	463	Inactive

The determination of the constitution of these carotenes and especially of the most important one, β-carotene, has been the subject of long investigations at our Zürich institute. Today the structural formula has been definitely proven. β-Carotene, $C_{40}H_{56}$, is an unsaturated hydrocarbon, containing eleven double linkages. Through catalytic reduction it takes up eleven moles of hydrogen. Degradation by oxidation has been particularly useful for elucidating the chemical structure. Ozonization gave geronic acid, permitting the conclusion that the carotene molecule must contain carbon rings like β-ionone. Comparing the yields of geronic acid obtained by ozonization of β-ionone and β-carotene, we came to the conclusion that the carotene molecule must contain two β-ionone rings as expressed by the following formula:

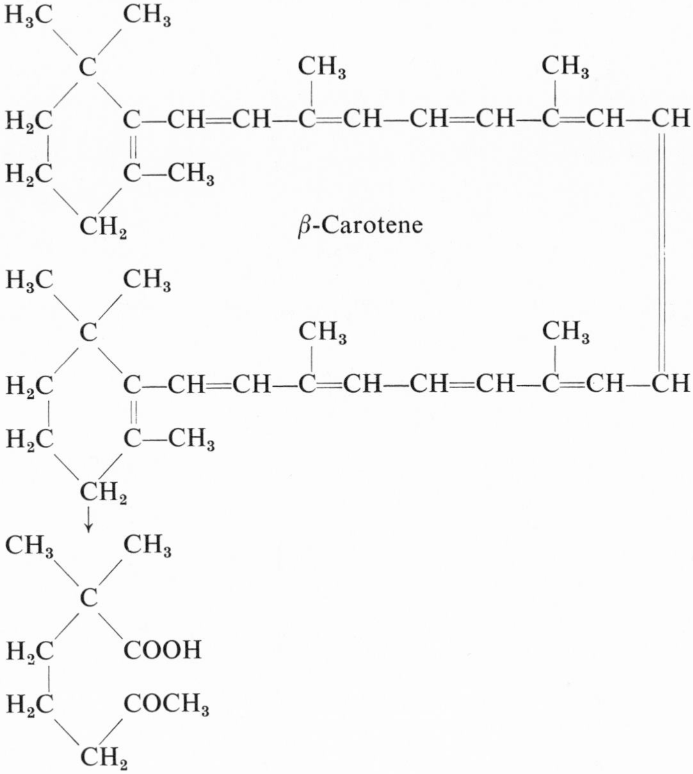

β-Carotene

Geronic acid

Degradation of β-carotene with potassium permanganate gives four moles of acetic acid; with chromic oxide six moles. This proves six methyl groups in the molecule. Four of these, those which give acetic acid already with permanganate, belong to the aliphatic chain.

Time is too short to give all the reasons for this formula for β-carotene. It suffices to say that it is so far in excellent agreement with all experimental data.

α- and β-Carotene are isomeric, and their isomerism is due to the different position of the double linkages. Ozonization of α-carotene yields geronic acid, and in contrast to β-carotene also isogeronic acid. The only formula which fully explains these results is the following:

α-Carotene

Geronic acid   Isogeronic acid

The asymmetric C atom in α-carotene accounts for the optical activity of this substance.

α-, β-, and γ-Carotene are not the only provitamins of the A factor. They are the only ones, as far as we know, occurring in nature.

Four carotene derivatives however have been prepared, which can act as provitamins. The first of these is carotene iodide, a well-crystallizing substance. Another one is the dihydrocarotene, which is a product of partial catalytic reduction and probably not a homogeneous substance. The third is a monohydroxy carotene, and the last an oxide of carotene, whose oxygen is most likely in the form of an inner ether.

In all four of these derivatives, at least one of the original two β-ionone rings is still unchanged. If both of these rings are altered, as is the case in the xanthophylls or phytoxanthins, through substitution of hydrogen atoms by hydroxyl groups, the ability to act as provitamins disappears completely. The presence of at least one β-ionone ring is therefore absolutely essential for the vitamin A effect. This fact is no longer surprising, since we know the close relationship between β-carotene and vitamin A.

Liver oils from various animal sources differ greatly in their vitamin A content. Not only does the amount vary between the different species, but it is also greatly influenced by their food. If the food is rich in carotene, the vitamin A, which is stored in the liver, increases enormously and far above the normal amount. Fish-liver oils are much richer in vitamin A in summer than in winter: for instance, halibut liver oil contains twenty times more in summer. According to von Euler's and our own investigations, the liver oil from *Hippoglossus hippoglossus*, *Scombresox saurus*, *Rhombus maximus* and of the Japanese fish *Stereolepis ishinagi*, contain from 200 to 2000 times as much vitamin A as common cod-liver oil. The discovery of this fact was of great importance. Without it we would hardly have been able to carry on our investigations.

Fractionation, the removal of foreign substances by freezing out at very low temperatures, and methods of adsorption led finally to vitamin A preparations with constant analytical data. These preparations could at least be regarded as highly concentrated forms of vitamin A.

This period of my work will always remain fixed in my memory as one of the most fascinating of my laboratory experiences. Up to the time when we started using those liver oils, very rich in vitamin A, we had of course experimented only with the unsaponifiable residue from cod-liver oil. Tedious processes of purification and concentration gave us products with as high as 400 C.L.O. units, the usual standard for measuring the vitamin A content. You can well imagine what it meant to us, when we found oils where this unsaponifiable residue, without any further purification, showed already C.L.O. units as high as 200 to 800. Methyl alcoholic solutions of these crude residues were purified by freezing out the sterines and other foreign substances at low temperatures. The C.L.O. unit rose promptly to 5000. A repetition of this process at 70° below freezing gave a product with 8000 C.L.O. units. Fractional adsorption on fibrous aluminum hydroxide gave a further rise to 9000, and a second adsorption finally even to about 10,000 C.L.O. units. Then it stopped, and renewed adsorptions on aluminum hydroxide did not give any further improvement. Quite recently we found in calcium hydroxide a much better and especially more selective absorbent. Through adsorption on calcium hydroxide a small amount of a foreign substance with a distinctly different absorption spectrum can be removed. The analytical data of the main fraction, however, remain unchanged. The final product is a very viscous light yellow oil. It can be distilled without decomposition under very much reduced pressure, boiling at a temperature of 137–138° C. Our investigations resulted in the following formula for vitamin A.

$$\text{H}_3\text{C} \quad \text{CH}_3$$
$$\begin{array}{c} \text{H}_3\text{C} \quad\quad \text{CH}_3 \\ \diagdown \diagup \\ \text{C} \\ \diagup \quad \diagdown \\ \text{H}_2\text{C} \quad\quad \text{C}-\text{CH}=\text{CH}-\overset{\overset{\displaystyle\text{CH}_3}{|}}{\text{C}}=\text{CH}-\text{CH}=\text{CH}-\overset{\overset{\displaystyle\text{CH}_3}{|}}{\text{C}}=\text{CH}-\text{CH}_2\text{OH} \\ | \quad\quad\quad \| \\ \text{H}_2\text{C} \quad\quad \text{C}-\text{CH}_3 \\ \diagdown \quad \diagup \\ \text{CH}_2 \end{array}$$

The degradation of vitamin A by oxidation is most illuminating and of great importance. Just like β-carotene, it gives geronic acid and three moles of acetic acid. Esterification establishes one alcoholic hydroxyl group. Catalytic reduction indicates five double linkages. Quite recently we synthesized the perhydro-vitamin A and now the structural formula has become a certainty.

We started from β-ionone and, by way of many intermediates, built up the perhydro-vitamin A. This, however, like the natural perhydro-vitamin A, is an oil. To make absolutely sure we therefore had to proceed one step further, and synthesize the higher ketone K. We did this with the perhydro-vitamin A obtained by catalytic reduction of the natural vitamin, as well as with our synthetic product. Both ketones gave well-crystallized semicarbazones, identical in every respect.

Equations are then given showing the steps in the synthesis.

A comparison of the formulas of β-carotene and vitamin A clearly reveals their structural and genetical relationship. The β-carotene molecule is split in half and one alcoholic hydroxyl appears at the end of the open chain.

Part IV   Biochemistry

From its earliest beginning chemistry held forth the promise of solving the basic problems of living matter. During the Middle Ages most of the men who contributed to the advance of the science were physicians or apothecaries, and interest in the processes of the human body was always high. The iatrochemists, followers of Paracelsus, made it their chief business to determine how the body worked and how it responded in disease to chemical remedies. However, their chemical knowledge was not sufficient for them to develop any but the most superficial theories. It was not until the nineteenth century that enough chemical information became available to permit any really fruitful speculation or laboratory investigation of the very complex reactions occurring in the living cell.

After the middle of the nineteenth century chemists, with their increased knowledge of organic compounds, turned more and more to biological problems. Justus Liebig in the latter part of his career undertook extensive studies in this area, and his great prestige among chemists helped to popularize this branch of chemistry. At the same time the physicists were expanding their concept of the various forms of energy and this work was soon applied to explaining the mechanism of energy production in animals. Physiologists, too, increasingly applied chemical tests in their work. Thus toward the end of the century visible signs of coöperation in this field had appeared. The science of biochemistry, or physiological chemistry as it was usually called then, was already in its infancy. Its growth in the twentieth century was amazingly rapid.

The first steps came with the discovery of the importance to life of minute amounts of substances such as hormones and vitamins. General mechanisms for energy production by oxidation of foods were soon worked out, and the roles of hormones and vitamins were fitted into the picture. Much attention was devoted to the intermediate metabolism of fats, proteins, and carbohydrates, and the central role of the latter compounds in energy production was explained. By mid-century many major metabolic pathways were worked out, and the advances in protein chemistry made possible by some of the techniques discussed in Part I had prepared the way for the rapid advances in understanding of enzyme formation and the genetic code that occurred shortly after 1950.

HORMONES AND VITAMINS

Early in the century Bayliss and Starling discovered that not all control of bodily processes was carried out by the nervous system. On the basis of their work on secretin from the pancreas they proposed the theory of chemical control by hormones, a term suggested by Starling in the second of the following selections.

During the same period the concept of auxiliary food factors began to develop. The work of Eijkman in Java led to the novel concept that disease could result from the lack of some essential substance as well as from the presence of a toxic one. The classic paper of Hopkins in 1906 developed the idea of vitamins very clearly, though the word itself was first proposed by Drummond in 1920.

The following selection is from page 353 in *The Journal of Physiology* (*London*) *28*, 325–353 (1902).

The Mechanism of Pancreatic Secretion

W. M. BAYLISS AND E. H. STARLING

Summary of Conclusions

1. The secretion of the pancreatic juice is normally evoked by the entrance of acid chyme into the duodenum, and is proportional to the amount of acid entering (Pawlow). This secretion does not depend on a nervous reflex, and occurs when all the nervous connections of the intestine are destroyed.

2. The contact of the acid with the epithelial cells of the duodenum causes in them the production of a body (secretin) which is absorbed from the cells by the blood-current, and is carried to the pancreas, where it acts as a specific stimulus to the pancreatic cells, exciting a secretion of pancreatic juice proportional to the amount of secretin present.

3. This substance, secretin, is produced probably by a process of hydrolysis from a precursor present in the cells, which is insoluble in water and alkalis and is not destroyed by boiling alcohol.

4. Secretin is not a ferment. It withstands boiling in acid, neutral or alkaline solutions, but is easily destroyed by active pancreatic juice or by oxidizing agents. It is not precipitated from its watery solution by tannic acid, or alcohol and ether. It is destroyed by most metallic salts. It is slightly diffusible through parchment paper.

5. The pancreatic juice obtained by secretin injection has no action on proteids until "enterokinase" is added. It acts on starch and to some extent on fats, the action on fats being increased by the addition of succus entericus. It is, in fact, normal pancreatic juice.

6. Secretin rapidly disappears from the tissues, but cannot be detected in any of the secretions. It is apparently not absorbed from the lumen of the intestine.

7. It is not possible to obtain a body resembling secretin from any tissues of the body other than the mucous membrane of the duodenum and jejunum.

8. Secretin solutions, free from bile salts, cause some increase in the secretion of bile. They have no action on any other glands.

9. Acid extracts of the mucous membrane normally contain a body which causes a fall of blood-pressure. This body is not secretin, and the latter may be prepared free from the depressor substance by acting on desquamated epithelial cells with acid.

10. There is some evidence of a specific localized action of the vaso-dilator substances which may be extracted from various tissues.

The following selection is from pages 339–340 in *The Lancet 1905, II* 339–341.

The Croonian Lectures on the Chemical Correlation of the Functions of the Body

ERNEST HENRY STARLING

Lecture I
Delivered on June 20th.

The Chemical Control of the Functions of the Body

Mr. President and Gentlemen—From the remotest ages the existence of a profession of medicine, the practise of its art and its acceptance as a necessary part of every community have been founded on a tacit assumption that the functions of the body, whether of growth or activity of organs, can be controlled by chemical means; and research by observation of accident or by experiment for such means has resulted in the huge array of drugs which form the pharmacopoeias of various civilized countries and the common armamentarium of the medical profession through the world. The practice of drugging rests on the supposition that the functions of the body can be influenced in a normal direction by such means. I propose in these lectures to inquire how far such a belief is consonant with our own knowledge of the physiological working of the body, how far, that is to say, the activities and growth of the different organs of the body are determined and coördinated among each other by chemical substances produced in the body itself but capable of classification with the drugs of the physician. If a mutual control, and therefore coördination, of the different functions of the body be largely determined by the production of definite chemical substances in the body, the discovery of the nature of these substances will enable us to interpose at any desired phase in these functions and so to acquire an absolute control over the workings of the human body. Such a control is the goal of medical science. How far have we progressed toward it? How far are we justified in regarding its attainment possible?

I hope to be able to vindicate to you the assumption which is at the basis of medical practice and to show that the activities of, at any rate, the large majority of the organs of the body are coördinated among themselves by the production and circulation of chemical substances, so that the results of physiological researches up to the present justify us in the faith that within a reasonable space of time we shall be in the possession of chemical substances which are normal physiological products, and by means of which we shall be in a position to control not only the activities but also the growth of a large number of the organs of the body.

In man and the higher animals the marvelous adaptations effected by means of the central nervous system are so much in evidence that physiologists have been tempted to ascribe every nexus between distant organs to the intervention of the nervous system; the more so because by this means an adaptation to changes, internal or external, can be effected in many cases within a fraction of a second. But in the evolution of life upon this earth this method of adaptation is of comparatively late appearance and is confined almost entirely to one division of living beings—i.e., the animal kingdom. In the lowest organisms, the unicellular, such as the bacteria and protozoa, the only adaptations into the mechanisms of which we can gain any clear insight are those to the environment of the organism and in these cases the mechanism is almost entirely a chemical one. The organism approaches its food or flies from harmful media in consequence of chemical stimuli; it prepares its food for digestion or digests it by the formation of chemical substances, toxins or enzymes. In the lowest metazoa, such as the sponges, there is still no trace of any nervous system. The coördination between the different cells of the colony is still determined by purely chemical means. The aggregation of the phagocytic cells round a foreign body is apparently due to the attraction exerted on them by the chemical substances produced in the death of the injured tissues.

With the appearance of a central nervous system or systems in the higher metazoa the quick motor reactions determined by this system form the most obvious vital manifestations of the animal. But the nervous system has been evolved for quick adaptations, not for the abolition of the chemical correlations which existed before a nervous system came into being. A study of the phenomena of even the highest animals shows that the development of the quick nervous adaptations involves no abrogation of the other more primitive class of reactions—*i.e.*, the chemical ones. Where the reaction is one occupying seconds or fractions of a second the nervous system is of necessity employed. Where the reaction may take minutes, hours, or even days for its accomplishment the nexus between the organs implicated may be chemical. Already we are able, in many cases, to prove the existence of such a chemical nexus and to employ it in artificially producing a state of growth or activity, which is in normal circumstances merely a phase in a complex series of physiological changes.

The chemical reactions or adaptations of the body, like those which are carried out through the intermediation of the central nervous system, can be divided into two main classes—(1) those which are evoked in consequence of changes impressed upon the organism as a whole from without; and (2) those which, acting entirely within the body, serve to correlate the activities, in the widest sense of the term, of the different parts and organs of the body.

The first class of adaptations includes those reactions of the body to chemical poisons produced by bacteria or higher organisms and represents one of the most important means by which the body maintains itself in the struggle for existence. The complicated phenomena involved in the formation of antitoxins, of cytolysins, of bactericidal substances, and such like means of protection, have been the subject of much study of recent years and their immediate interest to the practical physician renders it unnecessary for me to devote any time to their discussion, especially as the subject is one to which I have not given any personal attention. The investigation of the second class, that of correlation of the activities of organs, has by reason of its greater obscurity, or of the greater difficulty of its practical application in medicine, fallen largely to the province of the physiologist and I therefore propose to deal almost exclusively with those members of this class of reactions which have so far been definitely ascertained.

Before, however, entering into details of any particular correlation, it may be profitable to consider what we may expect to be the nature of the substance which will in any given case act as a chemical nexus between different organs. We are dealing here with a question of general pharmacology.

The author then presents Ehrlich's theory that toxins act by attaching themselves as side chains to a living protoplasmic molecule.

The first group therefore of pharmacological substances may be defined as substances presenting many points of resemblance to proteids, potent like enzymes in infinitesimal doses, and giving rise as a result of their introduction into the body to a reaction consisting in the production of an antibody.

Ehrlich's second group of substances, which includes practically all of our common drugs, probably act on the protoplasmic molecule or part of it by reason of their chemico-physical properties or their molecular configurations. It is difficult to give a more definite expression of their mode of action. We know that in many cases slight changes in the molecule, such as the introduction or withdrawal of an ethyl, methyl, or NH_2 group into or from a drug or group of drugs, alter their physiological actions in a regular manner. We know, moreover, that substances of the most diverse constitution, such as the various anaesthetics, may have little more than their fat solvent powers in common. All these drugs, however, are more or less stable compounds, generally to be obtained in a crystalline form and not easily destroyed by heat. On introduction into the body the incubation period of their physiological effects is generally determined only by the time necessary for their distribution to, and their diffusion into, the cells which they chiefly affect. Although repeated doses of them can set up a certain degree of tolerance, in no case is there any evidence of the formation of a physiological antidote or antitoxin to the poison.

To which of these two groups of bodies must we assign the chemical messengers which, speeding from cell to cell along the blood stream, may coördinate the activities and growth of different parts of the body? The specific character of the greater part of the toxins which are known to us (I need only instance such toxins as those of tetanus and diphtheria) would suggest that the substances produced for effecting the correlation of organs within the body, through the intermediation of the blood stream, might also belong to this class, since here also specificity of action must be a distinguishing characteristic. These chemical messengers, however, or "hormones" (from ὁρμάω, I excite or arouse), as we might call them, have to be carried from the organ where they are produced to the organ which they affect by means of the blood stream and the continually recurring physiological needs of the organism must determine their repeated production and circulation through the body. If they belong to the first class and are analogous to the toxins, each production of a given substance and its discharge into the blood stream must give rise to the formation of a specific antibody, which must increase in amount with each production of the substance in question and tend therefore to neutralize its physiological effects. It might be suggested that in the case of these chemical messengers the formation of an antibody was a local one and limited to the organ affected and that, in fact, their physiological effect—*e.g.*, secretion—was actually a pouring out of the antibody to the chemical messenger. But, as we shall see later, experimental evidence is entirely against this view, which, moreover, is not supported by any known instance of a similar localization of antibody as a result of injection into the organism of any of the substances which belong definitely to the toxin class. The formation of antibodies appears in fact, to be not a process of value in the normal physiological life of the organism, but one which has been evolved as a chemical means of defence to prevent the spread of injurious substances from the spot originally attacked.

We are therefore forced to the conclusion that if the processes of coördination of activities among the organs of the body are carried out under physiological conditions to any large extent by chemical means—*i.e.*, by the dispatch of chemical messengers along the blood stream—these emissary substances must belong to Ehrlich's second order of substances acting on the body, and must, in fact, fall into the same category as the drugs of our Pharmacopœia.

The following selection is from pages 425–427 and 449–452 in *The Journal of Physiology* (*London*) *44*, 425–460 (1912).

Feeding Experiments Illustrating the Importance of Accessory Factors in Normal Dietaries

F. GOWLAND HOPKINS

The experiments described in this paper confirm the work of

others in showing that animals cannot grow when fed upon so-called "synthetic" dietaries consisting of mixtures of pure proteins, fats, carbohydrates, and salts. But they show further that a substance or substances present in normal foodstuffs (*e.g.*, milk) can, when added to the dietary in astonishingly small amount, secure the utilization for growth of the protein and energy contained in such artificial mixtures.

The particular experiments, of which an account is now to be given, were undertaken to put upon a more quantitative basis results which I obtained as far back as 1906–1907.[1] Since that time, a fuller realization of the fact that (leaving on one side the influence of the inorganic constituents of dietaries) protein supply and energy supply do not alone secure normal nutrition, has arisen from the extremely interesting recent work upon the etiology of such diseases as beri-beri and scurvy. It is not surprising that much work is now being done in connection with the subject; and since the experimental results given in this paper were obtained, the publications of others have covered part of the ground. In particular I may refer to the work of Stepp upon mice, and to the extensive researches of Osborne and Mendel upon rats. But the observations now to be described differ in some important details from those of the authors quoted. They bring out in particular the marked influence of minute additions of normal food constituents in promoting the nutritive power of synthetic dietaries. Stepp approached the subject on the lines of an attempt to estimate the importance of lipoids in nutrition. He found that food mixtures after extraction with lipoid solvents could not maintain life in mice. The total material extracted by the solvents when added to the diet made the food efficient once more; but Stepp was unable to obtain this result by adding any known lipoid.

The earlier and greater part of the valuable and critical work of Osborne and Mendel was directed to the question as to whether life could be maintained upon a dietary containing a single individual protein instead of mixtures of proteins such as normal dietaries comprise. Their experiments led them to answer this question in the affirmative. Maintainance is possible so long as the protein stored is one not deficient in individual amino acid groupings, but as was inevitable, their earlier experiments led these authors to realize the importance of factors other than protein and energy supply, and they found in particular that synthetic dietaries which were

---

[1] The results of experiments made at the time were summarized in Lectures delivered at Guys Hospital in June 1909. Owing to subsequent ill health these Lectures were never published. The results given in the present paper were communicated to the Biochemical Club in October 1911. See also *Analyst* xxxi, p. 395, 1906.

capable of maintaining the life of full-grown rats (at least in individual cases), were quite unable, no matter what the protein, to maintain the growth processes in young animals. Of this fact I have long been aware, and I have known from my own observations that extremely small additions of tissue extracts, etc., were sufficient to induce growth, but until the present set of experiments were undertaken I had obtained no data as to how far the amount of food actually eaten intruded as a factor in the phenomenon. An accurate estimation of the amount of food eaten under the conditions of varied growth forms a special feature of the experiments now to be described.

Osborne and Mendel in their later experiments show that the addition of milk products to the food promoted rapid growth in rats which had remained stationary in weight when on the original artificial dietary. The material added they term "protein free milk." It was prepared by removing as far as possible, by precipitation and coagulation, the protein from fat-free milk, the fluid being then evaporated at low temperature, and the residue ground to a powder. This material was primarily used "to furnish the inorganic elements to the diet," and was added to the artificial dietaries in comparatively large amounts (28.2% of the total food mixture), in which it replaced part of the pure carbohydrate. In my experiments, while the artificial diet consisted of casein, fat, starch, sugar and inorganic salts, the addendum consisted of milk itself; but this was given in such small quantity that the total solids contained in it amounted to no more than from 1 to 3 or 4% of the whole food eaten. This small addition induced normal growth upon dietaries which without it were incapable even of maintainance. A special feature of my experiments was the rigorous use of controls. In each and every experiment two sets of rats, chosen carefully so as to show correspondence in the weight, sex, and origin of the individuals contained in them, were fed side by side. The sole difference in treatment consisted in the administration of the minute ration of milk to one of the sets compared. In some experiments after the relative rates of growth had been compared for a week or two, the small milk ration was transferred to the set which had been previously fed without it. In all cases the influence of the milk upon growth was so large that it could not have been due to any alteration in the quality of the protein eaten or in its ratio, nor, in my own belief, to the presence of any known milk constituent.

The experimental conditions and results are then described in detail. The conclusions follow.

Convinced of the importance of accurate diet factors by my own earlier observations, I ventured, in an address delivered in November 1906, to make the following remarks:

"But, further, no animal can live upon a mixture of pure protein, fat, and carbohydrate, and even when the necessary inorganic material is carefully supplied the animal still cannot flourish. The animal body is adjusted to live either upon plant tissues or the tissues of other animals, and these contain countless substances other than the proteins, carbohydrates, and fats. Physiological evolution, I believe, has made some of these well-nigh as essential as are the basal constituents of diet, lecithin, for instance, has been repeatedly shown to have a marked influence upon nutrition, and this just happens to be something already familiar, and a substance that happens to have been tried. The field is almost unexplored; only is it certain that there are many minor factors in all diets, of which the body takes account. In diseases such as rickets, and particularly in scurvy we have had for long years knowledge of a dietetic factor; but though we know how to benefit these conditions empirically, the scale errors in the diet are to this day quite obscure. They are, however, certainly of the kind which comprises these minimal qualitative factors that I am considering. Scurvy and rickets are conditions so severe that they force themselves upon our attention; but many other nutritive errors affect the health of individuals to a degree most important to themselves, and some of them depend upon unsuspected dietetic factors."

Evidence has now accumulated from various sides to justify these views. That a deficiency in quite other factors can induce disease is a fact which is now upon a firm experimental basis. That a deficiency, quite as little related to energy supply, may result in the failure of so fundamental a phenomenon as growth in young animals seems equally certain. To what extent bare maintainance of the body-weight is possible, in spite of such deficiencies, is perhaps less certain. Osborne and Mendel observed prolonged maintainance on artificial mixtures, but found that "sooner or later the animals declined; and unless a change in the diet was now instituted, within a comparatively short period the animals died." I have myself seen quite young rats maintain their weight practically unaltered upon a casein mixture for three weeks, and then begin to lose weight, or on the other hand, if given the necessary small addendum, begin to grow briskly. Such observations give the impression that the factor missing from the artificial food is one concerned solely with growth. But it is certain, as Stepp also found, that the presence of a most extraordinarily small remainder of the substance or substances removable by alcohol extraction, can affect the physiological value of artificial diets; and I am inclined to believe that apparent maintainance (which is usually very slow growth, or very slow decline) is only seen when the diet is not wholly free from them. If the food has been very thoroughly extracted, and if the fat subsequently added is wholly free from any tissue elements, I venture to think that only very short maintainance is possible. That "Denaturierung" plays no part here is shown by the fact that such food is clearly utilized when associated with a small addendum of the kind being discussed.

If there are any experiments in the literature of nutrition which might be thought to throw doubt upon the importance of such accessory substances, they would seem to be those demonstrating that fully hydrolized proteins can maintain growth. So far as these have been carried out with such material as autodigested pancreas, as in Otto Loewi's original experiments, or with digested flesh, the mixture would not be necessarily deficient in accessory substances, and inspection of the results would seem to show, that when, instead of gland or flesh, a separated protein was used, the effect upon nitrogenous equilibrium or growth was distinctly less favourable. Thus an experiment made by Abderhalden and Rona in which flesh was the source of the digested mixture, showed a much better nutrition balance than a similar one made by Abderhalden and Oppler who used casein. In Abderhalden's latest experiments of this kind, when digested casein was fed for any length of time, the results were also less favourable than when digested flesh was used. In any case, as Mendel and Osborne remark, the duration of all such experiments has been too short for deficiencies of the kind under discussion to manifest themselves in any pronounced manner. Thirty days in the case of a slow-growing animal such as a dog would be represented by a very few days in the growth period of a rat, and the latter nearly always grows for a brief period after being transferred to an artificial food mixture. A certain store of the missing factors is probably available in the body.

One point bearing on a comparison between Osborne and Mendel's experiments and my own, needs mention here. In the case of four rats, these observers state that they found inadequate growth upon an artificial casein mixture, although supplemented by a small milk addendum. The milk was not fresh milk, but "Trumilk" powder, given to the extent of 6% of the whole food mixture. When later the "protein free milk" (*vide supra*) was added to the extent of 28.2% of the food, normal growth was established.

It seems to me, however, from inspection of Osborne and Mendel's curves (Nos. L and LI) that, in the case of two of these rats, there was no break in the growth curve at the time of the change of food. Normal growth was established upon the casein and Trumilk mixtures some ten days before the change was made. In the case of the other two animals (Charts XLVIII and XLIX) the earlier consumption of food, so far as I can calculate from the food curves given, was certainly for some reason inadequate. Stepp found that milk contained material capable of restoring the nutritive efficiency of extracted diets; but the quantity he used was greatly in excess of that employed by me.

It is possible that what is absent from artificial diets and supplied in such addenda as milk and tissue extracts is of the nature of an organic complex (or of complexes) which the animal body cannot synthesize. But the amount which seems sufficient to secure growth is so small that a catalytic or stimulative function seems more likely. It is probable that our conception of stimulating substances, "Reizstoffe," may have to be extended. The original vague conception of such substances as being condiments, chiefly affecting taste, gained in definiteness by the work of the Pavlov school. But the place of specific diet constituents which stimulate the gastric secretory mechanism can be taken by the products of digestion itself, and in this connection the stimulant in the diet is by no means indispensable. Most observers agree that the addition to normal dietaries of meat extracts capable of stimulating the gastric flow, does not increase the actual absorption of the food, though this point could only be properly tested by adding them to an artificial dietary known to be free from analogous substances. As was emphasized above, the milk did not affect absorption in my experiments. But such undoubted stimulating effects due to diet constituents as those discovered by Pavlov may quite possibly be paralleled elsewhere in the body on more specific and indispensable lines. Stimulation of the internal secretions of the thyroid and pituitary glands, which are believed, on very suggestive evidence, to play an important part in growth processes, can be legitamately thought of. On the other hand the influence upon growing tissues may be direct. If the attachment of such indispensable functions to specific accessory constituents of diets is foreign to current views upon nutrition, so also is the experimental fact that young animals may fail to grow when they are daily absorbing a sufficiency of formative material and energy for the purposes of growth.

ENZYMES AND NUCLEOPROTEINS

It had long been recognized that bodily processes were catalyzed by some mysterious vital factor—a "ferment," as it was usually called. There were many controversies in the latter part of the nineteenth century as to whether fermenting activity was simply a vital function of a living cell, or whether it was due to a chemical compound that could be separated from the cell. At the end of the century, Buchner (H. M. Leicester and H. S. Klickstein, *A Source Book in Chemistry, 1400–1900*, Harvard University Press, Cambridge, Massachusetts, 1952, p. 506) settled this question by isolating an enzyme in impure state. It gradually became evident that these catalysts were proteins, or at least closely associated with proteins. In the third decade of the twentieth century, Sumner and Northrop succeeded in crystallizing certain enzymes and thus practically proving their protein nature. Shortly afterward, Stanley crystallized tobacco mosaic virus and so brought to light a remarkable new link between living and nonliving matter. These investigations, reported in the next three selections, revealed new and significant viewpoints, both theoretical and practical.

The following selection is from pages 435–439 in *The Journal of Biological Chemistry 69*, 435–441 (1926).

The Isolation and Crystallization of the Enzyme Urease
Preliminary Paper

JAMES B. SUMNER

After work both by myself and in collaboration with Dr. V. A. Graham and Dr. C. V. Noback that extends over a period of a little less than 9 years, I discovered on the 29th of April a means of obtaining from the jack bean a new protein which crystallizes beautifully and whose solutions possess to an extraordinary degree the ability to decompose urea into ammonium carbonate. The protein crystals, which are shown in Fig. 1, have been examined through the kindness of Dr. A. C. Gill, who reports them to be sharply crystallized, colorless octahedra, belonging by this definition to the isometric system. They show no double refraction and are from 4 to 5μ in diameter.

While the most active solutions of urease prepared in this laboratory by Sumner, Graham, and Noback and by Sumner and Graham possessed an activity of about 30,000 units per gm. of protein present, the octahedra, after washing away the mother liquor, have an activity of 100,000 units per gm. of dry material. In other words, 1 gm. of the material will produce 100,000 mg. of ammonia nitrogen from a urea-phosphate solution in 5 minutes at 20° C. At this temperature the material requires 1.4 seconds to decompose its own weight of urea.

The crystals, when freshly formed, dissolve fairly rapidly in distilled water, giving a water-clear solution after centrifuging from the slight amount of insoluble matter that is present. The solution coagulates upon heating and gives strongly the biuret, xanthoproteic, Millon, Hopkins and Cole, ninhydrin, and unoxidized sulfur tests.

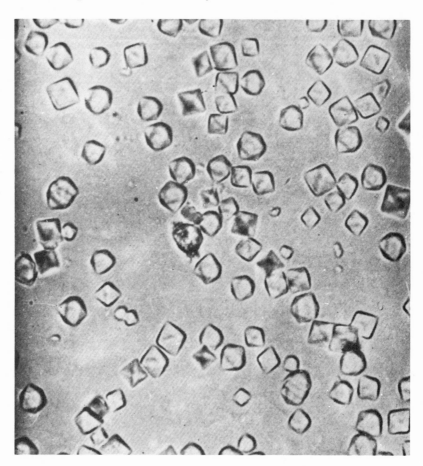

Fig. 1. Photomicrograph of urease crystals magnified 728 diameters

The phenol reagent of Folin and Denis gives a strong color, while the uric acid reagent gives none. The material can be entirely precipitated by saturating with ammonium sulfate. The Molisch test is negative and Bial's test is negative also. The absence of pentose carbohydrate, as shown by Bial's test, is especially pleasing as we have experienced a great deal of trouble in the past in freeing jack bean proteins from this substance.

The octahedral crystals, when freshly prepared, are very soluble in dilute alkali or dilute ammonia, and are either dissolved or coagulated by dilute mineral and organic acids, depending upon the concentration of acid. Even so weakly acid a substance as primary potassium phosphate is capable of causing an irreversible coagulation. Although the crystals dissolve in distilled water I am inclined to regard the material as globulin inasmuch as a precipitate is formed when carbon dioxide is passed into its solution and this precipitate immediately redissolves upon addition of a drop of neutral phosphate solution.

Owing to the fact that I have not had large enough amounts of the material to work with I am unable to give accurate figures for its nitrogen content at the present time, but this can be stated to be not far from 17 per cent, as shown by micro-Kjeldahl determinations made on several preparations. The content of ash is certainly low, so low that a considerable amount of material will have to be used to obtain this figure. Determination of the enzyme activity of the crystals has been somewhat interfered with, owing to the fact that dilute solutions of the crystals produce less ammonia from urea than one would calculate from results obtained from more concentrated solutions. If this effect is real, rather than apparent, it may be due to the instability of the enzyme at great dilutions. When in concentrated solution the activity is not lost very rapidly, provided the material is kept in the ice chest.

When old the crystals are entirely insoluble in distilled water, salt solutions, and dilute ammonia. In this condition the enzyme activity is almost nil. I have made several attempts to purify the fresh crystals by a second crystallization, but have never succeeded in obtaining more than traces of crystals and these have been insoluble in water and inactive.

It may be worth noting that practically all of our previous ideas concerning the nature of urease appear to be confirmed by the discovery of the octahedral crystals and by study of their properties. I undertook the task of isolating urease in the fall of 1917 with the idea that it might be found to be a crystallizable globulin, in which case the proof of its isolation would be greatly simplified. Other reasons for choosing urease were that the quantitative estimation of urease is both rapid and accurate, that urease can be reasonably expected to be an individual enzyme, rather than a mixture of enzymes, and that the jack bean appears to contain a very large amount of urease, if it is permissible to draw a parallelism between the urease content of the jack bean and the amounts of other enzymes found in other plant and animal materials.

In previous work in collaboration with Graham and Noback and in unpublished work of my own it has been found that urease is very completely precipitated, together with the jack bean globulins, by cooling its 35 per cent alcoholic solution to -5 to $-10°$ C., provided the reaction is sufficiently acid. We have found that urease can be precipitated by neutral lead acetate and neutralized cadmium chloride and that most of the urease can be reextracted by decomposing the precipitate with potassium oxalate; that urease can be precipitated by tannic acid without very much inactivation and that urease can be rendered insoluble, with loss of a part of its activity, by the action of dilute alcohol or very dilute acid.

Although the literature contains numerous references to a coenzyme of urease, I believe that no specific coenzyme exists. My evidence rests upon the fact that the loss of activity that occurs when the octahedral crystals are separated from a jack bean extract is almost exactly equal to the activity obtained when these crystals are washed with dilute acetone and then dissolved in water. If anything could separate an enzyme from its coenzyme crystallization might be expected to do so. The proteins in impure urease solution doubtless exert a protective action as buffers and both proteins and polysaccharides may exert protective colloidal action.

I present below a list of reasons why I believe the octahedral crystals to be identical with the enzyme urease.

1. The fact that the crystals can be seen by the microscope to be practically uncontaminated by any other material.

2. The great activity of solutions of the crystals.

3. The fact that solvents which do not dissolve the crystals extract little or no urease and that to obtain solutions of urease one must dissolve the crystals.

4. The fact that the other crystallizable jack bean globulins, concanavalin A and B, carry with them very little urease when they are formed from solutions that are comparatively rich in urease.

5. The unique crystalline habit of the octahedra and their ready denaturation by acid.

6. The fact that the crystals are purely protein in so far as can be determined by chemical tests, combined with evidence from previous work to the effect that urease behaves like a protein in its reactions toward heavy metals, alkaloid reagents, alcohol, and acids.

7. The fact that the crystals are nearly free from ash and the fact that we have previously prepared solutions of urease that contained neither iron, manganese, nor phosphorus.

The method which I have used to obtain the crystals is extremely simple. It consists in extracting finely powdered, fat-free jack bean meal with 31.6 per cent acetone and allowing the material to filter by gravity in an ice chest. After standing over night the filtrate is centrifuged and the precipitate of crystalline urease is stirred with cold 31.6 per cent acetone and centrifuged again. The crystals can now be dissolved in distilled water and centrifuged free from insoluble and inactive matter that has passed through the filter during the filtration. Of the urease extracted from the meal as much as 47 per cent may be present in the crystals. If one uses coarsely ground jack bean meal that has not been freed from fat the crystals are still obtained, but in traces only. I have carried out the process described above about fifteen times since first discovering the crystals and have always had success.

Exact details of the process are then described.

The following selection is from pages 739–743, 745, and 763–764 in *The Journal of General Physiology 13*, 739–766 (1930).

Crystalline Pepsin.
I. Isolation and Tests of Purity

JOHN H. NORTHROP

I

Introduction

Enzymes are in many respects connecting links between living and inanimate matter since their action is analogous to inorganic catalysts, although the enzymes themselves are found only in living organisms. As catalysts they increase the rate of one or more specific reactions and so act as directive agents for the reactions occurring in the organism. This directive property is undoubtedly essential for the existence of living cells. As a consequence of these properties the study of enzymes has been of interest to both chemists and biologists and has resulted in a great increase in the knowledge of their mode of action. The results of attempts to isolate the enzymes in pure form, however, have been singularly unsuccessful. There seems to be no convincing evidence that any enzyme has been obtained in the pure state; and only one, the urease described by Sumner, has been previously obtained in crystalline form. A number of methods have been found which allow the activity of an enzyme preparation to be increased almost indefinitely; at the same time, however, the preparation becomes more unstable and eventually the activity becomes lost.

In practically all the work the assumption has been made either explicitly or otherwise that the activity was a measure of the purity of the preparation and that any increase in activity was due to an increase in purity. This is not necessarily true. If the enzymes are analogous to inorganic catalysts then it is quite possible that the activity depends on the physical arrangement of the molecules or atoms. Evidence for this relation between the physical state and the activity was found by Fodor in the case of the proteolytic enzymes of yeast, and by Kuhn and Wasserman in the case of hemin. It is possible, on the other hand, that enzymes in general are of the type of hemoglobin (which might be considered an enzyme), and that they consist of an active group combined with an inert group. It might be possible under certain conditions to attach many more active groups to the inert group and so increase the activity above that of the original compound. Either of the above ideas would account for the well-known fact that crude preparations are much more stable than purified material and that the rate of inactivation of enzyme solutions practically always shows evidence of a mixture of stable and unstable forms.

There is some reason to think, therefore, that enzymes exist in a more stable form for either physical or chemical reasons, and in view of the uniformly negative results which have been obtained in attempting to isolate the most active preparations it seemed advisable in attempting the isolation of pepsin to study the more stable as well as the most active fraction.

II

Preliminary Experiments

A number of methods have been proposed for the purification of pepsin, such as precipitation with safranin, etc., fractionation by various adsorbents, and precipitation by dialysis from acid solution (Peckelharing). These and a number of other methods were tried and more or less active preparations obtained. The results with Peckelharing's method seemed the most encouraging, however, since the loss of activity was less and there was some indication that a constant activity was reached. This result has been reported by Peckelharing and also by Fenger, Andrew and Ralston using a similar method. It was found, however, that the dialysis could be dispensed with and the process made more rapid and efficient by solution with alkali and subsequent precipitation with acid, after a preliminary precipitation with half-saturated $MgSO_4$ or $(NH_4)_2SO_4$. The amorphous material so obtained contains about half the activity present in the original material and is 3 to 6 times as active as measured by the liquefaction of gelatin and about 5 times as active as measured by the digestion of casein or by the rennet action on milk. Repetition of this procedure gave products of increasing activity as measured by the liquefaction of gelatin, and apparently this activity could be increased indefinitely. Several samples were obtained which were 100 times as active as the original preparation. They were also more unstable, so that each succeeding precipitation was accompanied by a larger and larger percentage loss until finally no more active material remained. This has been the fate of all previous attempts to isolate the most active fraction of a number of enzymes. When the activity of the various fractions was determined by the rate of hydrolysis of casein or by the rennet action on milk, however, it was found that the activity increased until it reached about 5 times that of the crude preparation and then remained constant instead of increasing as did the gelatin-liquefying power. This was the result reported by Peckelharing and also by Fenger, Andrew and Ralston. This material appeared to be protein, as previous workers had found, and was reasonably stable. Efforts were therefore made to isolate this protein in crystalline form.

III

Isolation of the Crystalline Enzyme

It was noticed that the precipitate which formed in the dialyzing sac when the procedure of Peckelharing was followed appeared in more or less granular form and filtered rather easily, as though it were on the verge of crystallization. This precipitate dissolved on warming the suspension and it was eventually found that it could be induced to crystallize by warming to 45° C., filtering, and allowing the filtrate to cool slowly. The crystals so obtained were regular hexahedra and showed a tendency to grow in clusters, especially when appearing from more acid solutions. They are remarkably similar to the urease crystals pictured by Sumner and differ only in that they have a hexagonal base while the urease has an octagonal base. On one occasion a few crystals with truncated pyramids were obtained. They had the same activity and optical activity as the usual form. The crystals showed positive double refraction and were optically active in solution. They possessed proteolytic activity, when dissolved, equivalent to 5 times that of the U.S.P. 1 to 10,000 pepsin as measured by hydrolysis of casein, and 2.5 times as measured by the liquefaction of gelatin [see Fig. 1].

Improved Method for the Preparation of the Crystals. The isolation of the crystals in bulk by the above method was difficult owing to the dialysis. It was found that this could be avoided and the purification

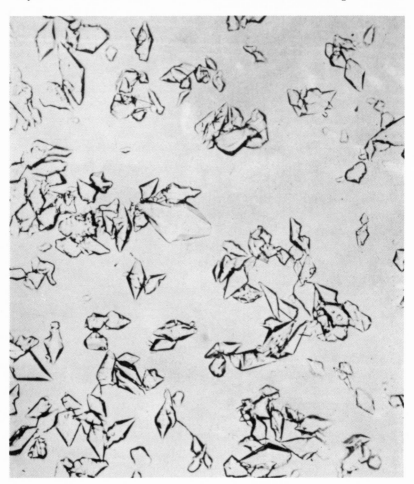

Fig. 1. Crystalline pepsin.

carried out as outlined above for the amorphous preparations except that the acid precipitate was dissolved at 45° C. in concentrated solution. On inoculation, this solution set to a solid paste of crystals.

A detailed description of the preparation of the crystals is given in tabular form at this point.

IV

General Properties and Analysis of the Crystals

The material prepared in this way has the general properties of a protein. It is coagulated by heat, precipitated by saturation of the solution with $MgSO_4$ or $(NH_4)_2SO_4$ and gives a strongly positive xanthoproteic test. The Millon test is negative. The crude material contains a large amount of yellowish pigment which is removed with difficulty. It may be largely removed by reprecipitation with $MgSO_4$ and becomes less as the material is recrystallized. All the preparations, however, give a slightly yellowish solution when dissolved although the dry crystals are pure white after several crystallizations. There is no relation between the activity and the color. Analysis of the material gave the results shown in Table II [not included here].

The crystals are difficult to dissolve after drying and are best kept under saturated $MgSO_4$ at 5° C. They are instantly inactivated by alkali in solution and lose activity slowly in acid solutions. The inactivated material is digested by the remaining active material and a large amount of tyrosine crystallizes out. This process also occurs slowly in the ice box so that the crystals on standing become mixed with nonprotein material that is not precipitated by salt nor by heat. The crystals can be freed from this soluble material by thorough washing with H_2O or by recrystallization. When freshly prepared in this way 98 to 99 per cent of the nitrogen is precipitated from solution by heating rapidly to boiling at pH 3 with sulfuric acid and Na_2SO_4, by saturation with $MgSO_4$ or $(NH_4)_2SO_4$, by the addition of alkali and subsequent neutralization, or by heating with 10 per cent trichloracetic acid.

Evidence is given for constant activity of various preparations, and for constant activity and composition on repeated crystallization. The paper concludes as follows.

VI

Conclusions as to the Purity of the Preparation

The preceding experiments have shown that no evidence for the existence of a mixture of active and inactive material in the crystals could be obtained by recrystallization, solubility determinations in a series of solvents, inactivation by either heat or alkali, or by the rate of diffusion. It is reasonable to conclude therefore that the material is either a pure substance or a solid solution of two very closely related substances. If it is a solid solution of two or more substances it must be further assumed that these substances have about the same degree of solubility in the various solvents used, as well as the same diffusion coefficient and rate of inactivation or denaturization by heat. It must also be assumed that both substances are changed by alkali at the same rate and to the same extent. This could hardly be true with the possible exception of two closely related proteins. It is conceivable that two proteins might be indistinguishable by any of the tests applied in this work. But in this case it would follow that the enzyme itself was a protein and this, after all, is the main point. It does not necessarily follow even if the material represents the pure enzyme that it is the most active preparation that can be obtained nor that it is the only compound which has proteolytic activity. There is some evidence that the activity of the preparation may depend on its physical state as is known to be the case with the catalytic activity of colloidal metals. It is possible, on the other hand, that hemoglobin is the type structure for the enzymes and that they consist of an active group combined with a protein as suggested by Peckelharing. The active group may be too unstable to exist alone, but it is quite conceivable that a series of compounds may exist containing varying numbers of active groups combined with the protein, and that the activity of the compound would depend on the number of these active groups. This hypothetical complex would not differ much from that assumed by Willstätter and his co-workers, except that it supposes a definite chemical compound with the protective group in place of an adsorption complex. It is of course possible that both types of complex may be formed under suitable conditions. The reactivation of enzymes as reported in the literature also suggests their protein nature since the conditions for this reactivation are similar to those found by Anson and Mirsky to be suitable for the formation of native from denatured protein. The fact that the crystalline urease prepared by Sumner is also a protein and that the temperature coefficient for the rate of inactivation of enzymes in general is that characteristic for the denaturization of proteins, suggests that the protein fraction in the purification of enzymes be given special attention even though it may not be the most active fraction.

The crystalline pepsin resembles the amorphous preparations obtained previously by Peckelharing, Ringer, Fenger, Andrew and Ralston and other workers. It is probable that the preparations obtained by these workers were nearly pure pepsin. Both Peckelharing and Ringer obtained preparations free from phosphorus so that there may be several proteolytically active forms.

Peckelharing showed that the same protein material could be obtained from gastric juice as from autolyzed gastric mucosa so that it is probable that the crystalline material could also be readily prepared from gastric juice. It seems fair to conclude therefore that the crystalline protein described in this paper is identical with the enzyme pepsin as secreted by the animal.

The following selection is in *Science 81*, 644–645 (1935).

Isolation of a Crystalline Protein Possessing the Properties of Tobacco-mosaic Virus

W. M. STANLEY

A crystalline material, which has the properties of tobacco-mosaic virus, has been isolated from the juice of Turkish tobacco plants infected with this virus. The crystalline material contains 20 per cent nitrogen and 1 per cent ash, and a solution containing 1 milligram per cubic centimeter gives a positive test with Millon's, biuret, xanthoproteic, glyoxylic acid and Folin's tyrosine reagents. The Molisch and Fehlings tests are negative, even with concentrated solutions. The material is precipitated by 0.4 saturated ammonium sulfate, by saturated magnesium sulfate, or by safranine, ethyl alcohol, acetone, trichloracetic acid, tannic acid, phosphotungstic acid, and lead acetate. The crystalline protein is practically insoluble in water and is soluble in dilute acid, alkali or salt solutions. Solutions containing from 0.1 per cent to 2 per cent of the protein are opalescent. They are fairly clear between pH 6 and 11 and between pH 1 and 4, and take on a dense whitish appearance between pH 4 and 6.

The infectivity, chemical composition and optical rotation of the crystalline protein were unchanged after 10 successive crystallizations. In a fractional crystallization experiment the activity of the first small portion of crystals to come out of solution was the same as the activity of the mother liquor. When solutions are made more alkaline than about pH 11.8 the opalescence disappears and they become clear. Such solutions are devoid of activity and it was shown by solubility tests that the protein had been denatured. The material is also denatured and its activity lost when solutions are made more acid than about pH 1. It is completely coagulated and the activity lost on heating to 94° C. Preliminary experiments, in which the amorphous form of the protein was partially digested with pepsin, or partially coagulated by heat, indicate that the loss in activity is about proportional to the loss of native protein. The molecular weight of the protein, as determined by two preliminary experiments on osmotic pressure and diffusion, is of the order of a few millions. That the molecule is quite large is also indicated by the fact that the protein is held back by collodion filters through which proteins such as egg albumin readily pass. The material readily passes a Berkefeld "W" filter.

The crystals are over 100 times more active than the suspension made by grinding up diseased Turkish tobacco leaves, and about 1,000 times more active than the twice-frozen juice from diseased plants. One cubic centimeter of a 1 to 1,000,000,000 dilution of the crystals has usually proved infectious. The disease produced by this, as well as more concentrated solutions, has proved to be typical tobacco mosaic. Activity measurements were made by comparing the number of lesions produced on one half of the leaves of plants of Early Golden Cluster bean, *Nicotiana glutinosa* L., or *N. langsdorffii*, Schrank after inoculation with dilutions of a solution of the crystals, with the number of lesions produced on the other halves of the same leaves after inoculation with dilutions of a virus preparation used for comparison.

The sera of animals injected with tobacco-mosaic virus give a precipitate when mixed with a solution of the crystals diluted as high as 1 part in 100,000. The sera of animals injected with juice from healthy plants give no precipitate when mixed with a solution of the crystals. Injection of solutions of the crystals into animals causes the production of a precipitin that is active for solutions of the crystals and juice of plants containing tobacco-mosaic virus but that is inactive for juice of normal plants.

The material herein described is quite different from the active crystalline material mentioned by Vinson and Petre and by Barton-Wright and McBain, which consisted, as Caldwell has demonstrated, largely of inorganic matter having no connection with the activity. These preparations were less active than ordinary juice from diseased plants, and the activity they possessed diminished on further crystallizations.

The crystalline protein described in this paper was prepared from the juice of Turkish tobacco plants infected with tobacco-mosaic virus. The juice was brought to 0.4 saturation with ammonium sulfate and the precipitated globulin fraction thus obtained was removed by filtration. The dark brown globulin portion was repeatedly fractionated with ammonium sulfate and then most of the remaining color was removed by precipitation with a small amount of lead subacetate at pH 8.7. An inactive protein fraction was removed from the light yellow colored filtrate by adjusting to pH 4.5 and adding 2 per cent by weight of standard celite. The celite was removed, suspended in water at pH 8, and the suspension filtered. The active protein was found in the colorless filtrate. This procedure was repeated twice in order to remove completely the inactive protein. Crystallization was accomplished by adding slowly, with stirring, a solution containing 1 cubic centimeter of glacial acetic acid in 20 cubic centimeters of 0.5 saturated ammonium sulfate to a solution of the protein containing sufficient ammonium sulfate to cause a faint turbidity. Small needles about 0.03 millimeters long appeared immediately and crystallization was completed in an hour. Crystallization may also be caused by the addition of a little saturated ammonium or magnesium sulfate to a solution of the protein in 0.001 N acid. Several attempts to obtain crystals by dialyzing solutions of the protein gave only amorphous material. To date a little more than 10 grams of the active crystalline protein have been obtained.

Although it is difficult, it is not impossible, to obtain conclusive positive proof of the purity of a protein, there is strong evidence that the crystalline protein herein described is either pure or is a solid solution of proteins. As yet no evidence for the existence of a mixture of active and inactive material in the crystals has been obtained. Tobacco-mosaic virus is regarded as an autocatalytic protein which, for the present, may be assumed to require the presence of living cells for multiplication.

BIOLOGICAL OXIDATIONS

As the knowledge of enzymes and biological mechanisms advanced, it became possible to attack many fundamental problems of biochemistry. Among the most important was the nature of biological oxidations and reductions by which the living cell obtained energy for life processes. The general mechanisms were considered from different viewpoints. Warburg and his school believed that enzymatically activated oxygen brought about direct oxidation of organic compounds, while Wieland proposed mechanisms for removal of hydrogen from organic compounds as the main oxidative process. These views are illustrated in the next two selections. The third illustrates how these viewpoints were reconciled by the discovery of the cytochromes by Keilin.

The following selection is from page 473 in *Biochemische Zeitschrift* *177*, 471–486 (1926).

The Action of Carbon Monoxide on the Metabolism of Yeast

OTTO WARBURG

The action of carbon monoxide on yeast is described and the Warburg manometric apparatus is explained. Then the results are discussed.

Table I [not included here] shows that carbon monoxide suppresses the respiration of yeast, by 22 to 77 per cent in the studies we carried out, according to the composition of the mixture. Here it is important that the effect depends not only on the pressure of carbon monoxide, but also on the oxygen pressure. For example, whether the inhibition of respiration at a carbon monoxide pressure of 583 mm. is 24 or 72 per cent depends on whether the prevailing oxygen pressure was high or low. Moreover, it is important that the inhibition by carbon monoxide is completely reversible. Yeast treated with carbon monoxide when placed in carbon monoxide-free gas does not respire more weakly, but even a little more strongly than the control yeast.

In what follows we call the oxygen-carrying part of the respiratory ferment for short the "respiratory enzyme," and so it follows from these studies that the respiratory enzyme combines with carbon monoxide which in the enzyme molecule occupies the same position that normally reacts with the oxygen. Thus the oxygen-carrying activity of the enzyme is suppressed.

The respiratory enzyme thus reacts like hemoglobin both with carbon monoxide and oxygen. Differing from hemoglobin, the respiratory enzyme binds oxygen more firmly than carbon monoxide. However, it is possible to drive out oxygen from hemoglobin by carbon monoxide, but it requires relatively more carbon monoxide to suppress respiration by carbon monoxide.

The remainder of the paper shows that while carbon monoxide inhibits respiration, it does not inhibit anaerobic fermentation.

The following selection is from pages 3327–3330 and 3339–3340 in *Berichte der Deutschen Chemischen Gesellschaft* 46, 3327–3342 (1913).

The Mechanism of Oxidation Processes

HEINRICH WIELAND

In recent years I have shown by many examples that it is possible

by using finely divided platinum metal even at ordinary temperatures to remove hydrogen from many compounds, to dehydrogenate
them. Palladium, which had chiefly been used, here loses its activity
when it is saturated with hydrogen, but since it is possible to separate
the hydrogen with oxygen or other hydrogen acceptors such as
quinone, methylene blue, etc., it is possible to use palladium black
in general in the sense of a transfer agent as a catalyst in oxidation, or
more exactly dehydrogenation, processes. By this method of considering the matter, the catalytic action of the platinum or palladium in
these processes does not occur by the metal activating a molecule of
oxygen (with intermediate formation of a peroxide), but much more
probably by the metal activating hydrogen, as is believed to occur
in the purification of detonating gas.

Studies to establish similar reaction behavior in other oxidation
processes have led to the result that apparently true oxidations in
which the oxygen is brought into the oxidizing molecule can also
occur through a dehydrogenation. Thus, aldehydes (through the
hydrates), like alcohols, can be dehydrogenated into carboxylic
acids:

$$R \cdot C{\overset{OH}{\underset{H}{\big|}}}OH \rightarrow R \cdot C{\overset{OH}{\underset{O}{\big\backslash}}} + H_2$$

For carbon monoxide, as an intermediate product in burning to
carbon dioxide, formic acid has been recognized:

$$C:O \rightarrow {\overset{HO}{\underset{H}{\big\backslash}}}C:O \rightarrow O:C:O + H_2$$

From the results thus obtained, I have taken this as the method
for a basic treatment of the most important processes of this type,
the biological oxidations, in order to test whether these reactions,
which mostly still lack an explained mechanism, can be brought
closer to understanding by the dehydrogenation theory. The general
dominant theory well known to biologists and also to chemists
who have occupied themselves with this theme is that oxidations and
combustions in the cells are due to their rapid occurrence with the
aid of oxygen-activating enzymes.

The following viewpoint was essential for an experimental treatment of the problem: it must first be shown that, as indicated by

the previously obtained results, the substances that form the materials for biological oxidations are especially easily dehydrogenated. Thus, it must be possible, with exclusion of oxygen, to decompose them with palladium black into hydrogen and their oxidation products. It is to be expected that this transformation will be slowed down as the metal is saturated with hydrogen. However, the reaction will continue if the hydrogen is removed by a suitable acceptor which continually separates it. Above all, oxygen is this type of acceptor, but since we here have excluded it, we take in its place, as above, other substances which easily take up active hydrogen, for example, quinone or methylene blue. It is also necessary first to show that oxidations that are of biological importance, can, in the presence of palladium, also occur without participation of oxygen. However, this is still only an imitation of the biological oxidation process when it is obtained with a substance foreign to the cell as the catalyst. If we recognize dehydrogenation as the driving force of biological oxidations, then first we can replace palladium black by an organic ferment which can act with another hydrogen acceptor besides oxygen. How far these experiments, with which I have now been occupied for a long time, have progressed will be shown in what follows.

I have always preferred as the simplest explanation the removal of hydrogen by the catalyst. In fact, in most cases, when palladium black is used, the hydrogen is removed as such and is absorbed by the metal. However, cases have also been found in which the hydrogen, without giving up its bond entirely, is only activated. Characteristic of this are the alcohols which are only slowly decomposed by palladium alone into aldehyde and hydrogen, but in which this decomposition occurs in much greater amount when the amount of hydrogen removed can be correspondingly taken up by quinone and quinoid dyes. I have therefore assumed that the first step in the action of the finely divided metal is dehydrogenation into an (apparently chemical) combination of the components expressed as a labile addition compound; in this the hydrogen becomes active in the same way as the palladium hydrogen. I might by the scheme:

$$Pd + RH_2 \rightleftarrows RPd\diagup^{H}_{\diagdown H} \quad \rightleftarrows R + Pd\diagup^{H}_{\diagdown H}$$

reconcile these ideas and thus the equilibrium relation between hydro RH_2 and the dehydro substance R. These separate hydrogen atoms should be called active hydrogen. In the organic ferments that will be discussed later the phase

$$R + Pd \diagup^{H}_{\diagdown H}$$

is mostly lacking.

Section 1. Combustion of Carbohydrates

Of the oxidative decomposition processes that occur within the cell, the most important is the slow combustion of grape sugar to carbon dioxide and water, the respiratory process. It has rightly aroused the astonishment of chemists and physiologists that the not especially easily oxidized molecule of glucose is smoothly burned to carbon dioxide and water even at low temperatures by the reaction of oxygen of the air carried into the tissues. On the basis of definition there can be no doubt that some sort of catalysts must take part in accelerating this reaction which in itself occurs infinitely slowly, but up to now it has not been possible to separate this sensitizer from the living processes. We have the general idea of its mode of action that this consists in an activation of oxygen which is taken up in a peroxide type of binding. Now with oxygen-free palladium black even at blood temperature (about 40°) I have been able to carry out a very rapid oxidation of grape sugar in which (and this is very important) *even from the beginning there is a rich formation of carbon dioxide.* With rising saturation of the metal by hydrogen, its activity weakens. However, we obtain a further rise of the reaction if the hydrogen split off is bound to quinone or methylene blue. *It is thus possible with the exclusion of oxygen to bring about extensive burning of grape sugar, using palladium black alone or in combination with quinoid compounds as hydrogen acceptors at low temperatures.*

Experimental details are given and oxidases are discussed. The paper then continues.

Section 3. The Reducing Ferments

If we consider oxidation processes as dehydrogenations, as the foregoing results have indicated exactly, at least for some important cases, then we have a reduction process at the same time, since the hydrogen activated by the ferment must be taken up by some sort of an acceptor. Naturally the hydrogenation of a molecule of oxygen to water $O{=}O + 4H \rightarrow 2H_2O$ is as much a reduction as the hydrogenation of methylene blue, of quinone, of plant pigments, or of nitrates to nitrites and ammonia, and others. I also consider the combined action of hydrogen peroxide in oxidation reactions such that it has the function of an easily hydrogenated substance in taking up hydrogen

$$HO-OH \xrightarrow{2H} 2H_2O$$

and dehydrogenating. Hydrogen peroxide is indeed known as the first step in hydrogenation of the oxygen molecule.

In this connection the so-called reduction enzymes so often discussed in the literature lose their special position, if we can recognize that their obvious reducing action, such as the decolorizing of a dye by some substrate, can also be used for the hydrogenation of an oxygen molecule, provided we can show that the "reductase" can equally function as an "oxidase" in the sense of the views expressed above. The reduction ferment most studied, the enzyme discovered by Schardinger in milk, permits this recognition. Its typical action consists in the fact that in its presence methylene blue is rapidly decolored by an aldehyde, that is, is reduced. The aldehyde naturally goes over to the corresponding acid. Now if we treat the dye with molecular oxygen, the ferment acts in the same way as the dehydrogenation of an aldehyde; we have the action of an oxidase. Without going into the matter more deeply, the theory given here certainly includes reduction and oxidation as two expressions of one process of dehydrogenation.

The aldehydes used in the Schardinger reaction, formaldehyde and acetaldehyde, were not suitable for this process, since at the optimum temperature of 60–70° they are themselves autooxidized, and also the resulting acids, formic and acetic, are not easily separated quantitatively for milk. Salicylic aldehyde was very suitable, however, and comparative studies with it have shown that under the same conditions with methylene blue or with molecular oxygen it is oxidized, that is, dehydrogenated, to salicylic acid.

Experimental results follow.

The following selection is from pages 269–271 in *Ergebnisse der Enzymforschung 2*, 239–271 (1933).

Cytochrome and Intracellular Respiratory Enzymes

D. KEILIN

VI Summary: respiratory function of cytochrome

Taking into account all possible deviations from the respiratory system described in this article, we can say however that the respiratory mechanism in which the oxidase-cytochrome system is involved is certainly by far the most important and the most widely distributed in nature, being common to cells belonging to all groups of organisms from bacteria and yeast to higher animals. The main respiratory system of the cell may be considered therefore as being composed of:

Dehydrogenase—substrates—cytochrome—oxidase—oxygen.

We can now summarize the main facts upon which is based the conception of the respiratory function of cytochrome and of the oxidase-cytochrome system.

(1) Cytochrome which is a mixture of three haemochromogen compounds (*a*, *b*, *c*) is the most widely distributed pigment present in cells of aerobic organisms but is absent from cells living anaerobically.

(2) There is marked parallelism in nature between the distribution of this pigment, the distribution of the oxidase and the respiratory activity of the cell.

(3) As in the reduced state cytochrome shows four distinct absorption bands which disappear on oxidation, the disappearance and reappearance of the bands in the cells corresponds to oxidation and reduction of cytochrome.

(4) Cytochrome has not only the property of reversible oxidation and reduction, but it can actually be seen in the living cells to undergo continual oxidation and reduction (yeast, bacteria, insects, etc.).

(5) The activity of cytochrome, in other words its oxidation and reduction, in living cells is affected by all inhibitors in the same way and to the same degree as the respiratory activity of the cell. While KCN, H_2S, NaN_3 and CO inhibit its oxidation, the narcotics such as urethane inhibit its reduction.

(6) Reduced cytochrome reacts with great velocity with the intracellular oxidase $+ O_2$, thus becoming immediately oxidized. For instance, a strong solution of reduced non-autoxidizable component *c* of cytochrome extracted from yeast when brought in contact with muscle oxidase preparation becomes immediately oxidized.

(7) Oxidized cytochrome, on the other hand, rapidly reacts with organic molecules or metabolites activated by dehydrogenases. For instance, oxidized cytochrome of washed muscle preparation (which has practically no oxygen uptake) remains indefinitely oxidized. It becomes reduced, however, when a small amount of succinic acid is added to the preparation. Cytochrome can be seen then to undergo oxidation and reduction as in a suspension of living

yeast cells and at the same time the muscle preparation takes up oxygen.

(8) It must be remembered that the reduction of oxidized cytochrome by activated molecules of metabolites means nothing else but the oxidation of these metabolites. In other words, it means respiration.

(9) The oxidase-cytochrome system can be reconstructed from the oxidase of heart muscle preparation and cytochrome c extracted from baker's yeast. It was found that neither oxidase by itself nor cytochrome c alone can appreciably oxidise cysteine. When, however, cytochrome and oxidase are brought together, they form a powerful catalytic system rapidly oxidizing cysteine to cystine.

(10) The activity of this reconstructed oxidase-cytochrome system toward cysteine is abolished by warming above 70° C. and is inhibited by KCN, H_2S, by CO in dark and to a smaller degree by CO in light, in the same way and to the same degree as is the respiration of living intact yeast cells. The reconstructed oxidase-cytochrome system behaves therefore like a true respiratory system in the cell.

(11) In intracellular oxidation the metabolites activated by dehydrogenases become "hydrogen donators." They undergo oxidation by reducing oxidized cytochrome which acts as a "hydrogen acceptor." The reduced cytochrome reacts with oxidase and oxygen, becoming thus oxidized.

We see therefore that generally for oxidation of intracellular metabolites both systems are essential: the Wieland-Thunberg system composed of dehydrogenases and their coferments and Warburg's system composed of oxidase and cytochrome.

FAT METABOLISM

The fate of foods in the body had been discussed by the early Greek philosophers and physicians. Iatrochemists had offered many theories on this subject. Little progress could be made, however, until the true chemical nature of food constituents became known. In the early twentieth century the composition of the carbohydrates, proteins, and fats was well established, but their fate in the body was still unknown, chiefly because only the end products of their oxidation—carbon dioxide, water, and ammonia (urea)—were recognizable. It was only when methods of labeling specific compounds became possible that intermediates in metabolism could be identified and metabolic pathways worked out. The first successful attempt at labeling occurred in 1905, before isotopic labeling was known. Knoop used the non-oxidizable benzene ring to label fatty acids and even as early as this showed the important fact that β-oxidation of these compounds took place in the body. When newer labeling materials became available, Schoenheimer used heavy hydrogen (see p. 91) to show that dynamic equilibrium always existed among the body fats. This concept, first applied to the fats, was later shown to be a general phenomenon of biological systems. Static conditions occurred only in the dead organism.

The following selection is from pages 150–151, 154, 155–156, and 160–161 in *Beiträge zur Chemischen Physiologie und Pathologie* 6, 150–162 (1905).

The Degradation of Aromatic Fatty Acids in the Animal Body

FRANZ KNOOP

In the burning of fats in the animal body there must be a successive formation of simpler products from the higher fatty acids before they are decomposed to carbonic acid and water; in the same way we must assume that the degradation of amino fatty acids in proteins occurs through simpler fatty acids, and also the decomposition of carbohydrates proceeds most probably through hydroxy fatty acids, for example, glycuronic and lactic acids. The oxidative degradation of the fatty acids therefore occupies a very important place in the animal body. In spite of this, our knowledge of the intermediate behavior is highly unsatisfactory, as far as can be judged, because the chemical processes in the animal body for the breakdown of the fatty acids of nutrition are so well adapted and interrelated with each other, and occur with such ease and speed that the intermediate members that must of necessity be formed escape observation.

Now, however, in many cases we can make such intermediate substances obtainable if the easily oxidizable compounds become accessible by introduction into them of less oxidizable groups which are difficult for the organism to handle; above all, of cyclic— that is, aromatic—complexes. Here we certainly must not overlook the fact that the path goes somewhat differently from a normal oxidation and only an indirect one is possible for the organism, for in great measure substances that are entirely burned have especially smoothly functioning specific mechanisms that do not work on homologous compounds burdened with groups foreign to the body. Such an idea is proved in the case of the phenylamino acids of proteins, tyrosine and phenyl alanine, since they differ from similar compounds by disappearing without residue.

What can be learned from the study of substances foreign to the body can then explain whether animal oxidations behave according to definite rules. We must next determine to what extent these rules also apply to the breakdown of nutritive substances, as we are greatly inclined to assume they do.

Very significant observations have been made on the oxidation of the aliphatic side chains of aromatic substances. These have shown that CH_3, CH_2OH, CHO, and CH_2NH_2 groups located on the benzene ring, though not without exceptions, are oxidized to carboxyl groups and the resulting benzoic acid or the acids corresponding to it are conjugated with glycocoll and excreted.

The literature on this subject is reviewed, and shows that phenyl propionic acid is converted to benzoic acid in the organism. The experimental method of feeding dogs gelating capsules containing the acid to be studied and determining the conjugated acid in the urine is then described. The paper then continues.

In this way I found by checking the older results:

I. In normal urine a vanishingly small amount of hippuric acid. By feeding of:

II. 2 g. of phenyl propionic acid (Kahlbaum): hippuric acid and no phenyl aceturic acid.

III. 2 g. of mandelic acid (inactive, Kahlbaum): unaltered mandelic acid.

IV. Phenyl acetic acid (Kahlbaum): phenyl aceturic acid, no increase in hippuric acid.

V. Ethyl benzene (Merck): hippuric acid, no phenyl aceturic acid.

I repeated the last study to be sure that there was actually a constant difference between oxidation of a hydrocarbon (ethyl benzene) and the corresponding acid (phenyl acetic acid), or else we would have had to reckon with the possibility that phenyl butyric acid would lead to somewhat similar results as phenyl butane. This is unnecessary, and from the above experimental results, I can now proceed to test phenyl butyric acid by an appropriate experimental method.

The synthesis of phenyl butyric acid is described.

The acid was fed twice, in the amount of 2 g. Both times I obtained from the urine an acid of the typical crystal form of phenyl aceturic acid, which like the latter melted at 142° and by splitting with dilute sulfuric acid in ether gave phenyl acetic acid with m.p. 76°. No hippuric acid was found.

Thus in fact there appears here the observation of an oxidation in the β-position, a finding which agrees with later evidence. The next step was to continue in the series and study phenyl caproic acid; it should go through phenyl butyric acid to phenyl acetic acid. Unfortunately, however, this acid has not been prepared. The phenyl valeric acid which lies between the two can be obtained, however; according to the same principle it must pass through phenyl propionic acid to hippuric acid if β-oxidation also takes place here.

Table I

Fed	Excreted	Alteration observed
$C_6H_5 \cdot COOH$	$C_6H_5 \cdot COOH$	Unaltered
$C_6H_5 \cdot CH_2 \cdot COOH$	$C_6H_5 \cdot CH_2COOH$	Unaltered
$C_6H_5 \cdot CH(OH) \cdot COOH$	$\left.\begin{array}{c} \\ \end{array}\right\} C_6H_5 \cdot CH(OH) \cdot COOH$	Unaltered (deaminated)
$C_6H_5 \cdot CH(NH_2) \cdot COOH$		
$C_6H_5 \cdot CH_2 \cdot CH_2 \cdot COOH$		Oxidized at the β-carbon atom
$C_6H_5 \cdot CH(OH) \cdot CH_2 \cdot COOH$	$C_6H_5 \cdot COOH$	
$C_6H_5 \cdot CO \cdot CH_2 \cdot COOH$		
$C_6H_5 \cdot CH{=}CH \cdot COOH$		
$C_6H_5 \cdot CH_2 \cdot CH(NH_2) \cdot COOH$		Apparently totally oxidized
$C_6H_5 \cdot CH_2 \cdot CH(OH) \cdot COOH$	0	
$C_6H_5 \cdot CH_2 \cdot CO \cdot COOH$		
$C_6H_5 \cdot CH{=}C(NH_2) \cdot COOH$		
$C_6H_5 \cdot CH_2 \cdot CH_2 \cdot CH_2 \cdot COOH$		Oxidized at the β-carbon atom
$C_6H_5 \cdot CO \cdot CH_2 \cdot CH_2 \cdot COOH$	$C_6H_5CH_2 \cdot COOH$	
$C_6H_5 \cdot CH{=}CH \cdot CH_2 \cdot COOH$		
$C_6H_5 \cdot CH_2 \cdot CH_2 \cdot CH_2 \cdot CH_2 \cdot COOH$	$C_6H_5 \cdot COOH$	Oxidized at the δ-carbon atom

$$C_6H_5 \cdot CH \cdot CH_2 \cdot CH_2 \cdot CO$$
$$|\qquad\qquad\qquad|$$
$$O\text{---------}$$

$$COOH$$
$$|$$
$$C_6H_5 \cdot CH \cdot CH \cdot CH \cdot CO$$
$$|\qquad\qquad\quad|$$
$$O\text{--------}$$

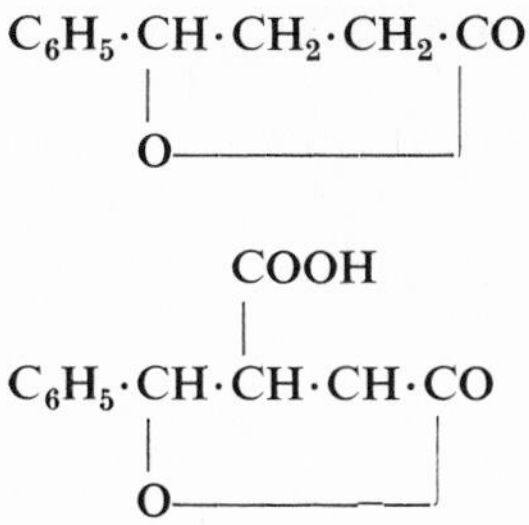

Unaltered   0

Synthesis of this acid is described.

We fed 1.5 g. of the resulting acid and in fact we obtained from the urine almost 0.5 g. of hippuric acid exclusively.

I did not continue the corresponding studies in the same series. However, I turned next to the question of whether the organism handled differently substances other than saturated normal acids of this series which had other types of substitution. I considered the possibility of complete combustion by analogy with phenyl alanine. What would happen, for example, if the amino group were in the β-position, or if another substituent were in the α- or β-position.

Reports of tests on a number of acids are given. The results are then summarized.

I give the results of all the preceding investigations as far as they concern aromatic acids with simple side chains, not substituted in the nucleus [Table I]:

If now on the basis of these results we test how far the views of E. and H. Salkowski on the degradation of aliphatic side chains and the experiments of Schotten and Baumann on the destruction of the benzene ring agree with our results, we see that in part they are incorrect and in part they must be extended.

Phenyl butyric acid, phenyl-α-lactic acid, phenyl pyruvic acid, and at least five other of the studied substances contain more than two C atoms in the side chain; none of them yields benzoic acid. Therefore E. and H. Salkowski's rule is far from general. On the contrary, it appears to me, at least for the saturated normal phenyl-substituted fatty acids, as far as the present position of synthetic organic chemistry permits testing, all the facts found correspond to the assumption of an oxidation in the β-position, and this can even be taken as the sole explanation.

Complete destruction of α-substituted acids is discussed in concluding the paper.

The following selection is in *The Journal of Biological Chemistry 111*, 175–181 (1935).

Deuterium as an Indicator in the Study of Intermediary Metabolism.
III The Role of the Fat Tissues

RUDOLF SCHOENHEIMER AND D. RITTENBERG

In this communication we report on some exploratory experiments connected with the metabolism of fat in which we have tested our methods and their application to biological problems. We have fed mice for several days on a diet comprising a deuterium-containing fat, and followed it after absorption. The animals were kept on a diet which was insufficient in quantity for them to maintain their weight. We expected that under these conditions almost all of the ingested fat would be burned and that relatively little would be deposited. Much to our surprise we found that, in spite of the fact that the animals lost weight, a large proportion of the absorbed fat was deposited in the depots, indicating that the fat which was burned was not oxidized directly after absorption but had been taken from the fat depots. We have direct proof that a part of the deuterium-rich fat was burned in our animals, as the body fluids which we distilled off from our animals contained appreciable amounts of heavy water.

It is well known that the properties of the storage fat in animals are somewhat dependent upon the properties of the food fat. It has been found possible to change the properties of the body fat somewhat by feeding either excessive amounts for a short period, or smaller amounts over a long period, of fats which differed markedly from body fat. The changes observed in the properties of the storage fat are usually small since there exists a tendency in the animal to alter the deposited fat to that typical for its species.

Our methods enabled us to follow the fate of small amounts of fats, which could not be traced by any other method. We analyzed mice after feeding them for 4 days on a diet with as little as 1 per cent fat, and were able to determine how much of the fat was deposited in the fat tissue and how much was burned.

Experimental

The fat which we fed was a partially hydrogenated linseed oil. It had properties similar to that of olive oil.

Partial Hydrogenation of Linseed Oil. 50 gm. of dry linseed oil (iodine number 170) were dissolved in 100 cc. of dry petroleum ether (b.p. 40°) and shaken with 0.5 gm. of active palladium in an atmosphere of deuterium. The petroleum ether was previously treated four times with concentrated H_2SO_4, washed with water, and distilled from P_2O_5. The linseed oil absorbed 5000 cc. of D_2 in about 4 hours. The petroleum ether was distilled off.

The water obtained by combustion of 0.609 gm. of the oil was purified by the methods described in Paper II of this series. The atom per cent of deuterium in this oil was 5.74. The iodine number of the oil was 79.5.

Feeding Experiments. Male mice were used in these experiments. Each animal was kept in a 600 cc. beaker containing 10 gm. of ether-extracted wool for bedding. The food was placed in a small glass cup suspended by a glass rod from a wire screen covering the beaker. Food was placed in the cup every day. Very little was spilled.

At the end of the feeding period, the mice were killed with ether, and weighed again. The whole intestinal tract from the esophagus to the anus was taken out and put back into the beaker which contained the food cup, the wool, some spilled food, and the feces. The organs (liver, spleen, kidneys, adrenals, heart, and testes) were removed and analyzed separately. The amount of consumed fat was calculated from the amount of fatty acids given and the amount of fatty acids remaining in the beaker after the mouse was taken out.

Analytical Methods

The carcasses of the mice, either individually or in groups, were placed in a 300 cc. round bottom flask with a short neck.

Distillation of Body Water. The flask was connected with a carbon dioxide-alcohol-cooled trap (see Paper I) and the system evacuated with an oil pump. The carcasses soon froze and ice sublimed into the trap. Several gm. were collected in this manner. The water collected in the trap was purified for the deuterium analysis in the manner described in Paper II.

Isolation of Fatty Acids and Unsaponifiable Material from Carcasses and Organs. The method used for separating the total unsaponifiable material was similar to that described by Schoenheimer and Breusch. With some modifications it could also be used for the quantitative separation of the total fatty acids of the animals and the residues in the beakers.

It is based on the observation that all the organic matter of animals dissolves easily in hot alkaline alcohol, which simultaneously saponifies the esters. The method was simplified and is now applicable to the determination of unsaponifiable material and fatty acids in organic material. We describe only the analysis of the mouse carcass. The procedure used in working up the organs and the material in the beakers was similar.

After a part of the body water had been distilled off, 70 cc. of 95 per cent ethyl alcohol, 10 cc. of water, and 7 gm. of solid KOH were added. The liquid was refluxed on a steam bath for 2 hours. All except the bones dissolved. The solution was filtered through glass wool, and the residue washed with hot alcohol. The filtrate and washings were combined and the alcohol distilled off. The remaining liquid was washed into a separatory funnel with ether and water. The aqueous layer was extracted three times with ether. The ether was washed with small amounts of water which were combined with the aqueous layer. The ether contained the unsaponifiable matter and was used to isolate the sterols.

In order to separate the fatty acids, the alkaline aqueous layer was acidified with hydrochloric acid and twice extracted with ether. On acidifying, a generally small but sometimes voluminous precipitate occurs; this is not soluble in ether, and collects at the water-ether interface. It packs together on stirring with a glass rod and the water can easily be drawn off. The ether is washed with water until it is neutral. Before the last separation of ether and water the liquid is allowed to stand for 24 hours so that the ether-insoluble precipitate packs together. The water is drawn off and the precipitate and ether layer are transferred to an Erlenmeyer flask, dried with Na_2SO_4, and treated with a small amount of norite which absorbs a brown-colored material but no fatty acids. The ether solution is filtered and the ether evaporated in an atmosphere of CO_2. The residue was weighed and the deuterium content was determined according to the procedure described in Paper II.

To estimate the amount of fat consumed, the fatty acids of the beaker were analyzed in a similar manner. The beaker contained the wool, small amounts of spilled food, the feces, and the intestines of the animals. A 500 cc. round bottom flask fitted with a rubber stopper and water inlet and outlet was placed over the beaker as a reflux condenser, and the contents were boiled with alkaline alcohol as described above. The bread particles did not dissolve and were filtered off through glass wool. The quantitative isolation was effected as described above.

Mice Kept on a Diet Containing 20 Per Cent Fat. The diet consisted of 80 per cent whole wheat bread and 20 per cent of deuterium-containing linseed oil prepared as described above. Each mouse and each beaker was analyzed separately. The amount of food given was such that the animals consumed almost all of it except a few particles which they spilled. Despite their noticeable hunger, they did not eat this spilled food as it was contaminated with urine. All the mice lost some weight during the feeding periods, which varied from 2 to 8 days. The body water was analyzed only from the mice of Experiments 5 and 6, as this method was developed during the experiment. The results are given in Table I.

Mice on 4 Per Cent Fat Diet. The mice were kept in separate beakers, but the analyses were carried out on the combined mice and the combined beaker contents. The values therefore give the average for all the mice (Table II).

Mice on 1 Per Cent Fat Diet. In order to obtain a homogeneous mixture the fat was dissolved in ether and mixed with the finely ground bread, and the ether evaporated. The procedure was the same as in the experiment with the 4 per cent fat diet (Table II).

Discussion

The partially hydrogenated linseed oil which we fed may, as a food component, be considered as equivalent to a natural fat. Its iodine number and physical properties correspond to those of olive oil. On theoretical grounds we cannot expect that molecules containing more deuterium than usual will be treated in a manner different from those in which the hydrogen is present in its ordinary isotopic ratio. We are confident that these results show us the route that the analogous natural compounds take in the organism.

We realize that our initial experiments have not given us all the information which our method could supply. Some of the analytical methods were developed during the course of the research so that our data are not complete. We have shown, however, that this method has a wide field of use so that, even on so small an animal as a mouse, we could follow the fat from a diet containing it to the extent of only 1 per cent.

The diet on which the mice were kept consisted principally of carbohydrate in order to avoid any disturbance of the fat metabolism. The small loss of body weight which all the animals showed resulted from insufficiency of food. The animals appeared healthy and ate almost all of the diet except the small amount which was scattered in the beaker and had become contaminated with urine or feces.

We worked up the animals in such fashion that no fat was lost. Since it is almost impossible to obtain quantitatively the fat of the depots alone, we have analyzed the total fat of the animal after the internal organs had been removed. The error involved in this procedure is small as the quantity of fat in the skin, muscles, and other organs is small in proportion to that in the depots. In this paper by depot fat is understood the total fat of the animal less that of the internal organs. The fact that in all our experiments a large part of the fat that we fed was found in the fat depots raises the problem as to whether all the fat, after absorption, is deposited in the depots before it is oxidized. From our experiments we can certainly say that the greater part takes this route.

The fat in the internal organs had a higher deuterium content than the fat in the depots. This means that a small part of the absorbed fat goes directly to the organs. The absolute amount is not large since the total amount of fat in the organs is very small. We can as yet draw no conclusions as to the content of the liver since this organ was not worked up alone, but in conjunction with the other organs. When we began this work, we did not expect that we should be able to analyze for the deuterium content of the liver fat of a mouse which had been fed for only a few days on a low fat diet. We are at present investigating this problem.

The analysis of the body fluids shows that a part of the ingested fat is burned. We did not attempt to determine the water balance of the animals in our experiments and cannot therefore directly estimate how much of the ingested fat was oxidized during the course of the experiment. Our analyses show that the mice which were fed a diet containing 1 per cent fat, for 4 days, consumed 251 mg. of fat. Of this we found 119 mg. (47 per cent) in the fat depots. The body fluids of the mice had a concentration of 0.008 per cent D_2O. This amount of heavy water would be formed by the combustion of 50 mg. of our fat (20 per cent). The remainder of the deuterium must have been lost in the water excreted (urine, respiration, feces, etc.).

After 8 days on a diet containing 20 per cent fat, about 50 per cent was found in the depots. As it is known that the properties of the fat depots are but slightly influenced by the fat of the diet, we must conclude that the absorbed fat is rapidly converted to the special fat of the animal. We must also expect that the deuterium-containing fatty acids have been converted to other fatty acids.

Summary

1. Mice were fed from 2 to 10 days on a diet comprising 20 per cent, 4 per cent, and 1 per cent deuterium-containing fats. At the end of this period the deuterium content of the fat depots, the fat of the internal organs, and the body fluids was determined.

2. A large part of the diet fat was found in the fat depots. In the case of the mice fed for 4 days on a diet containing 1 per cent fat, 47 per cent of the ingested fat could be found in the depots, and heavy water equivalent to 20 per cent of the ingested fat in the body fluids.

3. A small amount of the absorbed fat was found in the internal organs.

4. The experiments indicate that the largest part of the diet fat, even when it is present in small quantities, is deposited in the fat tissues before it is utilized.

Table I

Results of experiments on mice fed a diet containing 20 per cent fat
(The diet fat contains 5.74 atoms per cent of D)

Experiment No.	Feeding period (days)	Weight of animals (gm.)	Loss of weight (gm.)	Amount of fat consumed (gm.)	Amount of total fat in depots (gm.)	D_2 in— Depot fat (atom per cent)	D_2 in— Organ fat (atom per cent)	Diet fat in— Depot fat (per cent)	Diet fat in— Organ fat (per cent)	Heavy water in body fluids (per cent)
1	2	22.5	1.8	0.54	2.06	0.27		4.7		
2	2	13.8	0.1	0.58	0.42	2.17		37.8		
3	4	20.9	1.3	1.12	2.00	0.71		12.3		
4	4	15.1	0.4	1.28	0.39	2.61		37.6		
5	8	17.1	1.1	2.61	0.97	2.71		47.4		
6	8	15.9		2.72	0.94	2.36	3.33	41.3	58.0	0.33
7	8	19.2	0.6	2.53	0.64	2.78		48.6		0.47

Table II

Results of experiments on mice fed different amounts of fat

Experiment No.	Fat in diet (per cent)	Feeding period (days)	Weight of animals together (gm.)	Loss of weight (gm.)	Amount of fat consumed (gm.)	Amount of total fat in depots (gm.)	D_2 in— Depot fat (atom per cent)	D_2 in— Organ fat (atom per cent)	Diet fat in— Depot fat (per cent)	Diet fat in— Organ fat (per cent)	Heavy water in body fluids (per cent)
8	4	10	58.9	2.2		5.4	0.715	0.85	12.5	14.8	0.036
9	1	4	51.1	2.8	0.251	3.9	0.091	0.17	1.6	2.96	0.008

PROTEINS

METABOLISM. Once the structure of the proteins was known (p. 269) it was seen that the study of protein metabolism was largely the study of the metabolism of the individual amino acids. The interrelations between their metabolism and that of the carbohydrates soon became apparent, and it was realized that much of protein biochemistry was closely involved with that of the compounds formed in the oxidation of the carbohydrates. Reactions specific to the proteins involved the amino groups. The discovery of oxidative deamination was quickly followed by the unexpected discovery of the transamination reaction which brought proteins and carbohydrates into even closer relationship and added a new type of reaction to fit into the picture of the dynamic state of body constituents that had been revealed first for the fats.

The following selection is from pages 129, 130, and 135–136 in *Enzymologia 2*, 129–137 (1937).

The Degradation and Formation of Amino Acids by Transamination. I Exchange of 1(+) Glutamic Acid in Muscle Tissue

A. E. BRAUNSHTEIN AND M. G. KRITSMAN

Since the classic studies of Embden, Neubauer, Knoop, Krebs and others it has been generally accepted that the degradation of amino acids in animal organisms occurs chiefly through oxidative deamination, their synthesis by addition of free ammonia to α-keto acids with simultaneous reduction (reductive amination).

The literature on this subject is then reviewed and the paper continues.

The existence of such a process may be considered to be changed at several points by our views on nitrogen exchange in single organs, especially in muscle. On this basis we have carried out in our laboratory since 1936 systematic studies of the behavior of amino acids and especially the amino dicarboxylic acids in the metabolism of tissues, particularly of muscles.

As the first result of these studies, we report in this paper the discovery of *a new type of metabolic mechanism in muscle*, which is accomplished by the transfer of the amino group of glutamic acid to α-keto acids, with transformation of the latter into new amino acids, a reaction which is thus to be called *transamination*.

Experimental details are then described.

Discussion

As was stated at the beginning, in muscle there is no breakdown and no synthesis of amino acids with participation of free ammonia. If there had first been splitting of ammonia in our study, by oxidative deamination of glutamic acid, and this ammonia had then added to pyruvic acid with simultaneous hydrogenation of the latter (thus a trimolecular reaction whose probability is relatively very slight), then inevitably part of this ammonia would escape combination and would have been recognizable. Accordingly, the balance described above can only be the result of a process in which hydrogen and active amino groups are exchanged intermolecularly. Considered formally, the process consists of a "coupled" reaction by which the pyruvic acid (added or formed in the muscle) is reduced and at the same time aminated at the cost of the hydrogen atom and amino group given up by the glutamic acid.

By this process the glutamic acid is dehydrogenated and deaminated to α-ketoglutaric acid and is further degraded to CO_2 and succinic acid. The latter, under anaerobic conditions, accumulates in part, and in an oxybiotic study is almost completely oxidized further. In an aerobic study the added glutamic acid acts as an "accepting medium" for the pyruvic acid formed as an intermediate in lactic acid oxidation. The increased disappearance of lactic acid caused by addition of glutamic acid can then be considered to be based on the fact that dehydrogenation of lactic acid occurs at an increased rate because of rapid removal of the primary dehydrogenation product which in the further reaction is strongly inhibiting. In aerobic and anaerobic studies without glutamic acid, added pyruvic acid is gradually used up so that (in case of the presence of bromoacetate) only about half appears as lactic acid. The rest of the pyruvic acid changes in another way, apparently chiefly through the reaction recently recognized by Krebs to acetic acid and β-hydroxybutyric acid. In contrast to this, addition of glutamic acid leads here almost totally to increased appearance of the pyruvic acid which disappears in the form of its reduction products, lactic acid and alanine. Even under aerobic conditions pyruvic acid is practically completely reduced if glutamic acid is added (it should be remembered that the latter, like its closest transformation products, α-ketoglutaric and succinic acids, is an energetic hydrogen donor). The additional lactic acid formation observed in this case along with the alanine formation can be understood in the following way: in the reaction between glutamic acid and pyruvic acid, α-ketoglutaric acid is formed; the latter is then oxidatively decarboxylated to succinic acid, and a second molecule of pyruvic acid serves as the hydrogen acceptor, being hydrogenated to lactic acid according to the scheme of mixed dismutation of Krebs. . . .

Schematically we can express the balance of the transformations observed for glutamic acid in muscle by the following equations in which the secondary reactions and eventual halting of the processes at intermediate stages are neglected:

A. Under Aerobic Conditions

(1) 2 Lactic acid + O_2 = 2 pyruvic acid + $2H_2O$
(2) Glutamic acid + pyruvic acid = α-ketoglutaric acid + alanine
(3) α-Ketoglutaric acid + pyruvic acid = succinic acid + CO_2 + lactic acid
(4) Succinic acid + $3\frac{1}{2}O_2$ = $4CO_2$ + $3H_2O$

(1 + 2 + 3 + 4) Lactic acid + glutamic acid + $4\frac{1}{2}O_2$ = alanine + $5CO_2$ + $5H_2O$

B. Under Anaerobic Conditions (in the Presence of Pyruvic Acid)

(2) Glutamic acid + pyruvic acid = α-ketoglutaric acid + alanine
(3) α-ketoglutaric acid + pyruvic acid = succinic acid + CO_2 + lactic acid

---

(2 + 3) Glutamic acid + 2 pyruvic acid = succinic acid + alanine + lactic acid + CO_2

Reaction (2) represents the actual transamination. It is an enzymatic reaction—in the absence of tissues or with heated muscle homogenate glutamic acid does not react with pyruvic acid under our conditions.

As will be reported later, the transamination process is not limited to the system described here: it occurs not only in muscle tissue, but also in various other organs, and indeed the transfer of the amino group takes place not only from glutamic to pyruvic acid, but can also occur with other amino acids as donors and other α-keto acids as acceptors of the amino nitrogen.

The process recognized in the present work is the first example of a biochemical *synthesis of amino acids through intermolecular transfer of amino groups*. It is further for the first time a recognition of the synthesis of a new amino acid in muscle tissue. It is of interest that the amino acid synthesis by transamination occurs with greater intensity in minced muscle tissue in which most of the cellular elements are damaged, as opposed to the synthesis from free ammonia and keto acids (in liver and kidney), which presupposes the intactness of cell structures.

DETERMINATION OF STRUCTURE. The gradually improving methods for isolation of pure proteins permitted more intensive study of individual compounds among these very complex substances, and so the relatively crude methods for splitting or synthesis of proteins were replaced by methods by which a single, known amino acid could be removed from or added to a protein molecule. Thus the sequence of amino acids in a given protein could be determined and specific polypeptides built up. The method proposed by Sanger for determination of terminal amino acids as their dinitrophenol derivatives was a major step in structure determinations which led to synthesis of important protein hormones soon after the middle of the century.

The following selection is from pages 507–508 and 514–515 in *The Biochemical Journal 39*, 507–515 (1945).

The Free Amino Groups of Insulin

F. SANGER

That the free amino groups in proteins may be the ε-amino group of lysine was first suggested by Skraup and Kaas (1906) who failed to isolate lysine from deaminized proteins. Van Slyke and Birchard (1913) later found an apparent equality between the free amino-N of proteins and one-half of their total lysine-N, which suggested that the free amino groups were due exclusively to such a source. Methods were then developed to confirm the presence of the free ε-amino group of lysine in proteins; these consisted in treating a protein with a reagent that would react with free amino groups to give derivatives that were stable to acid hydrolysis, so that on hydrolysis of the substituted protein the derivative of lysine could be isolated. The most satisfactory was that of Gurin and Clark (1934), who treated gelatin with benzenesulphonyl chloride, hydrolyzed the resulting benzenesulphonyl gelatin and isolated ε-benzenesulphonyl-lysine from the hydrolysate.

In some proteins, and particularly in insulin, the number of free amino groups (Van Slyke) is far in excess of that which can now be ascribed to lysine, which suggests that the protein must contain residues of certain amino acids which are condensed in such a way that their α-amino groups remain free. Jensen and Evans (1935) have, in fact, been able to isolate the phenylhydantoin of phenylalanine from a hydrolysate of insulin that had been treated with phenyl*iso*cyanate, thus demonstrating that some free amino groups of insulin are present on phenylalanyl residues. Chibnall (1942) has suggested that the free amino groups of proteins over and above the ε-amino groups of lysine are due to terminal residues of polypeptide chains, and that the number of these groups must therefore give a measure of the number of polypeptide chains in the protein.

We found that methanesulphonyl amino acids were stable to acid hydrolysis and that they could be fractionated by partition chromatography (Gordon, Martin and Synge, 1943) with an indicator in the aqueous phase of the column. The rates at which the bands moved on the column were similar to those of the acetamino acids. The method was satisfactory when applied to synthetic peptides, but with insulin the number of terminal groups estimated by titration of the methanesulphonyl amino acids was far less than that suggested by the method of Van Slyke. The procedure was accordingly abandoned.

Abderhalden and Stix (1923) attempted to use 2:4-dinitrochlorobenzene (DNCB) for the identification of the terminal groups of a partial hydrolysate of silk fibroin. They did not meet with much success, chiefly owing to the presence of anhydrides in the hydrolysate and the difficulties of separating the products. It seemed, nevertheless, worth while to investigate this reagent, especially as all the 2:4-dinitrophenyl-amino acids (referred to henceforth as DNP-amino acids) produced are bright yellow, thereby facilitating chromatographic separation. DNCB will not react with amino acids in $NaHCO_3$ solution unless heat is applied, and this brings about a certain amount of hydrolysis of the protein. Fortunately, however, the corresponding fluoro-compound, 2:4-dinitrofluorobenzene (DNFB), was found to react readily at room temperature, and the use of this has met with considerable success, for the DNP-amino acids produced can be estimated colorimetrically and separated almost completely from one another by partition chromatography. The solvent systems normally used for separating the acetyl-derivatives were not entirely satisfactory for the DNP-monoamino acids, and several new systems had to be introduced; nevertheless, the method finally adopted embraced all amino acids, though this was not possible with the methanesulphonyl derivatives.

The method as applied to insulin consisted of three stages. In the first the protein was treated with DNFB, hydrolyzed, and the resulting colored compounds separated chromatographically. The identification of these was based upon band rates, and was confirmed by mixed chromatograms. Secondly, knowing which DNP-derivatives were present, one could assess the amount of each with reasonable accuracy by separating the fraction quantitatively and estimating the material present colorimetrically, using the pure DNP-amino acid as a standard. Thirdly, the whole operation was carried out on a larger scale, so that the DNP-amino acids could be isolated and satisfactorily characterized. The procedure should be applicable to the identification and estimation of the terminal residues in all peptides and proteins.

Experimental details are given, and the work is then summarized.

Summary

1. A new method is described for the identification and estimation of the free amino groups of proteins and peptides by the formation of derivatives with 2:4-dinitrofluorobenzene.

2. The method has been applied to insulin. Assuming a minimum mol. wt. of 12,000, it is shown that six free amino groups are present; two of these are located on glycine residues, two on phenylalanine residues and two represent the ε-amino groups of lysine.

3. The results suggest that the insulin submolecule of mol. wt. 12,000 is made up of four open peptide chains, two of these having terminal glycyl-residues and the other two terminal phenylalanyl-residues respectively.

CARBOHYDRATE METABOLISM

Probably the greatest advance in biochemistry in the first half of the twentieth century was the integration of various studies on yeast fermentation and muscle action together with work on energy production in the cell into a unified picture of the metabolism of carbohydrates. This furnished a framework into which a large number of the metabolic reactions of the body could be tied.

ANAEROBIC PHASE. The work began early in the century when Harden and Young showed that esters of phosphoric acid were important intermediates in carbohydrate breakdown, and that the enzymes involved in their formation required the presence of another substance, the coenzyme, to function. The ester that they isolated, fructose 1,6-diphosphate, was subsequently known as the Harden-Young ester.

Another essential step in elucidating the mechanism of the anaerobic phase was the isolation of the important phosphate carrier, adenosine triphosphate, now universally and familiarly known as ATP. This substance was found in 1929, independently by Lohmann and by Fiske and Subbarow.

As the compounds involved in the intermediate metabolism of carbohydrates were gradually identified, it began to be possible to propose mechanisms for the process. Essentially the correct path of breakdown through the phosphate esters to pyruvic acid was suggested by Embden and his co-workers in 1933. Thus the path of anaerobic oxidation and the reason for the occurrence of lactic acid in functioning muscle were finally explained. Further details were filled in by the Coris, husband and wife, who showed the importance of glucose-1-phosphate (the Cori ester) in the process and indicated the relationship of glycogen to the whole scheme. Thus, by midcentury, the anaerobic phase of carbohydrate metabolism was well understood, and its relationship to other phases of metabolism could be worked out. The next five selections illustrate steps in the unraveling.

The following selection is from pages 408–410, 414, and 417–418 in *Proceedings of the Royal Society* (*London*), *Series B, 77, 405–420 (1905).*

The Alcoholic Ferment of Yeast-Juice

ARTHUR HARDEN AND WILLIAM JOHN YOUNG

The authors describe their method of measuring the amount of fermentation by the amount of CO_2 evolved.

3. Dialysis of Yeast-juice

The facts above detailed suggested the possibility of dividing yeast-juice into two fractions by dialysis; an inactive residue and a dialysate which, although itself inert, would be capable of rendering this residue active.

This was experimentally realized by filtering the juice through a Martin gelatin filter.

This method of rapid dialysis was chosen because the yeast-juices at our disposal lost their activity too rapidly to permit of the ordinary process of dialysis through parchment being carried out. Either a 10- or a 7-per cent solution of gelatin was used to impregnate the Chamberland filter and the filtration was carried out under a pressure of 50 atmospheres.

Only a portion of the juice placed in the filter was actually filtered, the remainder being simply poured out of the case as soon as a sufficient quantity of filtrate had passed through. The residue adhering to the candle, which consisted of a brown viscid mass, was dissolved in water and made up to the volume of the juice filtered. Glucose was then added and one portion incubated at 25° with an equal volume of sugar solution and a second portion with an equal volume of the filtrate or of a boiled juice, containing an equal amount of glucose. Before incubation the carbon dioxide was pumped out of all the solutions. The filtrate was invariably found to be quite devoid of fermenting power, none of the enzyme having passed through the gelatin. The results (Table IV) show that in this way an almost inactive residue can be obtained which is rendered active by the addition of the filtrate (Experiments 1, 2, 3) or a boiled juice (experiment 4).

Table IV

Filtration of Yeast-juice through the Martin Gelatin Filter
15 c.c. residue + 3 grammes glucose + toluene

No.	Water	Filtrate	Boiled juice	Time	Carbon dioxide
	c.c.	c.c.	c.c.	hours	gramme
1	15	0	0	48	0.000
	0	15	0	48	0.035
2	15	0	0	60	0.001
	0	15	0	60	0.051
3	15	0	0	60	0.008
	0	15	0	60	0.064
4	15	0	0	60	0.024
	0	0	15	60	0.282

The total fermentations observed even in the presence of the filtrate are very low, this being, at all events in part, due to the fact that in this series of experiments the original juices themselves happened to be of low fermenting power.

In the second set of experiments (Table V) a smaller quantity of juice was placed in the filter and the filtration was continued until no more liquid would pass through. The residue was then washed several times by adding water and forcing it through the filter. The time occupied in this process varied greatly with different juices, the limits for the filtration and washing of 50 c.c. of juice, using two

Table V

Filtration of Yeast-juice through the Martin Gelatin Filter

No.	Vol. of juice filtered	Wash water	Residue	Filtrate	Boiled juice	Glucose	Carbon dioxide
	c.c.	c.c.	c.c.	c.c.	c.c.	grammes	c.c.
1	75	200	25	0	0	2.5	10.4
			25	0	25	5	396.3
2	80	260	20	0	0	2	8.3
			20	20	0	4	90.2
3	100	250	25	0	0	2.5	0.4
			25	0	25	5	268
4	50	200	25	0	0	2.5	0.9
			25	0	25	5	192

filters simultaneously, were about 6 to 12 hours. The carbon dioxide was not estimated by absorption in potash, as in the previous cases, but was collected and measured over mercury, by means of the apparatus described later on, the object of this procedure being to ascertain not only the total amount of carbon dioxide produced, but the rate and duration of the evolution. The residue was dissolved in water and made to the same volume as the original juice, and the filtrate was evaporated down to the same volume. All the solutions were saturated with carbon dioxide at the temperature of the bath (25°) before the measurements were commenced, and the observations were continued until all fermentation had ceased.

The boiled juice added in Experiments 1, 3 and 4 (Table V) was obtained by boiling a portion of the same preparation as was used for the filtration. The carbon dioxide is expressed in cubic centimetres under atmospheric conditions.

The process of filtration does not always produce an inactive residue, as on several occasions the residue after very thorough washing has been found to retain a considerable amount of activity. No reason has yet been found for this and it has not yet been ascertained whether it is due to some peculiarity in the particular specimen of juice or in the special filter employed.

It is of interest to note that in Experiment 2 (Table V) the residue alone gave 8.3 c.c. of carbon dioxide in 3 hours, the amount evolved in the last hour being only 0.1 c.c. At the close of this period the liquid still contained the alcoholic enzyme, since on the addition of 20 c.c. of the filtrate, fermentation recommenced and continued for many hours.

These two sets of experiments (Tables IV and V) show that the fermentation of glucose by yeast-juice is dependent upon the presence of a dialysable substance which is not destroyed by heat.

6. Production of the Initial Rapid Evolution of Carbon Dioxide by the Addition of Phosphates

As the result of a large number of attempts to isolate the constituent of boiled juice which brings about the increase in fermentation, it was found that whenever an increase was produced phosphoric acid in the form of a soluble phosphate was present. The effect of the addition of soluble phosphates to yeast-juice was, therefore, examined and it was found that a well-marked initial rapid evolution of carbon dioxide was thus produced. Since, moreover, the boiled juices employed invariably contained phosphates, precipitable by magnesia mixture, there can be no doubt that it is to the presence of these that the initial phenomenon is due. Quantitative estimations revealed the somewhat surprising fact that the extra quantity of carbon dioxide evolved in the initial period when a phosphate or a boiled juice is added, corresponds with the evolution of one molecular proportion of carbon dioxide for each atom of phosphorus added in the form of phosphate.

Experimental details are given and the limits of activity of phosphate and the production of alcohol by it are shown.

The paper then continues.

9. Fate of the Phosphoric Acid

When the fermented liquid is boiled and filtered almost the whole of the phosphorus present is found in the filtrate, but it is nearly all in a form which is not precipitated by ammoniacal magnesium citrate mixture.

In the following experiment three quantities of 25 c.c. of yeast-juice were taken:

A. Hot water was added, the solution heated in a boiling water-bath and the coagulate filtered off and well washed.

B. Ten cubic centimetres of a 30 per cent glucose solution and 10 c.c. of 0.3 molar potassium phosphate solution were added and the liquid at once heated to the boiling point, filtered, and the coagulate washed.

C. The same additions were made as to B and the liquid then fermented until the close of the initial period, after which it was heated and filtered like the others.

The total phosphorus was then estimated in each of the coagulates and in each of the filtrates, and the phosphorus precipitated by magnesium citrate in each of the three filtrates. The estimations of total phosphorus were made by heating with sulphuric and nitric acids until colorless, diluting, and precipitating with magnesium citrate mixture in presence of excess of ammonia.

The following [Table VII] were the results obtained, the numbers representing the grammes of magnesium pyrophosphate per 25 c.c. of juice.

Table VII

	A Original juice	B Juice + phosphate Not fermented	C Juice + phosphate Fermented
Coagulate	0.053	0.057	0.072
Filtrate—			
(a) Precipitated by Mg citrate	0.126	0.480	0.070
(b) Not precipitated by Mg citrate	0.271	0.282	0.679
Total	0.450	0.819	0.821

The amount of phosphate added was equivalent to 0.372 gramme of magnesium pyrophosphate.

A number of other results are given to show the extent to which phosphate is converted into the non-precipitable form by this reaction. All the estimations were made by boiling and filtering the fermented liquid immediately upon the close of the initial period. As before the numbers represent grammes of magnesium pyrophosphate obtained from 25 c.c. of juice.

The form in which this non-precipitable phosphorus is actually present in the fermented liquid, and in the liquid which has been boiled and filtered, has not yet been ascertained with certainty. Experiments which are still in progress, however, appear to indicate that it exists in combination with glucose, probably in the form of a phosphoric ester.

The following selection is from pages 369–370 in *Proceedings of the Royal Society* (*London*), *Series B, 78*, 369–375 (1906).

The Alcoholic Ferment of Yeast-Juice. Part II—The Coferment of Yeast-Juice

ARTHUR HARDEN AND WILLIAM JOHN YOUNG

In a previous communication it was shown that the fermentation of glucose by yeast-juice is dependent upon the presence of a dialyzable substance which is not destroyed by heat. This substance is contained in the active yeast-juice prepared by disintegrating living yeast, and, therefore, most probably exists in the yeast cell side by side with the zymase.

The occurrence of an analogous activating substance has been described by Magnus in the case of lipase of the liver. He observed that the active juice of this organ became inactive when dialyzed into water, but regained its activity when the dialysate or boiled liver juice was added. The term *coferment* was suggested by Bertrand to denote substances of this kind, and he applied it in two instances— to the calcium salt, which he considered was necessary for the action of pectase on pecten substances, and to the maganese of laccase, which he supposed to be essential for the activity of this enzyme. Although not entirely satisfactory, this term may be provisionally applied to activating substances such as those present in liver lipase and yeast-juice, until further knowledge of their nature and function permits of a more rational terminology.

(1) Preparation of the Inactive Residue from Yeast-juice in the Dry State

In the previous communication it was shown that when yeast-juice is filtered through a Martin gelatin filter, both the residue and the filtrate are incapable of fermenting sugar, whereas a mixture of the two produces a vigorous fermentation.

In carrying out the experiments which established this result, the residue left on the filter was always dissolved in water as soon as the filtration and washing were completed, and the activity of the solution was examined without delay. It has since been found possible to obtain the inactive residue in the solid form, in which condition it retains its properties for a considerable time.

This is accomplished by spreading the sticky mass left on the filter over a large watch-glass, and exposing it over sulphuric acid in a vacuum. The residue dries up in a few hours to a brittle mass which is converted by grinding into a light yellow powder.

Complete removal of the coferment is generally not effected by a single filtration, and the powder prepared as above is usually found to be slightly active. A completely inactive residue may, however, be obtained by redissolving in water and repeating the filtration and desiccation. The power prepared in this way and dried over sulphuric acid in a vacuum for 15 hours only loses its potential activity slowly.

The remainder of the paper describes the properties of this coenzyme preparation.

The following selection is from pages 310–311 in *Proceedings of the Royal Society (London)*, *Series B*, *80*, 299–311 (1908).

The Alcoholic Ferment of Yeast-Juice. Part III—The Function of Phosphates in the Fermentation of Glucose by Yeast-Juice

ARTHUR HARDEN AND WILLIAM JOHN YOUNG

Summary

1. The addition of a phosphate to a fermenting mixture of glucose and yeast-juice not only produces a temporary acceleration in the

rate of fermentation, but, in addition to this, an increased total fermentation.

2. The last effect is due to the fact that the hexosephosphate formed during the period of temporary acceleration is continually hydrolyzed by an enzyme with production of free phosphate, which again enters into reaction and thus brings about an increased fermentation.

3. It appears probable that the presence of phosphate is essential for the alcoholic fermentation of glucose by yeast-juice, the reaction which occurs being the following:

$$2C_6H_{12}O_6 + 2R_2HPO_4$$
$$= 2CO_2 + 2C_2H_6O + C_6H_{10}O_4(PO_4R_2)_2 + 2H_2O \qquad (1)$$

This reaction is only realized in the presence of the ferment and coferment discussed in previous communications, phosphate alone being unable, in the absence of coferment, to bring about fermentation in a mixture of ferment and glucose.

The hexosephosphate thus formed is then hydrolysed:

$$C_6H_{10}O_4(PO_4R_2)_2 + 2H_2O = C_6H_{12}O_6 + 2R_2HPO_4 \qquad (2)$$

The rate at which the second reaction occurs determines the rate of fermentation observed when glucose is fermented by yeast-juice.

4. An optimum concentration of phosphate exists which produces a maximum initial rate of fermentation. Increase of concentration beyond this optimum diminishes the rate of fermentation.

The following selection is in *Die Naturwissenschaften* 17, 624–625 (1929).

The Pyrophosphate Fraction in Muscle

K. LOHMANN

The phosphorus compound that occurs in large amounts in striated muscle and is easily split by hot solutions as well as being split enzymatically in bicarbonate solution at 37° has been isolated as a pyrophosphate. The earlier assumption that this pyrosphate in muscle is for the most part adsorbed and is not chemically bound cannot be considered correct, since now we have succeeded in isolating a compound that is decomposed by neutral hydrolysis of its barium salt into pyrophosphoric acid and adenosine phosphoric acid (adenylic acid). Adenylic acid has already been found in the blood of higher animals by Hoffman and in muscle by G. Embden and Zimmermann. Splitting of the adenyl pyrophosphoric acid, which I have isolated by brief heating in hot dilute acid, gave 2 moles of o-phosphoric acid and 1 mole each of adenine and a pentose (ribose) phosphoric acid. This hydrolysis of the Ba salt, very difficultly soluble in water, took place very slowly at room temperature in neutral or weak ammonia solution and was hastened with decrease in [H·].

The pyrophosphate fraction in muscle as well as in other cells can be characterized by the solubility of the alkali salts and the insolubility of the Ba salt in dilute acid alcohol, and by the ratio of easily hydrolyzed P to difficultly hydrolyzed P of 2:1. The discovery of this compound agrees with the observation of Davenport and Sacks that the color reaction discovered by these authors for inorganic pyrophosphoric acid is not found in deproteinated extract of fresh muscle. Embden and also Parnas have shown that the adenine residue split in muscle activity or by enzyme action in aqueous solution is hydrolyzed with loss of ammonia to hypoxanthine; according to Embden muscle adenylic acid goes to inosinic acid. A water extract of muscle acts on the adenyl pyrophosphoric acid with splitting off of 2 moles of o-phosphoric acid and 1 mole of NH_3 (= 1/5 the total N in the compound). However, the two processes do not occur synchronously. My studies further show that the acid-soluble adenine that occurs in fresh muscle appears in greatest part in the pyrophosphate fraction.

In an earlier investigation by Meyerhof, Lohmann and Meyer it was found that lactic acid formation by a widely distributed purified enzyme required a complement in addition to the glycogen, phosphate, and coenzyme, a complement which was no longer found in autolyzed muscle extract, but which could be isolated from fresh muscle in the form of a difficultly soluble barium salt. (This complement, which is necessary for the splitting of all carbohydrates, is not to be confused with the specific kinase-like activator obtained from autolyzed yeast which enables the otherwise difficultly attacked fermentable hexoses to form lactic acid enzymatically.) The adenyl pyrophosphoric acid now acts as this complement which we have long sought, as has been established with O. Meyerhof. Free muscle adenylic acid, but not the adenylic acid obtained from yeast, also exerts this effect, though to a small extent. It is remarkable that the analog of the pyrophosphate compound isolated from yeast, which is apparently identical with the adenyl pyrophosphoric acid from frog and dog muscles, is likewise able to cause lactic acid formation in purified, complement-free muscle enzyme solution which contains the coenzyme. Likewise, the adenyl pyrophosphoric acid, the muscle adenylic acid, or the analogous compound from yeast restores the fermenting system washed from dry yeast with purified coenzyme, the chief difference being only that the yeast preparation causes little or no ammonia splitting from the nucleotide compound and therefore the zymase system of yeast is considerably more stable than that of muscle.

The following selection is in *Science 70*, 381–382 (1929).

Phosphorus Compounds of Muscle and Liver

CYRUS H. FISKE AND Y. SUBBAROW

I. Muscle

Embden and Schmidt have recently made the highly interesting discovery that the adenosine phosphoric acid isolated about two years ago from voluntary muscle is not identical with that obtained from yeast nucleic acid. Among the chemical properties by which the two may be distinguished the difference in resistance to hydrolysis by acid is particularly striking. The muscle nucleotide ("myoadenylic acid") is hydrolyzed (by 0.1 N sulphuric acid at 100°) only about one-fifth as rapidly, as measured by the rate at which o-phosphoric acid is split off.

That adenine (in nucleotide combination) is the source of the ammonia formed in muscle during contraction has been amply demonstrated by Embden and his collaborators. The physiological significance of this important work is presumably quite unaffected by the fact, which we have now to report, that myoadenylic acid is not a normal constituent of muscle (except perhaps in traces), but a decomposition product. Our first intimation that this might be the case developed from the observation that when a protein-free muscle filtrate is treated with an alkaline solution of calcium chloride a large part of the purine nitrogen comes down in the precipitate. The calcium salt of myoadenylic acid is soluble in water, and should consequently—if present—remain dissolved under these conditions.

The purine derivative precipitated by calcium has been isolated by (1) precipitation with mercuric acetate in the presence of 2 per cent acetic acid, followed (after removal of the mercury) by (2) precipitation with calcium chloride and alcohol from hydrochloric acid solution, which yields an acid calcium salt. By repeating the entire process the acid calcium salt is finally obtained as a micro-crystalline precipitate. The yield is not far from quantitative, and accounts not only for most of the purine nitrogen of muscle, but also for most of the acid-soluble phosphorus not present as o-phosphoric acid, phosphocreatine, or hexose monophosphate. In the case of cat muscle the yield of purified material may be the equivalent of nearly 50 mg. of phosphorus per 100 gm. of muscle.

The acid calcium salt is not well suited for analytical purposes, owing to the difficulty of removing all the water. It may, however, be converted to a silver salt—by precipitation with silver nitrate from nitric acid solution—and the composition of this product has been found to be $C_{10}H_{13}O_{13}N_5P_3Ag_3$. It contains, in addition to adenine and carbohydrate, three molecules of phosphoric acid, or two more than in adenylic acid. Two of the three molecules of phos-phoric acid are readily removed by hydrolysis with acid, and this fact is doubtless sufficient to explain why Embden and Zimmermann obtained a nucleotide (myoadenylic acid) which still retains the one resistant phosphoric acid group.

The new substance includes also the phosphorus which Lohmann believes to be present in the muscle in the form of pyrophosphate, but whether or not it is an ester of pyrophosphoric acid remains to be determined.

In the second part of the paper the presence of α-glycerophosphate in liver is shown.

The following selection is in *Klinische Wochenschrift 12*, 213–215 (1933).

On Intermediate Behavior in Glycolysis in the Musculature

G. EMBDEN, H. J. DEUTICKE, AND GERT KRAFT

In studies extending over a long period in this Institute it has been shown that in muscle press juice and muscle homogenates large amounts of inorganic phosphoric acid have been made to disappear by the action of certain salts. By the addition of carbohydrate in the form of glycogen or starch this disappearance of phosphoric acid has been increased and in the studies with press juice it has been possible to isolate a hexose diphosphoric acid which in its properties agrees completely with the Harden-Young ester resulting from yeast fermentation.

In a later study of this reaction by Lohmann it was shown that the relationships were actually confused. Thus Lohmann established that the mixture of the resulting phosphorylation products did not split out phosphoric acid under the action of hot acid with the same ease as the Harden-Young ester, but was much more difficultly hydrolyzable. Thus the main mass of the phosphoric acid esters formed in this investigation must consist of a substance that differs from the known form of hexose diphosphoric acid. Attempts at its isolation led Lohmann to the view that the difficultly hydrolyzable substance was a different hexose diphosphoric acid from the Harden-Young ester.

In the course of a new study, begun with an entirely different purpose, to determine the carbohydrate phosphoric acid synthesis limitations, we obtained a large quantity of beautifully crystallized barium salt which we were able to identify as the secondary barium salt of a monophosphoric acid ester of *l*-glyceric acid.

We believe that the consequences of this discovery led us to far-reaching conclusions as to the events that take place in glycolytic lactic acid formation in muscles, at least insofar as glycolysis occurs through intermediate phosphorylation.

Next it was shown that under anaerobic conditions in muscle homogenates with addition of hexose diphosphate much more phosphoglyceric acid is formed than with starch; thus in spite of the ionic inhibition of dephosphorylation of the hexose ester, decomposition of the six-carbon chain into two fragments with three carbon atoms continues to occur. We may think that in the analogous study of Lohmann also the difficultly hydrolyzable ester consists in good part of phosphoglyceric acid.

We have previously observed the formation of this substance under the influence of sodium acetate, sodium fluoride, and sodium oxalate.

Our suggestion that the newly found substance is a normal intermediate product in glycolysis of the muscles could be supported by further studies.

It was next shown that fresh muscle homogenate splits added monophosphoglyceric acid very easily into phosphoric acid and pyruvic acid. The latter substance can be isolated without the use of a derivative in yields up to 80% of the theoretical. Glyceric acid not esterified with phosphoric acid forms under the same conditions no recognizable amount of pyruvic acid.

Glyceric acid and the pyruvic acid formed from its monophosphoric acid ester by splitting in the muscle are more highly oxidized substances than the six-carbon sugar and the lactic acid formed from this by glycolysis. The appearance of these oxidation products under anaerobic conditions occurs with large yield and this oxidative reaction is naturally possible only with the occurrence at the same time of reductive processes.

On the basis of results from previously reported experiments we form the idea that the formation of lactic acid which occurs by splitting the six-carbon chain in the middle in phosphorylation takes place in such a way that one molecule of hexose diphosphoric acid results in two molecules of triose monophosphate. For the *fructose* diphosphoric acid we must formulate this behavior as follows:

⟨Formula 1⟩

$$
\begin{array}{ccc}
\begin{array}{l}
CH_2-O-P(=O)(OH)\,OH \\
| \\
C=O \\
| \\
CHOH \\
| \\
CHOH \\
| \\
CHOH \\
| \\
CH_2-O-P(=O)(OH)\,OH \\
\text{Fructose diphosphoric acid}
\end{array}
&=&
\begin{array}{l}
CH_2-O-P(=O)(OH)\,OH \\
| \\
C=O \\
| \\
CH_2OH \\
\text{Dihydroxyacetone phosphoric acid} \\
+ \\
C(=O)(H) \\
| \\
CHOH \\
CH_2-O-P(=O)(OH)\,OH \\
\text{Glyceraldehyde phosphoric acid}
\end{array}
\end{array}
$$

By a dismutation process of the type of the Cannizzaro reaction both these triose phosphoric acid molecules can be changed to one molecule of *glycerol phosphoric acid* and one molecule of *phospho-glyceric acid* by the following formula:

⟨Formula 2⟩

$$
\begin{array}{cc}
\overset{\displaystyle O}{\overset{\displaystyle \parallel}{CH_2-O-P-OH}} + \overset{\displaystyle O}{\overset{\displaystyle \parallel}{CH_2-O-P-OH}} + H_2O = \\
\underset{CH_2OH}{\overset{C=O}{\big|}} \quad OH \qquad \underset{C}{\overset{CHOH}{\big|}} \quad OH
\end{array}
$$

Dihydroxyacetone
phosphoric acid

Glyceraldehyde
phosphoric acid

$$
\overset{\displaystyle O}{\overset{\displaystyle \parallel}{CH_2-O-P-OH}} \qquad \overset{\displaystyle O}{\overset{\displaystyle \parallel}{CH_2-O-P-OH}}
$$

CHOH   OH + CHOH   OH

CH₂OH   COOH

Glycerol
phosphoric acid

Phosphoglyceric
acid

The glycerol phosphoric acid whose rich occurrence in the liver has also been recently recognized by Fiske has not until now been isolated from these two dismutation products.

According to our just-reported finding, phosphoglyceric acid will be converted to pyruvic acid with splitting out of phosphoric acid. We are now studying whether the pyruvic acid thus formed can be hydrogenated to lactic acid and at the same time some of the glycerol phosphoric acid resulting from the dismutation can again be dehydrogenated to triose phosphoric acid.

In fact, it can be shown that in muscle homogenate the slight lactic acid formation ocurring from *phosphoglyceric acid* only and from *glycerol* phosphoric acid only, is greatly increased by *simultaneous* addition of *both* substances. The participation of the phosphoglyceric acid in this lactic acid formation corresponds to the demonstration that in the study with simultaneous addition of both substances the content of pyruvic acid is much less than in the study with phosphoglyceric acid alone and the participation of glycerol phosphoric acid indicates that the decreased content of pyruvic acid in the mixed study is not at all sufficient for the increased lactic acid in the study.

Experimental details are reported. The paper then continues.

Our collective previous experiments lead to the following picture of glycolytic lactic acid formation, so far as glycolysis occurs in general with participation of phosphorylation.

First phase: Synthesis of hexose diphosphoric acid from 1 molecule of hexose and 2 molecules of phosphoric acid or from 1 molecule of hexose monophosphoric acid and 1 molecule of phosphoric acid.

Second phase: Decomposition of the hexose diphosphoric acid molecule into 2 molecules of triose phosphate (see above, formula 1).

Third phase: Dismutation of 2 molecules of triose phosphate into 1 molecule of glycerol phosphoric acid and 1 molecule of phosphoglyceric acid by which, depending on whether the hexose diphosphoric acid has a ketose or an aldose character, there can result α- or β-glycerol phosphoric acid (formula 2).

Fourth phase: Splitting of phosphoglyceric acid into phosphoric acid and pyruvic acid by formula 3 below:

$$\text{Formula 3}$$

$$
\begin{array}{ll}
\underset{\displaystyle |}{CH_2}{-}O{-}\overset{\displaystyle O}{\overset{\displaystyle \|}{P}}{-}OH & \underset{\displaystyle |}{CH_3} \\
\underset{\displaystyle |}{CHOH} \qquad \; OH = \underset{\displaystyle |}{C}{=}O + H_3PO_4 \\
COOH & COOH \\
\text{Phosphoglyceric} & \text{Pyruvic} \\
\text{acid} & \text{acid}
\end{array}
$$

This formula expresses the fact that in the splitting, glyceric acid does *not* occur as an intermediate product, and the splitting thus takes place without uptake of water from outside.

Fifth phase: Reductive conversion of pyruvic acid to lactic acid at the cost of more oxidizable triose phosphoric acid formation from glycerol phosphoric acid by formula 4.

$$\text{Formula 4}$$

$$
\begin{array}{llll}
\underset{\displaystyle |}{CH_3} & \underset{\displaystyle |}{CH_2}{-}O{-}\overset{\displaystyle O}{\overset{\displaystyle \|}{P}}{-}OH & \underset{\displaystyle |}{CH_3} & \underset{\displaystyle |}{CH_2}{-}O{-}\overset{\displaystyle O}{\overset{\displaystyle \|}{P}}{-}OH \\
\underset{\displaystyle |}{C}{=}O + \underset{\displaystyle |}{CHOH} \qquad OH = \underset{\displaystyle |}{CHOH} + \underset{\displaystyle |}{CHOH} \qquad OH \\
COOH & CH_2OH & COOH & C \\
& & & \diagdown H
\end{array}
$$

Pyruvic	Glycerol	Lactic	Triose
acid	phosphoric acid	acid	phosphoric acid

The behavior we indicated as phases 3 to 5 is then repeated on the triose phosphoric acid.

The rest of the paper discusses the theories of other authors on glycolysis.

The following selection is from pages 288–290 in *Endocrinology 26*, 285–296 (1940).

Glycogen Breakdown and Synthesis in Animal Tissues

CARL F. CORI

The study of hexosemonophosphate formation was originally begun on intact muscle. Eggleton and Eggleton, Davenport and Sacks, and Lohmann showed that during stimulation of muscle a phosphate ester which is difficult to hydrolyze in acid accumulates, it was assumed to be the equilibrium ester. Cori and Cori devised a quantitative method in which this ester is separated from other phosphate esters and reducing substances and is determined by its reducing power for alkaline copper or ferricyanide solution and its organic P content. With this method the formation of hexosemonophosphate was investigated in mammalian and frog muscle under a variety of experimental conditions which included the administration of epinephrin and insulin and various forms of stimulation. In other experiments an attempt was made to determine the fate of hexosemonophosphate when it disappeared under anaerobic and aerobic conditions. Finally the hexosemonophosphate changes were correlated with simultaneously occurring changes in other phosphate fractions and in lactic acid content of muscle.

Following a short tetanic stimulation up to 50% of the glycogen which disappeared was present as hexosemonophosphate while the remainder was present as lactic acid. Traces of glucose and pyruvic acid were also formed. Since phosphocreatine decreased it was necessary to find out whether this was connected with the hexosemonophosphate formation. When epinephrin was injected into rats, the hexosemonophosphate content of muscle rose, but there occurred no change in phosphocreatine and the inorganic phosphate decreased. These same changes could be demonstrated more clearly when thin frog muscles were immersed in Ringer's solution containing epinephrin in a concentration of 1 to 10 million. The decrease in inorganic phosphate and increase in hexosemonophosphate occurred in equivalent proportions and there was no significant change in other phosphate fractions and only a slight increase in lactic acid. From these and other findings it was concluded that the mechanism of hexosemonophosphate formation in muscle consists in an esterification of glycogen with inorganic phosphate, but no inkling was obtained that the equilibrium ester is not the primary product of this reaction.

A participation of phosphocreatine in hexosemonophosphate formation from glycogen was definitely excluded when it was found that the ester is formed in muscle (and other tissue) extracts which contain no phosphocreatine. It has been shown that the breakdown of phosphocreatine during contraction is connected with the rephosphorylation of adenylic acid which is formed when adenosinetriphosphate transfers its mobile phosphate groups to fructose-6-phosphate to form fructose-1,6-diphosphate (Harden-Young ester).

Since it seemed doubtful that an insight into the mechanism of hexosemonophosphate formation from glycogen could be gained by continuing experiments with intact muscle, it was decided to work with a simpler system. Frog muscle was finely minced with scissors and extracted several times with large volumes of cold distilled water. This treatment removed inorganic and organic phosphates and coenzymes, but left considerable amounts of glycogen and enzymes in the muscle residue. When the muscle residue was suspended in phosphate buffer only small amounts of inorganic phosphate disappeared. Addition of minute amounts of adenylic acid greatly enhanced the disappearance of inorganic phosphate. The product formed after 3 hours of incubation was the equilibrium ester. When a time curve was made and the method of Cori and Cori for the determination of hexosemonophosphate was applied, it was noted that after short periods of incubation much more organic phosphate was present than corresponded to the reducing power. The formation of an intermediary product between glycogen and equilibrium ester was suspected and its isolation undertaken. The chief difficulty was its separation from the equilibrium ester which was finally accomplished by fractional crystallization of the brucine salts. After conversion to the barium salt the elementary analysis for C, H, P and Ba agreed with that of a hexosemonophosphate. It differed from other hexosemonophosphates by its lack of reducing power, the extreme ease with which it was hydrolyzed in weak acids (yielding equivalent amounts of glucose and inorganic phosphate) and the high optical rotation ($[\alpha]D + 120°$ for the free acid). The compound was assumed to be α-glucose-1-phosphate and this assumption was verified by synthesis. Its formation from glycogen is illustrated in the following diagram.

The glycogen molecule, which consists of an α-glucosidic chain, is disrupted by esterification of each glucose unit with phosphoric acid on carbon atom number one, a process which has been named "phosphorolysis." In this enzymatic process the phosphoric acid molecule may be pictured as playing the same role as the water molecule in the "hydrolysis" of glycogen by diastase.

Further experiments were undertaken with muscle extract. It was found that unless the extract was extensively dialyzed, glucose-1-phosphate did not accumulate. In this way the accelerating effect of Mg^{++} ions on reaction 2, the conversion of glucose-1- to glucose-6-phosphate, was detected. A method was described which permits the preparation of about 0.5 gm. of the barium salt of glucose-1-phosphate with 100 cc. of dialyzed extract. Kiessling described an enzymatic method in which the glucose-1-phosphate is obtained as the crystalline dipotassium salt. A synthetic method which permits the preparation of the compound on a larger scale was described by Cori, Colowick and Cori. The synthetic product was shown to be identical with the natural product in all chemical and biological properties. Mannose-1- and galactose-1-phosphate have also been prepared synthetically.

In their experiments with muscle extract Parnas and Baranowski and Ostern and collaborators observed the formation of equilibrium ester from glycogen and inorganic phosphate and the formation of hexosediphosphate from equilibrium ester and adenosinetriphosphate. Since their extracts remained active when dialyzed, they concluded that a coenzyme was not necessary for the formation of equilibrium ester. Later Parnas and Mochnacka obtained inactive extracts by dialyzing them more thoroughly and they were able to reactivate them by addition of adenylic acid and of inosinic acid. Cori, Colowick and Cori, Kendal and Strickland and Bauer and collaborators obtained only slight or no effects with inosinic acid. The difficulty of removing the last trace of adenylic acid by dialysis will be appreciated when it is realized that addition of 0.00003 M adenylic acid to an inactive extract produces a marked effect. When increasing amounts of adenylic acid are added to such an extract (which must be free of adenylic deaminase) a typical coenzyme-activity curve is obtained. Adenosinediphosphate is about one-half and inosinic acid one-thirtieth as active as adenylic acid. Adenosinetriphosphate (in extracts free of pyrophosphatase, an enzyme which converts adenosinetriphosphate to adenylic acid), cozymase, yeast adenylic acid (adenine-ribose-3-phosphoric acid), and adenosine are inactive.

It was to be expected that if adenylic acid is the coenzyme of the phosphorylase it would be necessary for reaction 1 in both directions, that is, not only for the formation of glucose-1-phosphate from glycogen but also for the synthesis of glycogen from glucose-1-phosphate. This was found to be the case with purified phosphorylase prepared from extracts of muscle, heart, brain and liver. Glycogen synthesis did not take place, unless adenylic acid was added. Inosinic and adenosinetriphosphoric acid could not be substituted for adenylic acid.

MECHANISM OF ENERGY UTILIZATION AND PRODUCTION. It was apparent from much of the earlier work that the contraction of muscles was intimately connected with the production of energy in the anaerobic phase of carbohydrate metabolism, but it was not immediately clear how the energy was produced and utilized. A startling observation by Engelhardt and Ljubimowa in 1939 was that myosin, one of the contractile proteins of muscle fibers, also had the properties of an adenosine triphosphatase, an enzyme essential in the transfer of phosphate groups from ATP to carbohydrates. Thus one of the participants in the mechanical process of contraction seemed also to be a chemical catalyst for some of the reactions that supplied the energy for that process. In 1941 Lipmann pointed out that the various transfers of phosphate groups in the anaerobic phase resulted in large turnover of energy and in the second following selection he discussed the concept of the high-energy phosphate bond as the main source of energy. Thus the significance of the anaerobic phase came to be understood.

The following selection is in *Nature 144*, 668–669 (1939).

Myosine and Adenosinetriphosphatase

W. A. ENGELHARDT AND M. N. LJUBIMOWA

Ordinary aqueous or potassium chloride extracts of muscle exhibit but a slight capacity to mineralize adenosinetriphosphate. Even this slight liberation of phosphate is mainly due, not to direct hydrolysis of adenosinetriphosphate, but to a process of secondary, indirect mineralization, accompanying the transfer of phosphate from the adenylic system to creatine, the corresponding enzymes (for which the name "phosphopherase" is suggested) being readily soluble.

In contrast to this lack of adenosinetriphosphatase in the soluble fraction, a high adenosinetriphosphatase activity is associated with the water-insoluble protein of muscle. This enzymatic activity is easily brought into solution by all the buffer and concentrated salt solutions usually employed for the extraction of myosine. On precipitation of myosine from such extracts, the adenosinetriphospha-tase activity is always found in the myosine fraction, whichever mode of precipitation be used: dialysis, dilution, cautious acidifica-tion, salting out. On repeated reprecipitations of myosine, the activity per mgm. nitrogen attains a fairly constant level, unless denaturation of myosine takes place. Under the conditions of our experiments (optimal conditions have not been determined) the activity of myosine preparations ranged in different experiments from 350 to 600 microgram phosphorus liberated per mgm. nitrogen in 5 min. at 37°. Expressed as

$$Q_p = \left(\frac{\mu\text{gm. P}/31 \times 22.4}{\text{mgm. N} \times 6.25 \times \text{hour}} \right),$$

this gives values of 500–850.

Acidification to pH below 4, which is known to bring about the denaturation of myosine, rapidly destroys the adenosinetri-phosphatase activity. Most remarkable is the extreme thermolability of the adenosinetriphosphatase of muscle: the enzymatic activity shown by myosine solutions is completely lost after 10 min. exposure to 37°. This corresponds with the well-known thermolability of myosine. In respect of its high thermolability adenosinetriphosphatase resembles the protein of the yellow enzyme, which when separated from its prosthetic group is also rapidly inactivated at 38° (Theorell). Evidently in the intact tissue of the warm-blooded animal (all experiments were performed on rabbit muscles), some conditions must exist which stabilize the myosine against the action of tempera-ture. A marked stabilizing effect on the adenosinetriphosphatase activity seems to be produced by the adenylic nucleotide itself. As can be seen from the accompanying graph, in the presence of adenosinetriphosphate the liberation of phosphate proceeds at 37° over a considerable period (Curves I, 1a and 1b), whereas the same myosine solution warmed alone to 37° for 10–15 min. shows on subsequent addition of adenosinetriphosphate an insignificant or no mineralization whatever [see figure].

Crude buffer extracts accomplish a quantitative hydrolysis of the labile phosphate groups of adenosinetriphosphate; myosine, reprecipitated three times, liberates but 50 per cent of the theoretical amount of phosphorus (see figure). It acts as true adenosine-*tri*-

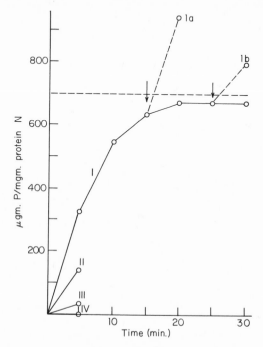

phosphatase and yields adenosinediphosphate, which is not further dephosphorylated and has been isolated in substance. This may serve as a convenient way of preparing adenosinediphosphate, instead of using crayfish muscle. The adenosinediphosphatase is thus associated with the more soluble proteins, occupying an intermediate position between adenosinetriphosphatase and the most readily soluble phosphopherases.

Under no conditions tested could we obtain a separation of adenosinetriphosphatase from myosine. Either the activity was found in the myosine precipitate or else it was absent from the precipitates and the remaining solution. This disappearance of the enzymatic activity we regard as the result of the start of denaturation of the very unstable myosine.

We are led to conclude that the adenosinetriphosphatase activity is to be ascribed to myosine or, at least, to a protein very closely related to and at present not distinguishable from myosine. Thus the mineralization of adenosinetriphosphate, often regarded as the primary exothermic reaction in muscle contraction, proceeds under the influence and with the direct participation of the protein considered to form the main basis of the contractile mechanism of the muscle fibre.

The following selection is from pages 100–102 in *Advances in Enzymology and Related Subjects of Biochemistry 1*, 99–162 (1941).

Metabolic Generation and Utilization of Phosphate Bond Energy

FRITZ LIPMANN

For a long time after its discovery by Harden and Young, phosphorylation of hexose in alcoholic fermentation was thought to be significant only as a means of modeling the hexose molecule to fit it for fermentative breakdown. However, as the outcome of intensive study of the intermediate reactions in fermentation and the relation between muscular action and metabolism, it later became evident that the primary phosphate ester bond of hexose changes metabolically into a new type of energy-rich phosphate bond. In this bond large amounts of energy made available by the metabolic process accumulate. The recent recognition that in nature there occurs a widespread utilization of such phosphate bonds as energy carriers, necessitates a still further revision of the earlier view concerning the biological significance of phosphate turn-over. During various metabolic processes phosphate is introduced into compounds not merely, or at least not solely, to facilitate their breakdown, but as a prospective carrier of energy. To outline the metabolic generation and the circulation of this peculiar type of chemical energy is the primary purpose of this paper. . . .

Through the discovery of creatine phosphate (Fiske and Subbarow, Eggleton and Eggleton) a compound of unusual properties was recognized as a component of the chemical make-up of cells. The more or less pronounced breakdown of creatine phosphate during muscular contraction early suggested its connection with energy supply. Interest in the compound became stronger after Meyerhof and Suranyi found that unexpectedly large amounts of heat were released by enzymatic decomposition. The biochemistry of the energy-rich phosphate bond was, in fact, herewith opened. Progress, however, was slowed by the conception then current as to the mechanism of muscle action, connecting contraction rigidly with glycogen breakdown to lactic acid. A profound revision of this conception became unavoidable when Lundsgaard showed that anaerobic contraction proceeded qualitatively, although not quantitatively, undisturbed after complete blocking of glycolysis by iodoacetic acid. He found "α-lactacid" contraction accompanied by a quite pronounced breakdown of creatine phosphate, exhaustion of the muscle being coincident with exhaustion of combined creatine. During the contraction period proportionality between creatine phosphate breakdown and action—measured as tension—was found. Using the heat data of Meyerhof, Lundsgaard calculated the tension-heat quotient of Hill (Tl/H). He found practical agreement with the quotient calculated earlier for normal muscle where heat of glycogen breakdown was compared with tension. In other words, equal amounts of ultimate heat energy, irrespective of its origin from either creatine phosphate or glycogen, did the same amount of mechanical work. By this finding of Lundsgaard the applicability of phosphate bond energy for the driving of the muscle machine was established.

With normal muscle the Eggletons and Fiske and Subbarow had already found that creatine phosphate, when largely decomposed during a long series of contractions, was reconstituted quite rapidly during recovery in oxygen. Anaerobically likewise creatine phosphate was resynthesized very effectively at the expense of glycolysis (Nachmansohn). Studying anaerobic resynthesis under the most favorable conditions, Lundsgaard found a remarkable efficiency of glycolysis. By breakdown of one-half mole of glucose to lactic acid approximately two moles of creatine phosphate were reformed. Comparing the heats of both reactions each about 24,000 cal. but of opposite sign it could be concluded that the total heat energy of glycolysis was utilized for conversion into phosphate bond energy. The free energy of glycolysis might be in fact somewhat greater than 24,000 cal. (Burk).

The availability of the energy-rich phosphate bond ($\sim$ph) in absence of glycolytic or combustion energy and the ease and effectiveness with which glycolysis and combustion energy could be converted into $\sim$ph, suggested that the energy utilized in the mechanical set-up of muscle under all circumstances was derived from energy-rich phosphate bonds, supplied constantly by glycolytic or oxidative foodstuff disintegration. The manner in which this supply took place remained, however, entirely obscure.

The study of intermediate reactions in glycolysis and fermentation with tissue and yeast extracts furnished the first explanation of the chemistry of such energy transfers.

The understanding of the transfer mechanism in anaerobic glycolysis still left much unexplained as to how creatine-phosphate could be synthesized in purely aerobic metabolism, especially in the presence of iodoacetic acid. The creatine in muscle must be considered as a natural trap or storehouse for ∼ph. Every metabolic process utilizable for the rebuilding of creatine phosphate must generate energy-rich phosphate bonds. A partial explanation developed when it was found that keto acid oxidation, undoubtedly occurring to some extent in aerobic carbohydrate breakdown, can furnish energy-rich phosphate, which, when brought over to creatine, would reform creatine ∼ph (Lipmann). A more general study of purely oxidative phosphorylation, found to occur abundantly in extracts of kidney and liver, was initiated by the work of Kalckar and is being conducted in Cori's laboratory. Here indications are found that present knowledge of the chemistry of generation and transfer of phosphate bonds is far from complete. More and more clearly it appears that in all cells a tendency exists to convert the major part of available oxidation-reduction energy into phosphate bond energy.

The metabolism of muscle is an almost unique case in nature of a straight-forward utilization of chemical energy. Here the need of organization into a uniform type is understandable. In all other cells the energy problem is much more complex. If, as in growth, foodstuff is transformed into protoplasm, the comparison of the free energies of starting material and final product frequently does not show appreciable difference, *i.e.*, storage of energy may be insignificant. The extra "energy of synthesis" needed here is used only in such a manner as to force chemical processes to go in desired directions. Ways and means by which phosphate bond energy is utilizable for such general cell purposes are recognizable and partly understood, and shall be discussed in due course.

AEROBIC PHASE. The remaining problem in carbohydrate oxidation was the fate of the pyruvic acid formed in the anaerobic phase. An important part of the aerobic mechanism involved the formation and reaction of succinic acid, a problem that was solved by Szent-Györgyi and his co-workers. The almost complete cycle was finally proposed by Krebs, and the next selection shows how thoroughly the process was understood in 1937. The main lack at this time was the failure to provide a direct path for entry of the pyruvic acid into the citric acid cycle, and this was furnished just after 1950 by the discovery of coenzyme A.

The following selection is from pages 148 and 152–156 in *Enzymologia* 4, 148–156 (1937).

The Role of Citric Acid in Intermediate Metabolism in Animal Tissues

H. A. KREBS AND W. A. JOHNSON

During the last decade much progress has been made in the analysis of the anaerobic fermentation of carbohydrate, but very little so far is known about the intermediate stages of the oxidative breakdown of carbohydrate. A number of reactions are known in which derivatives of carbohydrate take part and which are probably steps in the breakdown of carbohydrate; we know furthermore, from the work of Szent-Györgyi that succinic acid, fumaric acid and oxaloacetic acid play some role in the oxidation of carbohydrate, but the details of this role are still obscure.

In the present paper experiments are reported which throw new light on the problem of the intermediate stages of oxidation of carbohydrate; in conjunction with the work of Szent-Györgyi, Stare and Bauman and Martius and Knoop the new experiments allow us to outline the principal steps of the oxidation of sugar in animal tissues.

Experiments are then reported that show the catalytic effect of citrate on respiration and the conversion of citric acid into α-ketoglutaric acid and succinic acid, as well as its synthesis in the presence of oxaloacetic acid. On the basis of this and earlier work, the following general scheme is then presented.

VII. Role of Citric Acid in the Intermediate Metabolism

1. Citric Acid Cycle. The relevant facts concerning the intermediate metabolism of citric acid may now be summarized as follows:

1. Citrate promotes catalytically the oxidations in muscle tissue, especially if carbohydrates have been added to the tissue.

2. Similar catalytic effects are shown by succinate, fumarate, malate, oxaloacetate (Szent-Györgyi, Stare and Bauman).

3. The oxidation of citrate in muscle passes through the following stages: citric acid → α-ketoglutaric acid → succinic acid → fumaric acid → *l*-malic acid → oxaloacetic acid.

4. Oxaloacetic acid reacts with an unknown substance to form citric acid.

These facts suggest that citric acid acts as a catalyst in the oxidation of carbohydrate in the following manner

$$+ \, O_2 \quad \left(\begin{array}{c} \text{Oxaloacetic and} \\ \\ \text{Citric acid} \end{array} \right) + \text{``triose''}$$

According to this scheme oxaloacetic acid condenses with "triose" to form citric acid, and by oxidation of citric acid oxaloacetic acid is regenerated. The net effect of the "citric acid cycle" is the complete oxidation of "triose."

The synthesis of citric acid from oxaloacetic acid as well as the oxidation of citric acid to oxaloacetic acid has been experimentally verified. The only hypothetical point in the scheme is the term "triose," though we may consider it as certain that the substance condensing with oxaloacetic acid is related to carbohydrate.

The proposed scheme outlines a pathway for the oxidation of carbohydrate. Many details must necessarily be left open at the present time, but a few points will be discussed in the following sections.

2. *Origin of the C_4-dicarboxylic acid.* According to the scheme succinic acid or a related compound is necessary as "carrier" for the oxidation of carbohydrate and the question of the origin of succinic acid arises. We have shown previously that succinic acid can be synthesized by animal tissues in small amounts if pyruvic acid is available. The physiological significance of the synthesis is now clear: it provides the carrier required for the oxidation of carbohydrate.

3. *Further intermediate stages.* (a) iso-Citric acid. Wagner-Jauregg and Rauen and Martius and Knoop have suggested that iso-citric acid is an intermediate in the oxidation of citric acid. We find that iso-citric acid is indeed readily oxidized in muscle, the rates of oxidation of citric and iso-citric acids being about the same.

(b) cis-Aconitic acid. cis-Aconitic acid, discovered by Malachowski and Maslowski, was first discussed as an intermediate by Martius and Knoop and Martius showed that it yields readily citric acid with liver. We have examined the behavior of cis-aconitic acid in muscle and other tissues and find that it is oxidized as readily as citric acid. The conversion of cis-aconitic acid into citric acid is also brought about by tissue extracts. One milligramme muscle tissue (dry weight) converts up to 0.1 mg. cis-aconitic acid into citric acid per hour (40°; ph = 7.4).

Martius and Knoop assume that the reaction cis-aconitic $\leftrightarrows$ citric acid is reversible and believe that it plays a role in the breakdown of citric acid. It cannot yet be said, however, whether the reaction is an intermediate step in the breakdown or in the synthesis of citric acid.

(c) Oxalo-succinic acid. The oxidation of iso-citric acid would be expected to yield in the first stage oxalo-succinic acid (Martius and Knoop). This β-ketonic acid is only known in the form of its esters, since the free acid is unstable in the pure state. In acid solution it is readily decarboxylated and yields α-ketoglutaric acid (Blaise and Gault).

(d) Detailed citric acid cycle. The information available at present about the intermediate steps of the cycle may be summarized thus:

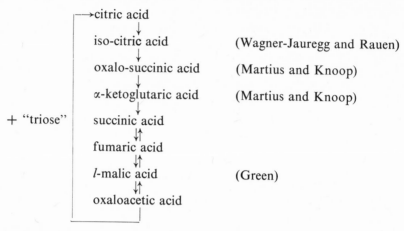

4. *Reversible steps*. Succinic acid arises according to our scheme by oxidative reactions from oxaloacetic acid, via citric and α-ketoglutaric acids. Anaerobic experiments, however, show succinic acid can also be formed by reduction from oxaloacetic acid (see also Szent-Györgyi). The reactions succinic acid → fumaric acid → *l*-malic acid → oxaloacetic acid are thus reversible under suitable conditions.

The outstanding problem in this connection is the question of the oxidative equivalent of the reduction. At least a partial answer may be given. The synthesis of citric acid as shown in section VI takes place anaerobically, although it is an oxidative process. A reductive process equivalent to the oxidation must therefore occur at the same time. The reduction of oxaloacetic acid to succinic acid is the only reduction of sufficient magnitude (see the next section) known so far to occur simultaneously with the citric acid synthesis and we assume therefore it is the equivalent for the synthesis of citric acid.

5. *Effect of malonate*. It follows from the preceding paragraph that succinic acid can arise from oxaloacetic acid in two different ways (a) oxidatively via citric and α-ketoglutaric acids (b) reductively via *l*-malic and fumaric acids. That two different ways and therefore two different enzyme systems bring about the conversion of oxalo-acetic into succinic acid can be demonstrated with the aid of malonate. Malonate inhibits specifically the reaction succinic acid ⇆ fumaric acid. Aerobically it will therefore increase the yield of succinic acid

from oxaloacetic acid since it prevents its secondary breakdown. Anaerobically, on the other hand, it will inhibit the formation of succinic acid, since in this case the succinic dehydrogenase is concerned with the formation of the succinic acid. The following experiment [Table V] shows that the results are as expected.

Table V

Effect of malonate on the aerobic and anaerobic
conversion of oxaloacetic into succinic acid.
(0.75 grammes wet muscle in 3 ccm
phosphate buffer; 40° C; ph 7.4)

	Experimental conditions (*Final concentration of the substrates*)	*μl of succinic* *acid formed in 40 min.*
1.	O_2; 0.1 M oxaloacetate	1086
2.	O_2; 0.1 M oxaloacetate; 0.06 M malonate	1410
3.	N_2; 0.1 M oxaloacetate	1270
4.	N_2; 0.1 M oxaloacetate; 0.06 M malonate	834

6. *Citric acid cycle in other tissues.* We have tested the principal points of the citric acid cycle in various other animal tissues and find that brain, testis, liver and kidney of the rat are capable of oxidizing citric acid as well as synthesizing it from oxaloacetic acid. Of these four tissues testis shows the highest rate of synthesis and this is of interest in view of the work of Thunberg's school on the occurrence of citric acid in spermatic fluid. 1 mg. (dry weight) rat testis forms anaerobically up to 0.02 mg. citric acid per hour if oxaloacetic acid is present.

Whilst the citric acid cycle thus seems to occur generally in animal tissues, it does not exist in yeast or in *B. coli*, for yeast and *B. coli* do not oxidize citric acid at an appreciable rate.

7. *Quantitative significance of the citric acid cycle.* Though the citric acid cycle may not be the only pathway through which carbohydrate is oxidized in animal tissues the quantitative data of the oxidation and resynthesis of citric acid indicate that it is the preferential pathway. The quantitative significance of the cycle depends on

the rate of the slowest partial step, that is for our experimental conditions the synthesis of citric acid from oxaloacetic acid. According to the scheme one molecule of citric acid is synthesized in the course of the oxidation of one molecule of "triose," and since the oxidation of triose requires 3 molecules O_2, the rate of citric acid synthesis should be one third of the rate of O_2 consumption if carbohydrate is oxidized through the citric acid cycle. We find for our conditions:

Rate of respiration $(Q_{O_2}) = -20$
Rate of citric acid synthesis $(Q_{citrate}) = +5.8$

The observed rate of citric acid synthesis is thus a little under the expected figure (-6.6) but it is very probable that the conditions suitable for the demonstration of the synthesis (absence of oxygen) are not the optimal conditions for the intermediate formation of citric acid, and that the rate of citric acid synthesis is higher under more physiological conditions. This is suggested by the experiments on the aerobic formation of succinic acid from oxaloacetic acid (Table IV) [not included here]. $Q_{succinate}$ in the presence of malonate and oxaloacetate is $+14.1$, and if citrate is an intermediate stage the rate of citrate formation must be at least the same. But even the observed minimum figures of the rate of the synthesis justify the assumption that the citric acid cycle is the chief pathway of the oxidation of carbohydrate in pigeon muscle.

8. *The work of Szent-Györgyi.* Szent-Györgyi, who first pointed out the importance of the C_4 dicarboxylic acids in cellular respiration, came to the conclusion that respiration, in muscle, is oxidation of triose by oxaloacetic acid. In the light of our new experiments it becomes clear that Szent-Györgyi's view contained a correct conception, though the manner in which oxaloacetic acid reacts is somewhat different from what Szent-Györgyi visualized. The experimental results of Szent-Györgyi can be well explained by the citric acid cycle; we do not intend, however, to discuss this in full in this paper.

Summary

1. Citric acid catalytically promotes oxidations in muscle, especially in the presence of carbohydrate.

2. The rate of the oxidative removal of citric acid from muscle was measured. The maximum figure for $Q_{citrate}$ observed was -16.9.

3. α-Ketoglutaric acid and succinic acid were found as products of the oxidation of citric acid. These experiments confirm Martius and Knoop's results obtained with liver citric dehydrogenase.

4. Oxaloacetic acid, if added to muscle, condenses with an unknown substance to form citric acid. The unknown substance is in all probability a derivative of carbohydrate.

5. The catalytic effect of citrate as well as the similar effects of succinate, fumarate, malate and oxaloacetate described by Szent-Györgyi and by Stare and Bauman are explained by the series of reactions summarized in section VII 3 d.

6. The quantitative data suggest that the "citric acid cycle" is the preferential pathway through which carbohydrate is oxidized in animal tissues.

Biographies   Index

Bibliography of Biographies

Aston, Francis William (1877–1945)
  Nobel Prize in Chemistry, 1922.
  Journal of the Chemical Society **1948,** 1468–1475.
  E. Farber, ed., *Great Chemists* (Interscience Publishers, New York, 1961), pp. 1454–1462.
Bayliss, William Maddock (1860–1924)
  Ergebnisse der Physiologie, Biologischen Chemie und Experimentellen Pharmakologie **25,** xx–xxiv (1926).
Bjerrum, Niels (1879–1958)
  Zeitschrift für Elektrochemie **53,** 101–102 (1949).
  Journal of Chemical Education **28,** 433 (1951).
  E. Farber, ed., *Great Chemists* (Interscience Publishers, New York, 1961), pp. 1490–1506.
Bodenstein, Max (1871–1942)
  Zeitschrift für Elektrochemie **37,** 341 (1931).
  Die Naturwissenschaften **19,** 625 (1932).
  Zeitschrift für Elektrochemie **48,** 585–587 (1942).
  Die Naturwissenschaften **30,** 737–739 (1942).
Bragg, William Henry (1862–1942)
  Nobel Prize in Physics, 1915.
  Die Naturwissenschaften **20,** 527–530 (1932).
  Kosmos **20,** 5–15 (1942).
  Science **95,** 595–596 (1942).
Bragg, William Lawrence (1890–   )
  Nobel Prize in Physics, 1915.
  Chemical and Engineering News **30,** 4364 (1952).
Braunshtein, Aleksandr Evseevich (1902–   )
  J. Turkevich, *Soviet Men of Science* (D. Van Nostrand Co., Princeton, N.J., 1963), pp. 64–65.
Brönsted, Johannes Nicolaus (1879–1947)
  Acta Chemica Scandinavica **3,** 1187–1209, 1215–1239 (1949).
  Journal of the Chemical Society **1950,** 409–419.
  E. Farber, ed., *Great Chemists* (Interscience Publishers, New York, 1961), pp. 1470–1488.
Butenandt, Adolf Friedrich Johann (1903–   )
  Nobel Prize in Chemistry, 1939.
  Journal of Chemical Education **26,** 91 (1949).
Carothers, Wallace Hume (1896–1937)
  Journal of the Chemical Society **1940,** 100–102.

E. Farber, ed., *Great Chemists* (Interscience Publishers, New York, 1961), pp. 1601–1611.
Condon, Edward Uhler (1902–   )
  National Cyclopedia of American Biography, vol. H, pp. 74–75.
Cori, Carl Ferdinand (1896–   )
  Nobel Prize in Medicine, 1947.
  National Cyclopedia of American Biography, vol. H, pp. 312–313.
Debye, Peter Joseph Wilhelm (1884–1966)
  Nobel Prize in Chemistry, 1936.
  Umschau **40,** 955–956 (1936).
  Zeitschrift für Elektrochemie **58,** 151–153 (1954).
  Chemical and Engineering News **41,** 97 (1963).
Diels, Otto Paul Hermann (1876–1954)
  Nobel Prize in Chemistry, 1950.
  Chemical and Engineering News **28,** 4266 (1950).
  Bayerische Akademie der Wissenschaften, Jahrbuch **1954,** 200–202.
Donnan, Frederick George (1870–1956)
  Journal of Chemical Education **18,** 282 (1941).
  Journal of Colloid Science **12,** 433 (1957).
Emich, Friedrich (1860–1940)
  Österreichische Chemiker-Zeitung **43,** 43–47 (1940).
  Journal of Chemical Education **35,** 608–611 (1958).
  The Microchemical Journal **4,** 423–444 (1960).
Engel'gardt, Vladimir Aleksandrovich (1894–   )
  Izvestiya Akademii Nauk SSSR, Seriya Biologicheskaya **1954,** 125–126.
  Fiziologicheskii Zhurnal SSSR imeni I. M. Sechenova **41,** 3–8 (1955).
  Uspekhi Sovremennoi Biologii **39,** 18–24 (1955).
Eyring, Henry (1901–   )
  Chemical and Engineering News **29,** 763 (1951).
  Chemical and Engineering News **41,** 88 (1963).
  Chemical and Engineering News **42,** 76 (1964).
Fajans, Kasimir (1887–   )
  Zeitschrift für Elektrochemie **61,** 773 (1957).
Fischer, Emil (1852–1919)
  Nobel Prize in Chemistry, 1902.
  Journal of the Chemical Society **117,** 1157–1201 (1920).
  Berichte der Deutschen Chemischen Gesellschaft, Special Number, 480 pp. (1921).
  Journal of Chemical Education **5,** 37–42 (1928).
  Angewandte Chemie **65,** 45–52 (1953).
  E. Farber, ed., *Great Chemists* (Interscience Publishers, New York, 1961), pp. 983–995.
Fischer, Hans (1881–1945)
  Nobel Prize in Chemistry, 1930.
  Zeitschrift für Naturforschung, Pt. b **1b,** 476–479 (1946).
  Die Naturwissenschaften **33,** 289–291 (1946).

Fischer, Hans (1881–1945)—*contd.*
  Angewandte Chemie **62,** 1–4 (1950).
  E. Farber, ed., *Great Chemists* (Interscience Publishers, New York, 1961), pp. 1527–1533.
Fermi, Enrico (1901–1954)
  Nobel Prize in Physics, 1938.
  Journal of Nuclear Energy **1,** 235–236 (1955).
  Die Naturwissenschaften **42,** 353–354 (1955).
  Scientia (Milan) **90,** 316–324 (1955).
  Laura Fermi, *Atoms in the Family; My Life with Enrico Fermi* (University of Chicago Press, Chicago, 1954).
Giauque, William Francis (1895–   )
  Nobel Prize in Chemistry, 1949.
  Tidsskrift for Kjemi, Bergvesen og Metallurgi **9,** 185–188 (1949).
  Chemical and Engineering News **27,** 3571 (1949).
  Les Prix Nobel en 1949 (Imprimerie royale, Stockholm, 1950) pp. 74–75.
Grignard, Victor (1871–1936)
  Nobel Prize in Chemistry, 1912.
  Bulletin de la Societe Chimique de France [5], **3,** 1434–1472 (1936).
  The Journal of the American Chemical Society **59,** No. 5, 17–19 (1937).
  Journal of Chemical Education **27,** 476–488 (1950).
  E. Farber, ed., *Great Chemists* (Interscience Publishers, New York, 1961), pp. 1334–1342.
Hahn, Otto (1879–   )
  Nobel Prize in Chemistry, 1944.
  Die Naturwissenschaften **35,** 161–163 (1948).
  Zeitschrift für Elektrochemie **53,** 51–53 (1949).
  Journal of Chemical Education **27,** 590 (1950).
  Angewandte Chemie **64,** 1–4 (1952).
  Journal of the Chemical Society **1956,** 3997–4003.
Hantzsch, Arthur Rudolf (1857–1935)
  Journal of the Chemical Society **1936,** 1051–1066.
  Zeitschrift für Elektrochemie **42,** 1–4 (1936).
  Berichte der Deutschen Chemischen Gesellschaft **68A,** 65–68 (1939).
  Berichte der Deutschen Chemischen Gesellschaft **74A,** 147–163 (1941).
  E. Farber, ed., *Great Chemists* (Interscience Publishers, New York, 1961), pp. 1066–1083.
Harden, Arthur (1865–1940)
  Nobel Prize in Chemistry, 1929.
  Journal of the Chemical Society **1943,** 334–340.
de Hevesy, George (1885–1966)
  Nobel Prize in Chemistry, 1943.
  Zeitschrift für Elektrochemie **59,** 823 (1955).
  Perspectives in Biology and Medicine **1,** 345–365 (1958).
  Journal of Chemical Education **40,** 36–37 (1963).

de Hevesy, George (1885–1966)—*contd.*
  Les Prix Nobel en 1940–1944 (Imprimerie royale, Stockholm, 1946),
    pp. 80–82.
Heyrovský, Jaroslav (1890–1967)
  Nobel Prize in Chemistry, 1959.
  Zeitschrift für Elektrochemie **60,** 105–106 (1956).
  Collection of Czechoslovak Chemical Communications **25,** 2945–2948
    (1960).
  Electrochimica Acta **2,** 233–234 (1960).
  Journal of Chemical Education **37,** 562–567 (1960).
Hönigschmid, Otto (1878–1945)
  Zeitschrift für Anorganische und Allgemeine Chemie **236,** 1–11
    (1938).
  Journal of Chemical Education **17,** 562 (1940).
  Die Naturwissenschaften **31,** 121–122 (1943).
  Die Naturwissenschaften **33,** 353–354 (1946).
  Chemische Berichte **82,** xi–lxv (1949).
  Angewandte Chemie **62,** 1–4 (1950).
Hopkins, Frederick Gowland (1861–1947)
  Nobel Prize in Medicine, 1929.
  Nature **141,** 989–993 (1938).
  The Biochemical Journal **71,** 1–9 (1959).
  Pharmaceutical Journal **186,** 527–528 (1961).
Ingold, Christopher Kelk (1893–   )
  Poggendorfs Handwörterbuch (1937), vol. 6, pp. 1192–1194.
  Encyclopaedia Britannica (1965), vol. 12, p. 250.
  Chemical and Engineering News **43,** 100 (1965).
Joliot, Frederic (1900–1958)
  Nobel Prize in Chemistry, 1935.
  Nuclear Physics **9,** 1–5 (1958).
  Die Pharmazie **13,** 723–725 (1958).
  Journal de Chimie Physique **56,** 617–621 (1959).
  Biographical Memoirs of Fellows of the Royal Society **6,** 87–105
    (1960).
Joliot-Curie, Irene (1897–1956)
  Nobel Prize in Chemistry, 1935.
  Nuclear Physics **4,** 497–502 (1957).
Karrer, Paul (1889–   )
  Nobel Prize in Chemistry, 1937.
  Les Prix Nobel en 1937 (Imprimerie royale, Stockholm, 1938), pp.
    99–101.
  Journal of Chemical Education **23,** 392–393 (1946).
  Chemical and Engineering News **33,** 2820 (1955).
Keilin, David (1887–1963)
  The Biochemical Journal **89,** 1–5 (1963).
Knoop, Franz (1875–1946)
  Hoppe-Seylers Zeitschrift für Physiologische Chemie **283,** 1–8 (1948).

Kossel, Walther (1888–1956)
  Zeitschrift für Naturforschung, Pt. a **2a,** 595 (1947).
  Nature **178,** 568–569 (1956).
Krebs, Hans Adolf (1900–   )
  Nobel Prize in Medicine, 1953.
  Les Prix Nobel en 1953 (Imprimerie royale, Stockholm, 1954), pp. 92–93.
  Nature **172,** 837 (1953).
  Science **118,** 711–712 (1953).
  Svensk Kemisk Tidskrift **65,** 281–285 (1953).
Kurnakov, Nikolai Semenovich (1860–1941)
  Uspekhi Khimii **8,** 785–812 (1939).
  Uspekhi Khimii **10,** 757–762 (1941).
  Uspekhi Khimii **21,** 1019–1057, 1068–1095 (1952).
  Zhurnal Obshchei Khimii **30,** 3509–3513 (1960).
  Yu. I. Solov'ev and O. E. Zvyagintsev, *Nikolai Semenovich Kurnakov, Life and Activities* (translated title) (U.S.S.R. Academy of Sciences Press, Moscow, 1960).
  Journal of Chemical Education **39,** 44–49 (1962).
Langmuir, Irving (1881–1957)
  Nobel Prize in Chemistry, 1932.
  Industrial and Engineering Chemistry (*News Edition*) **10,** 305–306 (1932).
  Proceedings of the Chemical Society **1959,** 80–83.
  E. Farber, ed., *Great Chemists* (Interscience Publishers, New York, 1961), pp. 1509–1523.
Latimer, Wendell Mitchell (1893–1955)
  Chemical and Engineering News **33,** 1291 (1955).
  Science **122,** 406–407 (1955).
  Biographical Memoirs, National Academy of Sciences **32,** 221–237 (1958).
Laue, Max von (1879–1960)
  Nobel Prize in Physics, 1914.
  Zeitschrift für Kristallographie, Kristallgeometrie, Kristallphysik, Kristallchemie **106,** 1–4 (1945).
  Die Naturwissenschaften **36,** 353–356 (1949).
  Acta Crystallographica **13,** 513–515 (1960).
  Zeitschrift für Kristallographie, Kristallgeometrie, Kristallphysik, Kristallchemie **114,** 163–169 (1960).
  Biographical Memoirs of Fellows of the Royal Society **6,** 135–156 (1960).
Levene, Phoebus Aaron Theodor (1869–1940)
  Science **92,** 392–395 (1940).
  The Journal of Biological Chemistry **141,** 1–2 (1941).
  Advances in Carbohydrate Chemistry **12,** 1–12 (1957).
  E. Farber, ed., *Great Chemists* (Interscience Publishers, New York, 1961), pp. 1314–1324.

Lewis, Gilbert Newton (1875–1946)
    Chemical and Engineering News **25,** 3290–3291 (1947).
    Biographical Memoirs, National Academy of Sciences **31,** 210–235 (1958).
Lipmann, Fritz Albert (1899–   )
    Nobel Prize in Medicine, 1953.
    Chemical and Engineering News **26,** 860 (1948).
    Nature **172,** 837–838 (1953).
    Science **118,** 712–713 (1953).
    Svensk Kemisk Tidskrift **65,** 281–285 (1953).
    Les Prix Nobel en 1953 (Imprimerie royale, Stockholm, 1954), pp. 94–95.
Lohmann, Karl (1898–   )
    Acta Biologica et Medica Germanica **1,** 365–367 (1958).
London, Fritz (1900–1954)
    Nature **174,** 63 (1954).
    Physics Today **7,** No. 1, 16–17 (1954).
    Die Naturwissenschaften **42,** 617–619 (1955).
Martin, Archer John Porter (1910–   )
    Nobel Prize in Chemistry, 1952.
    Les Prix Nobel en 1952 (Imprimerie royale, Stockholm, 1953), pp. 71–72.
McMillan, Edwin Mattison (1907–   )
    Nobel Prize in Chemistry, 1951.
    National Cyclopedia of American Biography, vol. H, pp. 236–237.
    Les Prix Nobel en 1951 (Imprimerie royale, Stockholm, 1952), p. 91.
Meitner, Lisa (1878–   )
    Die Naturwissenschaften **35,** 161–163 (1948).
Meyerhof, Otto (1884–1951)
    Nobel Prize in Medicine, 1922.
    Biochimica et Biophysica Acta **4,** 1–3 (1950).
    Die Naturwissenschaften **39,** 217–218 (1952).
    Science **115,** 365–368 (1952).
Nernst, Hermann Walther (1864–1941)
    Nobel Prize in Chemistry, 1920.
    Berichte der Deutschen Chemischen Gesellschaft **75A,** 79–104 (1942).
    Physikalische Zeitschrift **43,** 109–116 (1942).
    Scientific Monthly **54,** 195–196 (1942).
    E. Farber, ed., *Great Chemists* (Interscience Publishers, New York, 1961), pp. 1204–1208.
Northrop, John Howard (1891–   )
    Nobel Prize in Chemistry, 1946.
    National Cyclopedia of American Biography, vol. G, p. 272.
    Les Prix Nobel en 1946 (Imprimerie royale, Stockholm, 1947), pp. 106–107.
    Annual Review of Biochemistry **30,** 1–10 (1961).
Ostwald, Wolfgang (1883–1943)
    Kolloid-Zeitschrift **103,** 89–94 (1943).

Ostwald, Wolfgang (1883–1943)—contd.
  Journal of Chemical Education **22**, 263–264 (1945).
  Kolloid-Zeitschrift **115**, 3–5 (1949).
  Kolloid-Zeitschrift **145**, 1–2 (1956).
Paneth, Friedrich Adolf (1887–1958)
  Zeitschrift für Elektrochemie **61**, 1121–1122 (1957).
  Österreichische Chemiker-Zeitung **59**, 289–295 (1958).
  Nature **182**, 1274 (1958).
  Biographical Memoirs of Fellows of the Royal Society **6**, 227–246 (1960).
Pauling, Linus (1901–   )
  Nobel Prize in Chemistry, 1954.
  Nobel Peace Prize, 1963.
  Chemical and Engineering News **27**, 28 (1949).
  Chemical and Engineering News **29**, 5349 (1951).
  Chemical and Engineering News **32**, 4486 (1954).
  Les Prix Nobel en 1954 (Imprimerie royale, Stockholm, 1955), pp. 66–67.
  Chemical and Engineering News **33**, 242, 244 (1955).
  Les Prix Nobel en 1963 (Imprimerie royale, Stockholm, 1964), pp. 113–114.
Pregl, Fritz (1869–1930)
  Nobel Prize in Chemistry, 1923.
  Mikrochemie **3**, 105–116 (1931).
  Journal of Chemical Education **35**, 608–611 (1958).
  E. Farber, ed., *Great Chemists* (Interscience Publishers, New York, 1961), pp. 1326–1331.
  The Microchemical Journal **6**, (1), 5–16 (1962).
Randall, Merle (1888–1950)
  National Cyclopedia of American Biography **39**, 200 (1954).
Richards, Theodore William (1868–1928)
  Nobel Prize in Chemistry, 1914.
  Proceedings of the Royal Society (*London*), *Series A* **121**, xxix–xxxiv (1928).
  Science **68**, 333–339 (1928).
  Journal of the Chemical Society **1930**, 1937–1969.
  Journal of Chemical Education **9**, 453–458 (1932).
Robinson, Robert (1886–   )
  Nobel Prize in Chemistry, 1947.
  Chemical and Engineering News **31**, 3844 (1953).
  E. Farber, *Nobel Prize Winners in Chemistry*, 1901–1950 (Henry Schuman, New York, 1953), pp. 190–191.
Rodebush, Worth H. (1887–1959)
  Frontiers in Chemistry **3**, 137–161 (1945).
  Biographical Memoirs, National Academy of Sciences **36**, 277–288 (1962).
Ruzicka, Leopold (1887–   )
  Nobel Prize in Chemistry, 1939.

Ruzicka, Leapold (1887–   )—*contd.*
  Arhivza Hemiju i Tehnologiju **13**, 73–97 (1939).
  Les Prix Nobel en 1939 (Imprimerie royale, Stockholm, 1940), pp.
    109–110.
  Current Science (India) **9**, 5–8 (1940).
Sanger, Frederick (1918–   )
  Nobel Prize in Chemistry, 1958.
  Les Prix Nobel en 1958 (Imprimerie royale, Stockholm, 1959),
    p. 67.
Schoenheimer, Rudolf (1898–1941)
  Science **94**, 553–554 (1941).
Seaborg, Glenn Theodore (1912–   )
  Nobel Prize in Chemistry, 1951.
  National Cyclopedia of American Biography, vol. H, pp. 274–275.
  Les Prix Nobel en 1951 (Imprimerie royale, Stockholm, 1952), pp.
    89–90.
Segrè, Emilio (1905–   )
  Nobel Prize in Physics, 1959.
  Les Prix Nobel en 1959 (Imprimerie royale, Stockholm, 1960), pp.
    80–81.
Semenov, Nikolai Nikolaevich (1893–   )
  Nobel Prize in Chemistry, 1956.
  *Bulletin de l'Academie des Sciences de l'URSS, Classe des Sciences
    Chimiques* **1946**, 337–343.
  Zhurnal Fizicheskoi Khimii **30**, 722–728 (1956).
  Les Prix Nobel en 1956 (Imprimerie royale, Stockholm, 1957), pp.
    65–66.
  Priroda **46**, No. 2, 43–48 (1957).
Sidgewick, Nevil Vincent (1873–1952)
  Proceedings of the Chemical Society **1958**, 310–319.
  E. Farber, ed., *Great Chemists* (Interscience Publishers, New York,
    1961), pp. 1376–1387.
Soddy, Frederick (1877–1956)
  Nobel Prize in Chemistry, 1921.
  Biographical Memoirs of Fellows of the Royal Society **3**, 203–216
    (1957).
  E. Farber, ed., *Great Chemists* (Interscience Publishers, New York,
    1961), pp. 1464–1468.
Sörensen, Sören Peter Lauritz (1868–1939)
  Journal of the American Chemical Society **61**, 2573–2574 (1939).
  Kolloid-Zeitschrift **88**, 129–139 (1939).
  Svensk Kemisk Tidskrift **51**, 248–251 (1939).
  Journal of the Chemical Society **1940**, 554–561.
  Uspekhi Khimii **10**, 111–112 (1941).
Spedding, Frank Harold (1902–   )
  Chemical and Engineering News **26**, 3752–3753 (1948).
  Chemical and Engineering News **30**, 1201 (1952).

Stanley, Wendell Meredith (1904–)
Nobel Prize in Chemistry, 1946.
National Cyclopedia of American Biography, vol. G, pp. 410–411.
Les Prix Nobel en 1946 (Imprimerie royale, Stockholm, 1947), p. 108.
Starling, Ernest Henry (1866–1927)
The Biochemical Journal **22,** 618–620 (1928).
Proceedings of the Royal Society (*London*), *Series B* **102,** xvii–xxvii (1928).
Staudinger, Hermann (1881–1965)
Nobel Prize in Chemistry, 1953.
Journal of Chemical Education **16,** 1 (1939).
Journal of Chemical Education **28,** 120–122 (1951).
Chemiker Zeitung **75,** 159–163 (1951).
Angewandte Chemie **63,** 229–231 (1951).
Hermann Staudinger, *Arbeitserinnerungen* (A. Huthig Verlag, Heidelberg, 1961).
Sumner, James Batcheller (1887–1955)
Nobel Prize in Chemistry, 1946.
Les Prix Nobel en 1946 (Imprimerie royale, Stockholm, 1947), pp. 101–105.
Biographical Memoirs, National Academy of Sciences **31,** 376–396 (1958).
The Enzymes **1,** xiii (1959).
Svedberg, The (1884–)
Nobel Prize in Chemistry, 1926.
Les Prix Nobel en 1926 (Imprimerie royale, Stockholm, 1927), pp. 77–78.
Chemical and Engineering News **31,** 3464 (1953).
Tiselius, Arne Wilhelm Kaurin (1902–)
Nobel Prize in Chemistry, 1948.
Tidsskrift for Kjemi, Bergvesen og Metallurgi **8,** 157–160 (1948).
Les Prix Nobel en 1948 (Imprimerie royale, Stockholm, 1949), pp. 69–74.
Journal of Chemical Education **28,** 538 (1951).
Chemical and Engineering News **31,** 3464 (1953).
Tswett, Michael (1872–1920)
Isis **36,** 108–109 (1946).
Journal of Chemical Education **36,** 144–147 (1959).
Chymia **6,** 146–161 (1960).
Urey, Harold Clayton (1893–)
Nobel Prize in Chemistry, 1934.
National Cyclopedia of American Biography, vol. E, p. 475.
Journal of Chemical Education **39,** 583–584 (1962).
Warburg, Otto Heinrich (1883–)
Nobel Prize in Medicine, 1931.
Kaplan, F., *Nobel Prizewinners* (Nobelle Publishing Co., Chicago, 1939), pp. 79–80.

Warburg, Otto Heinrich (1883–   )—*contd.*
  Annual Review of Biochemistry **33**, 1–14 (1964).
Wieland, Heinrich Otto (1877–1957)
  Nobel Prize in Chemistry, 1927.
  Journal of Chemical Education **7**, 1763–1777 (1930).
  Die Naturwissenschaften **30**, 333–373 (1942).
  Biographical Memoirs of Fellows of the Royal Society **4**, 341–352
    (1958).
  Bayerische Akademie der Wissenschaften, Jahrbuch **1959**, 160–170.
  E. Farber, ed., *Great Chemists* (Interscience Publishers, New York,
    1961), pp. 1442–1451.
Zsigmondy, Richard Adolf (1865–1929)
  Nobel Prize in Chemistry, 1925.
  Les Prix Nobel en 1926 (Imprimerie royale, Stockholm, 1927), pp.
    73–76.
  Chemiker Zeitung **53**, 849–850 (1929).
  Zeitschrift für Angewandte Chemie **42**, 1068–1070 (1929).
  Zeitschrift für Elektrochemie **35**, 876 (1929).
  *Nachrichten von der Gesellschaft der Wissenschaften zu Göttingen,
    Geschäftliche Mitteilungen* **1929–1930**, 54–59.

Name Index